SpringBoard®

Level 3

Mathematics with Meaning™

THE COLLEGE BOARD
inspiring minds™

The College Board is a mission-driven not-for-profit organization that connects students to college success and opportunity. Founded in 1900, the College Board was created to expand access to higher education. Today, the membership association is made up of more than 5,900 of the world's leading educational institutions and is dedicated to promoting excellence and equity in education. Each year, the College Board helps more than seven million students prepare for a successful transition to college through programs and services in college readiness and college success — including the SAT® and the Advanced Placement Program®. The organization also serves the education community through research and advocacy on behalf of students, educators and schools.

For further information, visit www.collegeboard.com.

ISBN: 0-87447-881-2
ISBN: 978-0-87447-881-5

4 5 6 7 8   11 12 13 14
Printed in the United States of America

Acknowledgments

The College Board gratefully acknowledges the outstanding work of the classroom teachers and writers who have been integral to the development of this revised program. The end product is a testimony to their expertise, understanding of student learning needs, and dedication to rigorous but accessible math education.

Virginia Bohme
School Specialist
University of Arizona
Mathematics Department
Tucson, Arizona

Tammy Buckshi
Mathematics Teacher
Iredell-Statesville Schools
Iredell County, North Carolina

Marcia Chumas
Math Department Chair
East Mecklenburg High School
Charlotte, North Carolina

Betty Davis
Mathematics Teacher
Boston Latin School
Boston, Massachusetts

Wendy L. DenBesten
Mathematics Teacher
Hoover High School
Fresno Unified School District
Fresno, California

Karen Flowers
STEM Coach, Mathematics
Nashville Public Schools
Nashville, Tennessee

Megan Gerstenzang
Mathematics Teacher
Gibbons Middle School
Westborough Public Schools
Westborough, Massachusetts

Shawn Harris
Mathematics Instructor
Ronan Middle School
Ronan, Montana

Melinda Herman
Mathematics Teacher
Christ Presbyterian Academy
Nashville, Tennessee

Marie Humphrey
Mathematics Teacher
David W. Butler High School
Matthews, North Carolina

Andrew Kearns
Math Department Chair
Dr. Michael M. Krop Senior High
Miami-Dade County Public Schools
Miami, Florida

Dean Packard
Mathematics Teacher
Tucson High Magnet School
Tucson, Arizona

Aaron Smith
Mathematics Curriculum Specialist
Duval County Public Schools
Duval County, Florida

Jill Stevens
Mathematics Teacher
Trinity High School
Euless, Texas

Andrea Sukow
Instructional Specialist, SpringBoard
Math Coordinator, retired
Metro Nashville Public Schools
Nashville, Tennessee

Sue Swanda
Mathematics Teacher, retired
Charlotte-Mecklenburg Schools
Cornelius, North Carolina

Judy Windle
Instructional Specialist, SpringBoard
Mathematics Teacher, retired
Charlotte-Mecklenburg Schools
Charlotte, North Carolina

Special thanks also go to the writers and teachers whose excellence in creating the previous Mathematics with Meaning™ program provided the strong foundation on which this program rests.

Sandy Campo
Mathematics Consultant
Providence, Rhode Island

James R. Choike
Professor of Mathematics
Oklahoma State University
Stillwater, Oklahoma

Jill Gough
Mathematics Teacher
The Westminster Schools
Atlanta, Georgia

Sam Gough
Mathematics Teacher
The Westminster Schools
Atlanta, Georgia

Christopher Kribs-Zaleta
Associate Professor of Mathematics
University of Texas at Arlington
Arlington, Texas

Guy Mauldin
Mathematics Teacher
Science Hill High School
Johnson City, Tennessee

Chris Sollars
Mathematics Teacher
Alamo Heights High School
San Antonio, Texas

J. T. Sutcliffe
Mathematics Teacher
The St. Mark's School of Texas
Dallas, Texas

Acknowledgments *continued*

Assessment Advisors

The assessment advisors provided valuable input during the development of the Math Standards Review to ensure the format of this practice was aligned with national and state assessment formats. We especially thank Beverly Whittington for her work on rubrics.

Margaret Bambrick
K-12 Mathematics Specialist
Volusia County Public Schools
DeLand, Florida

Gail Burton
Middle School Math Teacher on
   Assignment
Volusia County Public Schools
DeLand, Florida

Patra Cooks
SpringBoard Coordinator for Math
Hillsborough County Public Schools
Tampa, Florida

Johnnie Ebbert
Mathematics Teacher
Volusia County Schools
DeLand. Florida

Vicki Ewing
District Resource Teacher for
   Promise /former Middle School
   Math Teacher
Hillsborough County Public Schools
Tampa, Florida

Bonnie Fenwick
Mathematics Teacher
Volusia County Public Schools
Port Orange, Florida

Nicki Junkins, Ed. D.
Director of K-12 Curriculum and
   Program Accountability, retired
Volusia County Public Schools
DeLand, Florida

Beverly Whittington
Mathematics Consultant
Bordentown Township, New Jersey

Program Reviewers

The following reviewers contributed immeasurably to this revised edition, and we gratefully thank them for all their suggestions for improvements and clarifications.

James Choike
Professor of Mathematics
Oklahoma State University
College Board, Mathematical
   Sciences AAC
Stillwater, Oklahoma

Kristi Connally
Mathematics Teacher
Broward County Public Schools
Ft. Lauderdale, Florida

Landy Godbold
Mathematics Teacher
The Westminster Schools
Atlanta, Georgia

Janice Martin
Mathematics Teacher/Principal,
   retired
Charlotte-Mecklenburg Schools
Charlotte, North Carolina

Julie Skalka Martin
Mathematics Curriculum
   Coordinator
Metropolitan Nashville Public
   Schools
Nashville, Tennessee

Karen Martinez
Mathematics Teacher and Coach
Broward County Public Schools
Ft. Lauderdale, Florida

Jerry McMahon
Mathematics/Computer Science
   Teacher
Charlotte-Mecklenburg Schools
Charlotte, North Carolina

Joanne Patchin
A. P. Mathematics Teacher
Palm Beach County Public Schools
West Palm Beach, Florida

Carla Richards
Title I Math Coach
Franklin Special School District
Franklin, Tennessee

Sandra Ammons Sullivan
Mathematics Teacher
York County School District #2
Clover, South Carolina

Research and Planning Advisors

We also wish to thank the members of our SpringBoard Advisory Council, the SpringBoard Math Trainers, and the many educators who gave generously of their time and their ideas as we conducted research for the program. Your suggestions and reactions to ideas helped immeasurably as we planned the revisions. We gratefully acknowledge the teachers and administrators in the following districts:

Broward County Public Schools
Fort Lauderdale, Florida

Cherry Creek School District
Cherry Creek, Colorado

Chicago Public Schools
Chicago, Illinois

DeKalb County School System
DeKalb County, Georgia

Duval County Public Schools
Jacksonville, Florida

Guilford County Schools
Greensboro, North Carolina

Hillsborough County Public Schools
Tampa, Florida

Hobbs Municipal Schools
Hobbs, New Mexico

Indianapolis Public Schools
Indianapolis, Indiana

Miami-Dade County Public Schools
Miami, Florida

Metropolitan Nashville Public Schools
Nashville, Tennessee

The City School District of New Rochelle
New Rochelle, New York

Orange County Public Schools
Orlando, Florida

School District of Palm Beach County
Palm Beach, Florida

Penninsula School District
Gig Harbor, Washington

Pinellas County Schools
Largo, Florida

San Antonio Independent School District
San Antonio, Texas

Spokane Public Schools
Spokane, Washington

Volusia County Schools
DeLand, Florida

Editorial Leadership

The College Board gratefully acknowledges the expertise, time, and commitment of the math editorial team.

Betty Barnett
Educational Publishing Consultant

John Nelson
Director of Curriculum and
Instructional Products, SpringBoard

Contents

Level 3

Instructional Units

Unit 1 Patterns and Numerical Relationships

Contents *continued*

Unit 4 Proportional Relationships

Unit 5   Probability and Statistics

Unit 6   Three-Dimensional Geometry

Contents *continued*

Resources

To the Teacher

Welcome to SpringBoard *Mathematics with Meaning,* a highly engaging, student-centered instructional program. This revised edition of SpringBoard offers a standards-based mathematics program that may be used as a core curriculum. The mathematics instruction follows a balanced approach in which concepts are presented based on the most effective instruction: *directed* for basic mathematics principles, including examples and practice; *guided* for concepts that need a combination of direct instruction and investigatory learning; and *investigative* activities that allow students to explore and discover mathematics concepts through a contextual setting.

SpringBoard is the College Board's official Pre-AP program, developed to provide a roadmap for attaining the knowledge and skills students require for success in Advanced Placement courses and in college-level work. Based on the College Board Standards for Success in Mathematics and current research on best instructional practices, SpringBoard uses a "back-mapping" instructional design that starts with the end in mind, namely, the Embedded Assessments. The skills and knowledge needed for these assessments are scaffolded into the activities leading to each assessment. By using the Embedded Assessments as a starting point for planning instruction, teachers have a clear picture of what students need to know and be able to do as they progress through the unit and the course to more easily adjust the learning plan to meet individual needs.

What Sets SpringBoard Apart from Other Mathematics Programs?

The College Board developed SpringBoard as a clearly articulated, engaging, and rigorous framework for mathematics instruction for middle school through Precalculus that develops the skills and knowledge necessary to prepare students for college and to compete in the 21st century. Students need to be able to solve complex math problems using a variety of mathematical knowledge and skills, collaborate with others to complete a task, and communicate effectively using the language of mathematics. In SpringBoard, rigor is made accessible, and all students have ample opportunity to refine and master mathematics content.

SpringBoard's approach is just the opposite of the "inch deep, mile wide" philosophy that permeates so much of mathematics instruction today. With SpringBoard, students explore the "big ideas" and develop the critical thinking skills needed to apply and communicate concepts in real-world situations.

Unique features of SpringBoard include:

- **Rigorous, standards-based instruction:** The College Board Standards for College Success in Mathematics provide the instructional framework for developing the skills students need for both Advanced Placement and college-level work.

- **Research-based instruction:** The SpringBoard program integrates the research findings on best practices for helping students learn, as well as underlying research on how best to present and reinforce new content learning. A key element of the organization of the program is orienting it around the desired results; i.e., what must students know to perform well and then scaffolding instruction to deliver that performance.

- **Student-centered, interactive, collaborative activities:** Each grade level or course is organized into short, interactive activities that require students to participate through discussions, making their own notes about concepts, and demonstrating learning through multiple means of evaluation.

- **Integrated teaching and learning strategies:** Embedded in each activity are Suggested Learning Strategies that help students use a methodical approach to learning new content. These learning activities are designed to encourage students to take control of their own learning by identifying which strategies work best for them. Teachers also make use of these strategies by using them as part of strategic instruction that demands a reflective and metacognitive approach to teaching and learning.

- **Assessment for learning:** Multiple opportunities are provided to assess student learning: before starting a unit of instruction to assess prerequisite knowledge (Getting Ready), during instruction to monitor understanding (Check Your Understanding), and after instruction to evaluate knowledge of concepts and how to apply them in a variety of situations (Practice, Embedded Assessments, Reflections, Math Standards Review, Unit Tests).

- **Professional development:** Unparalleled professional development builds teacher capacity to deliver challenging curriculum to meet the needs of all students while honoring the creativity and intelligence teachers bring to the classroom. Face-to-face training is supported by an online system featuring resources that includes an interactive professional learning *Community* that allows peer-to-peer sharing and sustains successful teaching.

Preparing All Students to Meet Rigorous Standards

The CBSCS standards define mathematics content expectations with a focus on college readiness and 21st century skills and knowledge. As the pipeline to AP, SpringBoard is the vehicle that makes rigorous standards attainable for all students through strategic instruction. Integrated into the program are the five NCTM process standards (Problem Solving, Reasoning and Proof, Communication, Connections, and Representations) to equip students with the thinking skills needed to acquire and apply significant math content.

Founded on these content and process standards, SpringBoard provides an instructional pathway that equips teachers with the resources to deliver effective instruction and students with the knowledge, skills, and strategies to demonstrate high levels of learning.

Meeting or exceeding your state standards, SpringBoard provides the assurance that your students will be well prepared to meet the curriculum goals set by your state. Access to the alignment of curriculum and assessments to your state standards is available at SpringBoard Online.

Search by State Standards or College Board Standards or Keyword to access:

- Student Activities
- Teaching Plans
- Embedded Assessments
- End-of-Unit Tests

How Educational Research Informs SpringBoard

Research plays an increasingly significant role in fostering learning and in closing the performance gap so that all students have access to college. As classroom practitioners, SpringBoard writers understand the role research plays in curricular design and instructional practice. They also have the hands-on experiences of what works in the classroom. Incorporating both research from experts in the field and practical experience, Springboard facilitates learning by providing deep experience with contextually based mathematics concepts so that students not only learn the concepts but also how to apply and represent them in multiple situations and applications.

SpringBoard Begins with the End in Mind

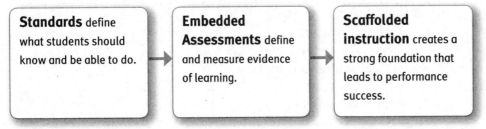

Standards define what students should know and be able to do.

Embedded Assessments define and measure evidence of learning.

Scaffolded instruction creates a strong foundation that leads to performance success.

Instructional Strategies Build Student Success

Research has shown that students learn by doing. To develop a deep understanding of mathematical concepts and their applications, the SpringBoard curriculum addresses all learning modalities by including all students in rich discussion and application of concepts. Research also supports the use of specific learning strategies to help students "learn how to learn." Through the use of multiple learning and instructional strategies, students not only acquire the knowledge they need but also the confidence in their own abilities to learn and use mathematics in real-world situations.

Assessment Informs Instruction

Research supports assessment to provide the instructor with knowledge about what individual students know and can do. The program provides multiple opportunities for formative assessment, including quick assessments of prerequisite skills, ongoing checks of understanding through frequent debriefing where students explain the math in their own words, and more structured tests for students to demonstrate knowledge. See pages xxii and xxiii for more on assessment opportunities.

Making Mathematics Relevant to Today's Students

SpringBoard helps students understand that mathematics does not occur only in the confines of a classroom. Activities present engaging contexts for students to connect mathematics to the world around them with insights into how math is used in diverse applications from construction to food to music or art.

Contextually Based Activities

Activities in the student books are developed around real-world contexts that allow students to relate what they already know to how mathematics is used by the people and organizations around them. These contexts provide a rich understanding for students as they learn not only the mathematics concepts but also their real-world applications. Seeing mathematics from multiple perspectives provides insights for students into how they personally use mathematics.

Interactive Participation

In the SpringBoard classroom, students are encouraged to engage in academic discourse and reflection and to articulate their thoughts and ideas, providing a sense of relevance to and engagement in the learning process. Working in collaborative groups, students also explore their own and others' ideas about what they are studying. The collaborative techniques in SpringBoard classrooms not only involve all students, they also create a setting where students can gain confidence in their own ideas and skills in communicating those ideas to classmates.

Student Ownership of Learning

Students thrive in SpringBoard classrooms as they learn through participation and active engagement with mathematic concepts that stretch and inspire their thinking. As they develop confidence in their ability to succeed in mathematics, students begin to take ownership of their learning in new and exciting ways.

Students are guided toward the goal of being independent learners with point-of-use strategies for learning, development of mathematics language through frequent definitions and reminders, tips for reading and writing math, and built-in opportunities to reflect on personal learning. All these elements combined lead toward preparing students to take ownership of their learning for this course and in future studies.

Teaching and Learning Support

SpringBoard provides educators with effective methods to reach students who enter today's classrooms with a broad spectrum of skills, knowledge, experiences, and interests. SpringBoard encourages an atmosphere of responsive teaching, promoting a learning-centered environment in which teachers can differentiate instruction based on their knowledge of the students, curriculum goals, and instructional strategies.

Strategic Instruction Is Differentiated Instruction

Virginia Rojas, a leading educator on instructional practices for English language learners, describes four steps to promote effective standards-based instruction:

1. Identify expectations.
2. Determine acceptable evidence of learning through assessment.
3. Plan the student learning experience.
4. Build scaffolds to help students reach the learning goals.

Expectations for Learning   Beginning with the end in mind, expectations are set through the knowledge and skills students will need to complete the Embedded Assessments. Students are encouraged to begin each unit with a look at the Embedded Assessments, including the accompanying rubric. Giving students an assessment rubric in their books clearly sets the level of learning expected.

Assessment as Evidence of Learning   The SpringBoard classroom provides multiple opportunities to assess for learning, beginning each unit with a quick pre-assessment to evaluate students' prerequisite knowledge and skills. Through strategies and Teacher-to-Teacher notes in the Teacher's Edition, teachers are encouraged to debrief students frequently to assess their progress and to look at multiple ways of addressing instruction both to challenge students and to address the needs of those who may be more visual learners or who may need a step-by-step approach.

Other ongoing assessments include Check Your Understanding questions for each activity, math standards reviews that mimic high-stakes tests, and unit tests. In addition, students are encouraged through an end-of-unit reflection to self-assess and to reflect on their own learning—both how they learn and what they learn. Through ongoing self-assessment, students become reflective thinkers and examine how they think and solve complex problems, and how effectively they communicate mathematically with others, effectively promoting learning.

The Student Learning Experience   A SpringBoard classroom is one where students participate in their own learning rather than sitting back and "receiving" knowledge from a lecture. SpringBoard presents mathematics content in the context of how mathematics is used in real-world situations, and students interact with that content in multiple ways, learning through the use of strategies that work best for them. Ongoing use of collaborative and other purposeful instructional strategies provide students with the tools they need to attain a higher level of learning. By addressing all learning modalities and levels of readiness, strategic instruction makes rigorous content accessible and develops the math process skills that are necessary for Advanced Placement courses and college readiness.

Scaffolded Student Learning   Beginning with the expectations for what students need to know and be able to do, mathematics content is divided into instructional activities to address those needs. Activities provide scaffolded instruction by:

- introducing students to new content through worked-out examples and immediate reinforcement with "Try These" practice problems,
- using a "laddering" approach where successive questions and problems gradually remove the props and require students to do more of the analysis and problem solving, and
- developing higher level critical-thinking skills through investigative activities that allow students to explore mathematics concepts in real-world situations.

The flexible design of SpringBoard provides multiple opportunities and resource tools to differentiate instruction in order to support the growth and development of all students. Using a range of teaching strategies, teachers can monitor and adjust instruction adding more or less scaffolding where needed.

Professional Development

The SpringBoard program provides unparalleled teacher support through initial and advanced teacher training institutes that focus on:

- hands-on instruction in best instructional practices,
- use of strategies to improve instruction and student learning,
- mapping a standards-based curriculum and vertical articulations of concepts across the grade levels, and
- using assessment to inform instruction.

In addition to training workshops, the program provides train-the-trainer workshops to build district training capacity, support for in-district trainings, online teacher mentors, and access to an online community of SpringBoard teachers and admininstrators for sharing and learning from best practices.

A Preview of the Annotated Teacher Edition

Middle School Mathematics, Level 3, has six units focused on the big ideas in math at this level, chunked into meaningful portions within a unit. Within the units are three types of activities (direct, guided, investigative) which scaffold to two or three Embedded Assessments in a unit. Each unit ends with Practice Problems, Reflection, and Math Standards Review. End-of-Unit Tests can be found online to print or for students to take online.

Planning the Unit Identifies the big ideas and student learning expectations on key math concepts presented and assessed in the unit.

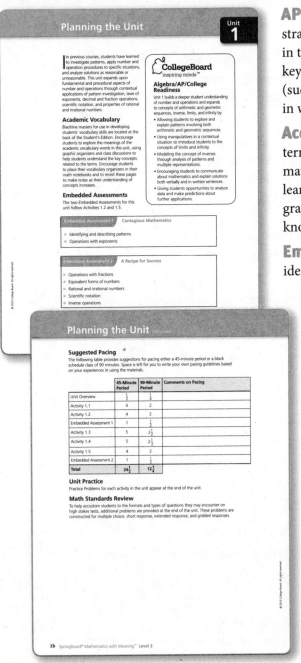

AP /College Readiness connects Pre-AP strategies with higher order thinking skills developed in the unit. More than just math skills, these are key factors for successful communication in math (such as interpreting and modeling a problem in writing).

Academic Vocabulary focuses on key math terms to help students develop the language of mathematics. Based on research for supporting learning, students explore these words in detail using graphic organizers and revisiting the terms as their knowledge about them increases.

Embedded Assessment skills and knowledge identify the expectations for what students will be expected to know and do for each Embedded Assessment; helps teachers scaffold their own instruction to facilitate student learning.

Suggested Pacing provides time frames for teaching either a 45-minute or 90-minute period with suggestions based on the SpringBoard writers' personal teaching experience. Knowing that classes will vary, space has been provided to reflect, record, and adjust pacing to your students needs.

Introducing the Unit
Helps students focus on the essential skills they will be learning and what they will be assessed on at the end of the unit.

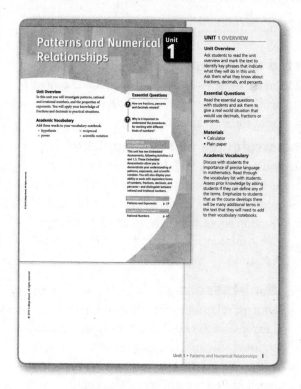

Unit Overview helps set the stage by connecting students' past learning with what they will be learning in the unit.

Essential Questions focus on the big ideas in the unit and help students make connections between mathematical ideas as well as connections to real-world mathematics. Students revisit their answers to Essential Questions in the end-of-unit reflection.

Embedded Assessments set up the expectations for learning in the unit.

Prerequisite Skills Check
Identifies prerequisite skills students will need for the unit.

Getting Ready is a quick assessment of where students are.

- Identifies math concepts for review.
- Helps you address individual student needs.
- Skills needed for each question are identified in the teaching notes
- Suggested answers provide convenience.

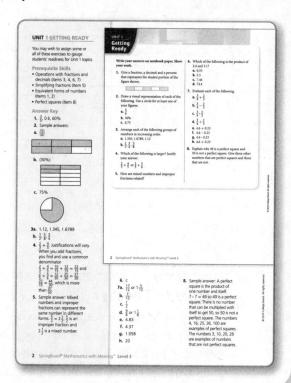

Instructional Support

Activity focus statements give a quick look at what students will learn in the activity.

Materials list provides a handy reference for organizing the instructional materials you'll use in the activity.

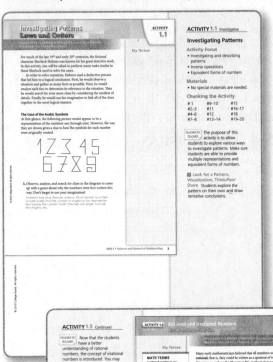

Suggested chunking helps you plan how to pace the instruction for students and identifies natural points at which to debrief students to ensure understanding before moving to the next chunk.

Teaching strategies and commentary

provide suggestions from a SpringBoard teacher's perspective and background information for the activity. Aligned to questions on the student page, suggestions include information about the problem, the intent of the problem, possible misconceptions, and a variety of ways to present the lesson.

Mini-Lessons give access to supplementary content relating to the focus of the activity. Lessons can be used in a variety of ways: to support students needing review, to present additional content, or to provide alternative methods for presenting information.

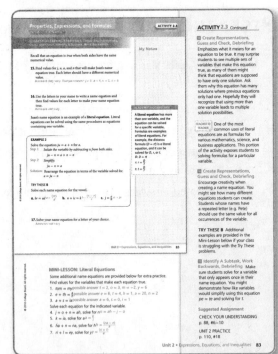

Teacher to Teacher tips from a math mentor provide deeper explanations on the math being developed on the page and suggestions for addressing topics such as student misconceptions, alternative ways of presenting content, or ways to make connections to other mathematical concepts.

Instructional Support *(continued)*

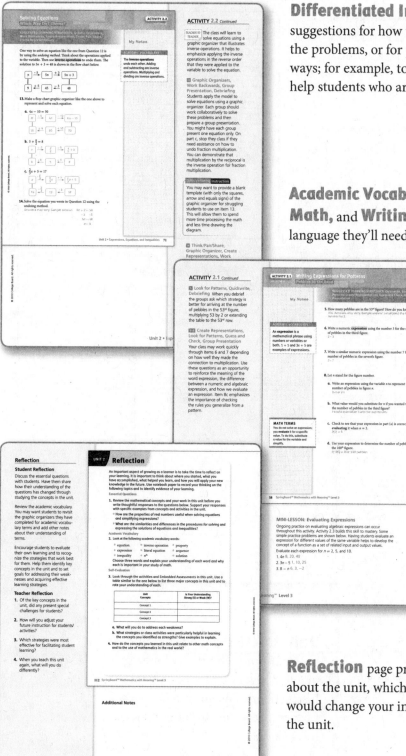

Differentiated Instruction tips at point of use give suggestions for how to help students better comprehend the problems, or for presenting information in different ways; for example, to use a more visual presentation to help students who are visual learners.

Academic Vocabulary, Math Terms, Reading Math, and **Writing Math** help students master the language they'll need to reason and communicate in mathematics. Call-out boxes on the student pages serve as reminders to debrief with students to ensure their understanding of math terms and to have students

- Use graphic organizers to explore academic vocabulary terms.
- Write math terms in their math notebooks.

Reflection page provides opportunity to make notes about the unit, which strategies worked best, or how you would change your instruction the next time you teach the unit.

Assessing for Instruction
Multiple informal assessment opportunities help you track individual student learning and adjust instruction as needed.

Try These practice problems follow a worked-out example and give a quick look at whether students mastered the concept or need further instruction or practice.

Check Your Understanding ends each activity and helps you assess student learning. Problems can be used during the activity or at the end.

The Mathematical Reflection question requires students to think about the concepts they learned in the activity, make connections among concepts, and communicate their understanding about concepts and how they are used in real-world situations. Students' answers to these questions give you insight into their skills at reasoning and communicating their understanding of concepts.

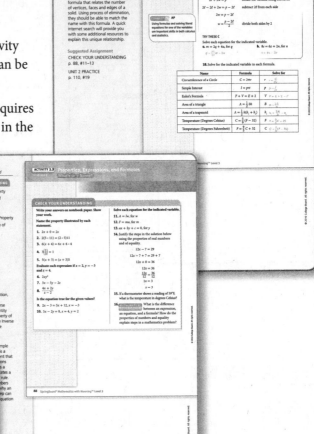

Unit Practice provides additional problems for each activity for extra practice, review, or for additional instruction. Problems can be used to further assess learning after review or instruction.

Performance Based Assessments

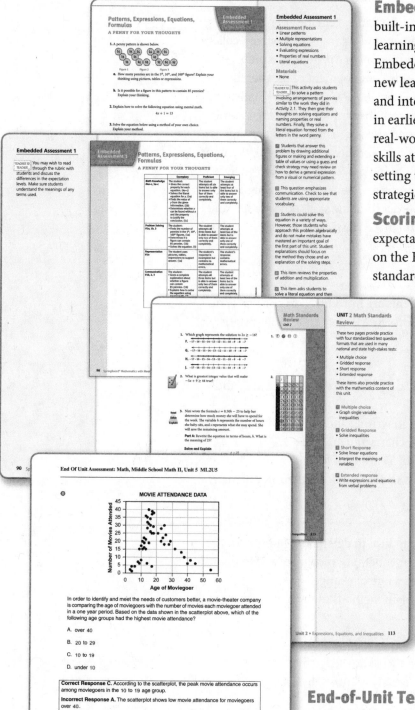

Embedded Assessments provide built-in opportunities to evaluate student learning. Each unit contains two to three Embedded Assessments that cover both new learning in the preceding activities and integrate skills and knowledge learned in earlier units. Most assessments present real-world scenarios to assess students' skills at transferring knowledge from one setting to another, consistent with AP strategies.

Scoring Rubrics clearly spell out expectations for student performance on the Embedded Assessment. Process standards and math knowledge are assessed in areas of communication, connections, problem solving, representations, and reasoning and proof.

Math Standards Review provides practice on new math concepts in formats found on standardized tests.

End-of-Unit Tests offer online and printable test formats with distractor rationales to inform learning and instruction.

The Pathway to Advanced Placement and College Readiness

SpringBoard provides a comprehensive and systematic approach to preparing ALL students for the demands of rigorous AP courses, college classes, and other post-secondary experiences. SpringBoard prepares students through sequential, scaffolded development of the prerequisite skills and knowledge needed for success in AP Calculus and Statistics. In each unit of study, explicit AP Connections are outlined in the Planning the Unit pages of the teachers' edition and are reinforced as they appear in student activities. Through ongoing exposure to rigorous mathematics content and experience with the thinking processes needed to analyze, solve, and explain complex math problems, students exit SpringBoard equipped with the kind of higher order thinking skills, knowledge, and behaviors necessary to be successful in AP classes and beyond.

From Pre-AP to AP

Beginning in middle school, students are introduced to concepts and skills that are fundamental to success in AP mathematics and statistics courses.

Middle School 1 students learn to:
- Model functions in numerical, symbolic (equation), table, and graphical forms.
- Communicate mathematics in writing and verbally, justifying answers and clearly labeling charts and graphs.
- Explore and represent data in a variety of forms.
- Use multiple representations to communicate their mathematical understanding.

Middle School 2 students:
- Acquire an algebraic and graphical understanding of functions.
- Write, solve, and graph linear equations; recognize and verbalize patterns; and model slope as a rate of change.
- Communicate clearly to explain methods of problem solving and to interpret results.
- Investigate concepts presented visually and verbally.

Middle School 3 students extend their knowledge by:
- Writing algebraic models from a variety of physical, numeric, and verbal descriptions.
- Solving equations using a variety of methods.
- Justifying answers using precise mathematical language.
- Relating constant rate of change to verbal, physical, and algebraic models.
- Using technology to solve problems.
- Reinforcing and extending the vocabulary of probability and statistics.

Algebra 1 students:

- Gain an understanding of the properties of real numbers.
- Formalize the language of functions.
- Explore the behavior of functions numerically, graphically, analytically, and verbally.
- Use technology to discover relationships, test conjectures, and solve problems.
- Write expressions, equations, and inequalities from physical models.
- Communicate mathematics understanding formally and informally.

Geometry students:

- Read, analyze, and solve right triangle and trigonometric functions within contextual situations.
- Develop area formulas necessary for determining volumes of rotational solids, solids with known cross sections, and area beneath a curve.
- Explain work clearly so that the reasoning process can be followed throughout the solution.

Algebra 2 students:

- Develop the algebra of functions through operations, composition, and inverses.
- Read and analyze contextual situations involving exponential and logarithmic functions.
- Work with functions graphically, numerically, analytically, and verbally.
- Learn optimization problems.
- Compare the relative rate of change of linear and exponential functions.
- Learn the concept of infinite sum as a limit of partial sums.
- Work with statistics in numerical summaries, calculations using the normal curve, and the modeling of data.

Precalculus students:

- Gain an introductory understanding of convergence and divergence.
- Collect, analyze, and draw conclusions from data.
- Solve problems in contextual situations dealing with polynomial, rational, logarithmic, and trigonometric functions.
- Model motion using parametric equations and vectors.
- Develop an intuitive understanding of the limiting process and of continuity.
- Justify their reasoning and understanding verbally, in writing, and with models.
- Use technology to explore and support conclusions.

Concepts and Skills: A Progression to AP

| Middle School 1 | Middle School 2/3 | Algebra 1 |

Patterns/Limits

Middle School 1

Use a Venn diagram to find the LCM of 30 and 42.

First, place the prime factors in the Venn diagram.

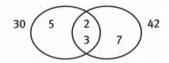

Then, multiply the factors in the intersection of the circles by the factors that are not in the intersection.

$$2 \times 3 \times 5 \times 7$$

Middle School 2/3

Place each number in the appropriate region of the Venn diagram.

$$5, -1, 0, 3, -12, -11, 15, 23, 2, -9$$

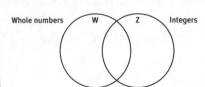

Algebra 1

Travis Smith and his brother, Roy, are co-owners of a trucking company. The company needs to transport two truckloads of fruit grown in Pecos, Texas, to a Dallas, Texas, distributing plant. If the fruit does not get to Dallas quickly, it will spoil. The farmers offer Travis a bonus if he can get both truckloads to Dallas within 24 hours.

Due to road construction, Travis knows it will take 10 hours to drive from Pecos to Dallas. The return trip to Pecos will take only 7.5 hours. He estimates it will take 1.5 hours to load the fruit onto the truck and 1 hour to unload it.

Why is it impossible for Travis to earn the bonus by himself?

Ratio/Rates of Change

Middle School 1

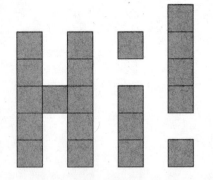

Look at the tiles that make up the message, Hi! Find the percent of the tiles in Hi! that are in the H.

In this situation, was it easier to find a fraction or a decimal before determining the percent? Explain and write your answer.

Middle School 2/3

Write and solve the proportion needed to calculate the hoist of a flag whose fly is 17 inches if $\dfrac{\text{hoist}}{\text{fly}} = \dfrac{1}{1.9}$.

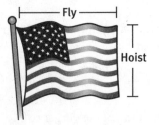

Algebra 1

A growler was found floating in the ocean just off the shore of Greenland. Its volume above water was approximately 27 cubic meters.

Two icebergs float near this growler. One iceberg's volume is 3^4 times that of the growler. The second iceberg's volume is 2^7 times that of the growler. Which iceberg has the larger volume? Explain.

Geometry

Use each of the following sets of triangle side lengths to build triangles using the manipulatives (straws) provided by your teacher.

Triangle side lengths	Type of triangle	c^2	$a^2 + b^2$
5, 12, 13			
6, 6, 12			
5, 6, 12			
5, 12, 15			
5, 12, 12			
6, 12, 13			
6, 12, 15			

What does your work suggest about the relationship between a^2, b^2, c^2, and the type of triangle?

Algebra 2

Many young children practice a form of cryptography when writing notes. The following message is written using a secret code.

What is needed to decipher the seven-letter word?

Precalculus

Let $f(x) = \dfrac{x^2 - 1}{x - 1}$. Use the following methods to explore the values of y as the value of x approaches 1.

Complete the table below.

	x approaches 1 from the left				x approaches 1 from the right		
x	0.9	0.99	0.999	1	1.001	1.01	1.1
$f(x)$							

Which two similar triangles allow us to state that $\dfrac{x}{t} = \dfrac{t}{z}$?

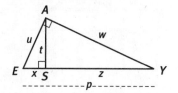

Wesley is interested in a four-year private college whose tuition and fees for the current year are about $24,000 and a four-year public university whose tuition and fees for the current year are about $10,000. In the last decade, tuition and fees have increased an average of 5.6% per year in four-year private colleges and 7.1% per year in four-year public colleges.

Complete the table to show the estimated tuition for the next four years.

Years From Present (t)	Private College Tuition and Fees	Public College Tuition and Fees
0	$24,000	$10,000
1		
2		
3		
4		

Write two functions to model the data in the table. Let $R(t)$ represent the private tuition and fees and $U(t)$ represent the public tuition and fees.

Lester worked during the time that Maurice attended graduate school. Each month, Lester saves $200 and deposits this amount into the $5000 money market account that his parents set up for him when he graduated.

Lester's money market account earns him 3% interest, compounded monthly. Complete the table to record Lester's money market account balance each month for the first five months that he worked.

Month	Account Balance
0	
1	
2	
3	
4	
5	

| Middle School 1 | Middle School 2/3 | Algebra 1 |

Expressions, Equations, Functions

Middle School 1

To keep the scale balanced, if you add something to one side, you must also add the same thing to the other side. If you subtract something from one side you must also subtract the same thing from the other side.

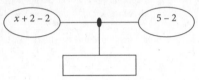

You can subtract 2 from the left side to isolate the x, because $+2$ and -2 are a zero pair. To keep the scale balanced you must also subtract 2 from the right side.

Middle School 2/3

Consider the relation $\{(1, 2), (2, 4), (4, 5), (8, 3)\}$.

Use mapping to determine if the relation is a function. Explain.

Step 1: Write all domain values in an oval.

Step 2: Write all range values in another oval.

Step 3: Connect the input values with their output values using arrows.

Algebra 1

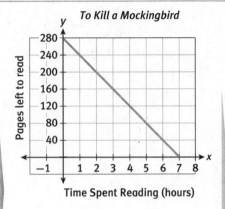

To Kill a Mockingbird

Pages left to read (y-axis): 40, 80, 120, 160, 200, 240, 280

Time Spent Reading (hours) (x-axis): −1, 1, 2, 3, 4, 5, 6, 7, 8

Identify the x-intercept and y-intercept from this model. What does each intercept represent in the problem situation?

Write the equation of this line using the intercepts. Identify the form of the equation that you have created.

Area/Accumulation

Middle School 1

Joseph is taking a summer cooking class taught by a chef named Dotty. She is an excellent cook but often forgets to tell the class how much of something to use. So Joseph is never quite sure if he has what he needs.

On the first day of class, he measures 6 cups of rice. When Dotty sees it, she says "Too much rice! Only 2 cups of rice are needed for this recipe."

Draw a model for 6 cups of rice. Use your drawing to find how many 2-cup amounts of rice are in 6 cups of rice.

Middle School 2/3

Use the formula Lillie found $(SA = Ph + 2B)$ to determine the surface area of this triangular prism.

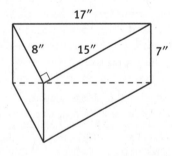

17″, 8″, 15″, 7″

Algebra 1

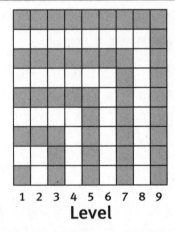

Level: 1 2 3 4 5 6 7 8 9

Investigate the patterns in the logo by completing the table below.

Level	# of Squares Added	Perimeter	Total Area
1	1	4	1
2			
3			
4			

Geometry	Algebra 2	Precalculus

Geometry

For each polygon, plot the ordered pair (number of sides, sum of angle measures) on the axes below.

Carefully choose and label your scale on each axis.

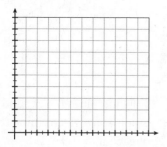

The data points you graphed above should appear collinear. Write an equation for the line determined by these points.

Algebra 2

Write the equation and graph the hyperbola described.

center (−1, 4), transverse axis 6 units, vertical conjugate axis 8 units

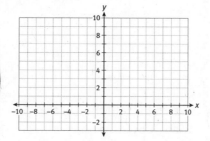

Precalculus

The number of minutes of daylight for any location at 60° N latitude is modeled by the function below.

$$m(d) = 390 \sin\left[\frac{2\pi}{365.25}(d - 80)\right] + 738$$

where d = day of the year

Use a calculator to graph the function $m(d)$. Then sketch the graph on the axes below.

Table tops are made with laminate delivered to *A Cut Above* in different rectangular sizes. Before making any cuts, a cardboard template is made to be used as a guide. Lorena uses the templates to investigate the areas.

One of the templates that Lorena must determine the area of is shown.

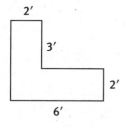

Determine the area of this shape. Be sure to include units of measure with your answer. Describe the method used.

To expand a series to show the terms of the series, substitute 1, 2, 3, and 4 into the expression for the general term. To find the sum of the series, add the terms.

$$\sum_{n=1}^{4} (2n + 5) = (2 \cdot 1 + 5)$$
$$+ (2 \cdot 2 + 5)$$
$$+ (2 \cdot 3 + 5)$$
$$+ (2 \cdot 4 + 5)$$
$$= 7 + 9 + 11 + 13$$

Write the first four terms and the last term in the series $\sum_{n=1}^{100} (2n - 3)$. Then find the indicated partial sum.

Rainwater harvesting is becoming a viable alternative for supplying households and businesses with water. Rain collects in gutters that channel the water into a cistern or a rain barrel.

A manufacturer needs to use the least amount of material to build a cistern to maximize profits.

For a cylindrical cistern with a volume of 25 cubic meters, create an equation that represents the total surface area of aluminum that it would take to build the cistern in terms of the radius x.

Use your graphing calculator with a window set to $0 \le x \le 5$ and $0 \le y \le 150$. Determine the intervals on this window that the function is increasing or decreasing.

What is the minimum amount of aluminum needed to build this cistern, to the nearest whole number?

Middle School 1	**Middle School 2/3**	**Algebra 1**

Graphs/Coordinate Plane/Transformations

One sunny day, Sen T. Pede and his friend Lady Bug start out from the elm tree and move toward a rose bush that is 45 feet away. Sen crawls at 5 feet per minute and Lady crawls at 3 feet per minute.

Use the diagram below to show where each critter is exactly three minutes after they start their journey. Place the letter S at Sen's location and the letter L at Lady's location.

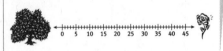

To perform a reflection, each point of a pre-image is copied on the opposite side of a given line and remains equidistant from the line.

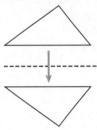

Sketch the reflection of the triangle over the line $y = 4$.

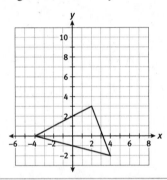

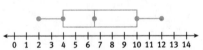

Consider lines l_1, l_2, l_3, and l_4 on the graph above. Determine the slope of each line.

In the graph above, l_1 is parallel to l_2 and l_3 is parallel to l_4. Write a conjecture about the slopes of parallel lines.

Data Analysis & Probability

In Xander's hat are cards numbered 1–20. He will draw out one card and replace it each time. He is interested in getting a card with an odd number (event A) or a multiple of 3 (event B).

a. Write the sample space for each event.

b. Find the probability of each event occurring. Write the probability three ways, as a fraction, a decimal, and a percent.

c. For each probability in Part b, describe what the fraction, the decimal, and the percent mean in terms of the event.

d. Find $P(\text{not } A)$ and $P(\text{not } B)$.

e. Make a Venn diagram of the relationship between the outcomes of events A and B.

The box-and-whisker plot below shows the average number of points scored per game by each player on the basketball team this season.

What is the median number of points scored by a player?

What is the lower quartile?

What percent of the players have average scores that are less than 10 points?

What is the range of the average number of points scored in a game as displayed in the box-and-whisker plot above?

To find the absolute mean deviation of Zach's data, begin by completing the table. Recall that Zach's mean time is 60 min.

Time x	Time − Mean $= (x - \bar{x})$	|Time − Mean| $= \|x - \bar{x}\|$
10	$10 - 60 = -50$	$\|10 - 60\| = 50$
60		
20		
135		
75		

Geometry

Use coordinate geometry to prove the following triangles similar.

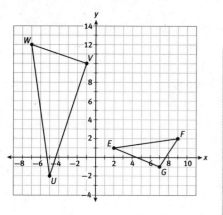

Algebra 2

For the absolute value function, describe the transformations represented in the rule and use them to graph the function.

$$g(x) = |x + 2| - 3$$

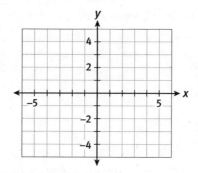

Precalculus

Graphs of polynomials can be sketched by plotting the x- and y-intercepts and considering the end behavior of a function.

Use what you know about end behavior and zeros of a function to sketch a small graph of each function.

a. $f(x) = x + 3$

b. $g(x) = (x + 5)(x - 5)$

c. $h(x) = (x + 4)(x - 4)(x + 1)$

d. $k(x) = (x + 2)(x - 2)(x + 1)(x - 1)$

Jamming Gems		
Shapes	Lengths	Gemstone colors
Square Cut	18 inches	Pink
Princess Cut	24 inches	Clear
Pear shape	36 inches	Blue
Marquise		Purple
Round		Green
Oval		

How many necklaces with one shape, length, and gemstone color can be created at *Jamming Gems*? Explain how you arrived at your answer.

Janet and Bob both have type A blood. Each carries the dominant gene for the type A antigen and the recessive gene for the type O antigen. A Punnett Square that represents the possible gene combinations for their children is below.

	A	O
A	AA	AO
O	AO	OO

A gene combination of AA or AO represents a child with Type A blood and a gene combination of OO represents a child with Type O blood.

1. What is the probability that a child of Janet and Bob will be type O?

2. What is the probability that a child of Janet and Bob will be type A?

Year	G	Ln(G)
1	7.475	
2	9.663	
3	13.696	
4	18.039	
5	24.320	
6	31.164	
7	39.290	
8	47.693	
9	59.003	
10	74.153	
11	93.849	

The table displays G the global installed wind capacity (the amount of energy created from all installed wind turbines) in Megawatts from 1997 to 2007, with 1996 as year 0.

Create a scatter plot of the re-expressed data. Then find a linear regression equation for the re-expressed data.

The SpringBoard Math Classroom

A SpringBoard classroom is an environment which supports high expectations for all students as they develop problem solving, critical thinking, and reasoning skills.

Collaborative Groups

The **student-centered classroom** capitalizes on collaboration. It is an environment where students are able to engage in purposeful conversation with partners and small groups. Collaborative groups provide a setting in which students feel safe to explore ideas and venture ideas. Group structure should encourage all members to work together to complete a given task while insuring that each student is held accountable for equal participation in the assignment. Collaborative groups allow learning to be active as students engage in discussions making conjectures, questioning, discovering and as they fulfill tasks within the group. Collaborative groups promote the exploration of a variety of ideas and approaches.

Debriefing / Reflections

Frequently in a mathematics classroom students and teachers should engage in **debriefings**. The purpose of debriefing is to allow learners to reflect on their learning, correct misconceptions, identify thinking processes used during an activity, summarize information, and process what they have learned. Debriefing can be accomplished in a variety of ways including whole class discussion, small group discussion, group presentation, and individual writing.

Interactive Word Wall

The **Word Wall** facilitates vocabulary development for the class. Creating and maintaining a Word Wall is an ongoing activity. It should be an instructional tool, not just a display. Designate a specific space (such as a bulletin or blank wall space) in the classroom for the Word Wall. Words may be written on index cards, sentence strips, or blank paper by you or by your students.

- As your students encounter new words, you or your students may add them to the Word Wall.
- Spend time revisiting words on the Wall whenever possible.
- Emphasize the categorization of words to help students see the logic in language. Invite them to generate a list of potential categories to sort words. (alphabetical order, mathematical concepts, problem solving techniques, etc.)
- Make the words into manipulatives by writing them on cards so that they can be shifted, added, and/or eliminated.
- Encourage students to use words from the Wall correctly in their writing, specifically on the Embedded Assessments.

Vocabulary Notebook

The **Vocabulary Notebook** facilitates vocabulary development for the individual student. It is an intentional tool for students to expand their understanding of academic terms and concepts. The Vocabulary Notebook may be a spiral notebook, a section of the students' mathematics notebook, or a composition notebook. As students are introduced to Academic Vocabulary, they can explore terms and concepts and discuss other math terms that are encompassed by the word. Students can complete vocabulary graphic organizers for Academic Vocabulary and add to the organizers as relevant terms are introduced, saving the completed graphic organizers in their Vocabulary Notebook.

In previous courses, students have learned to investigate patterns, apply number and operation procedures to specific situations, and analyze solutions as reasonable or unreasonable. This unit expands upon fundamental and procedural aspects of number and operations through contextual applications of pattern investigation, laws of exponents, decimal and fraction operations, scientific notation, and properties of rational and irrational numbers.

Academic Vocabulary

Blackline masters for use in developing students' vocabulary skills are located at the back of the Student's Edition. Encourage students to explore the meanings of the academic vocabulary words in this unit, using graphic organizers and class discussions to help students understand the key concepts related to the terms. Encourage students to place their vocabulary organizers in their math notebooks and to revisit these pages to make notes as their understanding of concepts increases.

Embedded Assessments

The two Embedded Assessments for this unit follow Activities 1.2 and 1.5.

CollegeBoard
inspiring minds™

Algebra/AP/College Readiness

Unit 1 builds a deeper student understanding of number and operations and expands to concepts of arithmetic and geometric sequences, inverse, limits, and infinity by:

- Allowing students to explore and explain patterns involving both arithmetic and geometric sequences.

- Using manipulatives in a contextual situation to introduce students to the concepts of limits and infinity.

- Modeling the concept of inverses through analysis of patterns and multiple representations.

- Encouraging students to communicate about mathematics and explain solutions both verbally and in written sentences.

- Giving students opportunities to analyze data and make predictions about further applications.

Embedded Assessment 1   Contagious Mathematics

- Identifying and describing patterns
- Operations with exponents

Embedded Assessment 2   A Recipe for Success

- Operations with fractions
- Equivalent forms of numbers
- Rational and irrational numbers
- Scientific notation
- Inverse operations

Suggested Pacing

The following table provides suggestions for pacing either a 45-minute period or a block schedule class of 90 minutes. Space is left for you to write your own pacing guidelines based on your experiences in using the materials.

	45-Minute Period	90-Minute Period	Comments on Pacing
Unit Overview	$\frac{1}{2}$	$\frac{1}{4}$	
Activity 1.1	4	2	
Activity 1.2	4	2	
Embedded Assessment 1	1	$\frac{1}{2}$	
Activity 1.3	5	$2\frac{1}{2}$	
Activity 1.4	5	$2\frac{1}{2}$	
Activity 1.5	4	2	
Embedded Assessment 2	1	$\frac{1}{2}$	
Total	$24\frac{1}{2}$	$12\frac{1}{4}$	

Unit Practice

Practice Problems for each activity in the unit appear at the end of the unit.

Math Standards Review

To help accustom students to the formats and types of questions they may encounter on high stakes tests, additional problems are provided at the end of the unit. These problems are constructed for multiple choice, short response, extended response, and gridded responses.

Patterns and Numerical Relationships

 Unit 1

Unit Overview
In this unit you will investigate patterns, rational and irrational numbers, and the properties of exponents. You will apply your knowledge of fractions and decimals to practical situations.

Academic Vocabulary
Add these words to your vocabulary notebook.
- hypothesis
- power
- reciprocal
- scientific notation

Essential Questions

 How are fractions, percents and decimals related?

 Why is it important to understand the procedures for working with different kinds of numbers?

EMBEDDED ASSESSMENTS

This unit has two Embedded Assessments, following Activities 1.2 and 1.5. These Embedded Assessments allow you to demonstrate your understanding of patterns, exponents, and scientific notation. You will also display your ability to work with equivalent forms of numbers, fractions, decimals, and percents—and distinguish between rational and irrational numbers.

1

UNIT 1 OVERVIEW

Unit Overview
Ask students to read the unit overview and mark the text to identify key phrases that indicate what they will do in this unit. Ask them what they know about fractions, decimals, and percents.

Essential Questions
Read the essential questions with students and ask them to give a real world situation that would use decimals, fractions or percents.

Materials
- Calculator
- Plain paper

Academic Vocabulary
Discuss with students the importance of precise language in mathematics. Read through the vocabulary list with students. Assess prior knowledge by asking students if they can define any of the terms. Emphasize to students that as the course develops there will be many additional terms in the text that they will need to add to their vocabulary notebooks.

You may wish to assign some or all of these exercises to gauge students' readiness for Unit 1 topics.

Prerequisite Skills

- Operations with fractions and decimals (Items 3, 4, 6, 7)
- Simplifying fractions (Item 5)
- Equivalent forms of numbers (Items 1, 2)
- Perfect squares (Item 8)

Answer Key

1. $\frac{3}{5}$, 0.6, 60%

2. Sample answers:

a. $\left(\frac{5}{6}\right)$

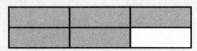

b. (30%)

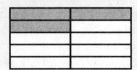

c. 75%

3a. 1.12, 1.345, 1.6789

b. $\frac{1}{2}, \frac{5}{8}, \frac{3}{4}$

4. $\frac{2}{3} + \frac{4}{5}$. Justifications will vary. When you add fractions, you find and use a common denominator
$\frac{2}{3} + \frac{4}{5} = \frac{10}{15} + \frac{12}{15} = \frac{22}{15}$ and
$\frac{2}{5} + \frac{5}{6} = \frac{12}{30} + \frac{25}{30} = \frac{37}{30}$
$\frac{22}{15} = \frac{44}{30}$, which is more than $\frac{37}{30}$.

5. Sample answer: Mixed numbers and improper fractions can represent the same number in different forms. $\frac{5}{2} = 2\frac{1}{2}$, $\frac{5}{2}$ is an improper fraction and $2\frac{1}{2}$ is a mixed number.

Write your answers on notebook paper. Show your work.

1. Give a fraction, a decimal and a percent that represents the shaded portion of the figure shown.

2. Draw a visual representation of each of the following. Use a circle for at least one of your figures.
  a. $\frac{5}{6}$
  b. 30%
  c. 0.75

3. Arrange each of the following groups of numbers in increasing order.
  a. 1.345, 1.6789, 1.12
  b. $\frac{1}{2}, \frac{3}{4}, \frac{5}{8}$

4. Which of the following is larger? Justify your answer.
  $\frac{2}{3} + \frac{4}{5}$ or $\frac{2}{5} + \frac{5}{6}$

5. How are mixed numbers and improper fractions related?

6. Which of the following is the product of 2.4 and 3.1?
  a. 0.55
  b. 5.5
  c. 7.44
  d. 74.4

7. Evaluate each of the following.
  a. $\frac{3}{4} + \frac{2}{3}$
  b. $\frac{3}{4} - \frac{2}{3}$
  c. $\frac{3}{4} \cdot \frac{2}{3}$
  d. $\frac{3}{4} \div \frac{2}{3}$
  e. $4.6 + 0.23$
  f. $4.6 - 0.23$
  g. $4.6 \cdot 0.23$
  h. $4.6 \div 0.23$

8. Explain why 49 is a perfect square and 50 is not a perfect square. Give three other numbers that are perfect squares and three that are not.

---

6. c

7a. $\frac{17}{12}$ or $1\frac{5}{12}$

b. $\frac{1}{12}$

c. $\frac{1}{2}$

d. $\frac{9}{8}$ or $1\frac{1}{8}$

e. 4.83

f. 4.37

g. 1.058

h. 20

8. Sample answer: A perfect square is the product of one number and itself. $7 \cdot 7 = 49$ so 49 is a perfect square. There is no number that can be multiplied with itself to get 50, so 50 is not a perfect square. The numbers 4, 16, 25, 36, 100 are examples of perfect squares. The numbers 3, 10, 20, 28 are examples of numbers that are not perfect squares.

Investigating Patterns
Laws and Orders

SUGGESTED LEARNING STRATEGIES: Look for a Pattern, Visualization, Think/Pair/Share

My Notes

For much of the late 19th and early 20th centuries, the fictional character Sherlock Holmes was known for his great detective work. In this activity, you will be asked to perform many tasks similar to those Sherlock used to solve his cases.

In order to solve mysteries, Holmes used a deductive process that led him to a logical conclusion. First, he would *observe* a situation and gather as many facts as possible. Next, he would *analyze* each fact to determine its relevance to the situation. Then he would *search* for even more clues by considering the smallest of details. Finally, he would use his *imagination* to link all of the clues together in the most logical manner.

The Case of the Arabic Symbols

At first glance, the following picture would appear to be a representation of the numbers one through nine. However, the way they are drawn gives a clue to how the symbols for each number were originally created.

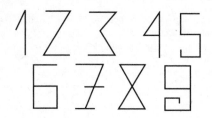

1. Observe, analyze, and search for clues in the diagram to come up with a guess about why the numbers were first written this way. Don't forget to use your imagination!

Answers may vary. Sample answer: Each number is written in such a way that the number of angles in the representation equals the number itself. One has one angle, two has two angles, etc.

Investigating Patterns

Activity Focus
- Investigating and describing patterns
- Inverse operations
- Equivalent forms of numbers

Materials
- No special materials are needed.

Chunking the Activity

# 1	#9–10	#15
#2–3	#11	#16–17
#4–6	#12	#18
#7–8	#13–14	#19–20

TEACHER TO TEACHER The purpose of this activity is to allow students to explore various ways to investigate patterns. Make sure students are able to provide multiple representations and equivalent forms of numbers.

1 Look for a Pattern, Visualization, Think/Pair/Share Students explore the pattern on their own and draw tentative conclusions.

2 Discussion Group, Visualization, Look for a Pattern Students explore the pattern in groups. They should reach the conclusion that the number of angles in each representation corresponds to the numerical value of the numbers. Some groups may have difficulty recognizing the pattern and may benefit from additional questioning about their observations.

3 Discussion Group, Visualization, Look for a Pattern Students should extend their explanation of the patterns to determine that the symbol for zero contains no angles.

My Notes

SUGGESTED LEARNING STRATEGIES: Discussion Group, Visualization, Look for a Pattern

2. Discuss your observations with your group.

a. List some observations that you had in common with your group members.
Answers may vary.

b. List some observations that your group members had that you didn't think of.
Answers may vary.

c. As a group, write an official conclusion based on your shared observations.
Answers may vary but should include connections to the number of angles in each of the representations.

3. Based on your group's conclusion, explain how this pattern could also be used to describe zero with the symbol **0**.
The symbol for zero has no angles.

SUGGESTED LEARNING STRATEGIES: Look for a Pattern, Create Representations, Quickwrite

My Notes

The Case of the Multiple Viewpoints

The next case at hand involves investigating the pattern shown below. In order to reconstruct the pattern and solve the mystery, several witnesses have been asked to describe the pattern.

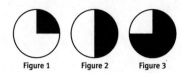

Figure 1   Figure 2   Figure 3

4. The description provided by the first witness is given in terms of percents. Provide an example of what this description might be.

Answers may vary. Sample answer: Each successive circle has 25% more shading than the last.

5. The second witness used fractions to describe the pattern. Provide an example of what this description might be.

Answer may vary. Sample answer: Each successive circle has $\frac{1}{4}$ more shading that the last.

6. Witnesses #3 and #4 have provided different accounts of the pattern. One of them describes the pattern as increasing, and the other describes it as decreasing. Explain how both of their descriptions could be considered correct.

Answers may vary. Sample answer: The amount of shaded area is increasing, and the amount of unshaded area is decreasing.

---

4 Look for a Pattern, Create Representations, Quickwrite
This question provides background information for the students' prior knowledge of percents.

5 Look for a Pattern, Create Representations, Quickwrite
Together, Items 4 and 5 provide background information for the students' prior knowledge of equivalent forms of numbers. There may be a need to provide additional support based on student responses.

6 Look for a Pattern, Create Representations, Quickwrite
Students explore the idea that some problems have multiple approaches and multiple solutions. The pattern can be described as an increase in shaded area or a decrease in unshaded area, and both descriptions are correct.

7 Create Representations, Look for a Pattern Students should recognize that either description of the pattern (increasing or decreasing) will generate the same fourth figure.

8 Quickwrite It is important for students to understand that solutions can often be reached in a variety of ways. Throughout this course, students will have the opportunity to explore and validate multiple approaches to the same problem.

Suggested Assignment

CHECK YOUR UNDERSTANDING
p. 12, #1a, 2a

UNIT 1 PRACTICE
p. 50, #1a, 1b

9 Look for a Pattern, Quickwrite The pattern of the figures is a little more complicated than the previous two examples. While most students will correctly determine that the number of line segments increases by 1, and the number of squares increases by two, some may not recognize that the figures are rotating ninety degrees counterclockwise.

My Notes

7. Analyze the descriptions of all four witnesses and draw a representation of what Figure 4 would look like if the pattern continued.

8. Explain why it is necessary to gather as much evidence about the pattern from as many different viewpoints as possible.

Answers may vary. Sample answer: Gathering evidence from different viewpoints will give you a more complete idea of the pattern, and can confirm or rule out your original analysis.

The Case of the Revolving Figure
Case #3 involves the pattern shown below:

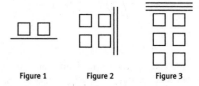

Figure 1   Figure 2   Figure 3

9. Observe and analyze the pattern, then describe it in as much detail as possible.

Answers may vary. Student answers should include observations about the number of segments and squares in each figure as well as the rotation of the figures.

Investigating Patterns
Laws and Orders

SUGGESTED LEARNING STRATEGIES: Discussion Group, Self/
Peer Revision, Look for a Pattern, Create Representations

My Notes

10. Share your description with your group members and list any details you may not have considered before.
    Answers may vary.

11. Use the evidence gathered in Questions 9 and 10 to draw representations of the fourth and fifth figures in the pattern.

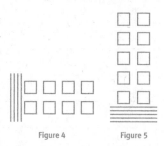

Figure 4   Figure 5

12. Answer the following based on your observations of the pattern.

    a. Describe the pattern for the number of line segments in each figure.
    The number of segments increases by one each time.

    b. How many line segments would appear in Figure 16?   16

    c. How many line segments would appear in Figure 49?   49

    d. Explain how you could determine the number of line segments in *any* figure in the pattern.
    The number of line segments is equal to the figure number.

> **WRITING MATH**
> One way to describe number patterns is to list several terms in order, followed by ellipses (...) to indicate that the pattern continues. For example, writing
>
> 1, 3, 5, 7, ...
>
> implies that the pattern of adding two to each digit continues indefinitely.

ACTIVITY 1.1 *Continued*

10 Discussion Group, Self/Peer Revision All groups should have recognized by now that the figures are rotating.

11 Look for a Pattern, Create Representations Some students may need to use notebook paper for their drawings.

12 Look for a Pattern Students who struggle with parts c and d may need additional questions about earlier figures in the pattern. While they may recognize the number of line segments increases by 1 each time, they may not make the connection that the number of line segments is equal to the figure number.

13 Graphic Organizer, Look for a Pattern, Work Backward

The first column of the table organizes the students' answers from Item 12. While most students are able to determine the number of squares and the sum of squares and line segments in the first five figures, some may have difficulty making the connection that the number of squares is twice the figure number and the sum is three times the figure number. Additional questioning about the sixth and seventh figures may benefit these students.

14 Look for a Pattern Although expressions have yet to be introduced, accelerated learners may be able to describe the patterns as *n*, 2*n*, and 3*n*, respectively.

My Notes

13. Organize the evidence you gathered about line segments, and continue to explore the pattern in the table below.

Figure	Number of Line Segments	Number of Squares	Sum of Line Segments and Squares
1	1	2	3
2	2	4	6
3	3	6	9
4	4	8	12
5	5	10	15
16	16	32	48
49	49	98	147

14. Explain how you could determine the number of squares and the sum of line segments and squares in any figure in the pattern.

Answers may vary. Sample answer: The number of squares is twice the figure number. The sum of squares and segments is three times the figure number.

SUGGESTED LEARNING STRATEGIES: Look for a Pattern,
Work Backward, Discussion Group, Graphic Organizer

My Notes

TRY THESE A

Describe the pattern, and list the next three terms in the following
sequences:

a. 0, 8, 16, 24, ...   Add 8; 32, 40, 48

b. 2, −4, −10, −16, ...   Subtract 6; −22, −28, −34

c. 27, 9, 3, 1, ...   Divide by 3; $\frac{1}{3}, \frac{1}{9}, \frac{1}{27}$

15. Complete the table below by investigating each sequence.

Sequence	Increasing or Decreasing?	Next Term in the Sequence	Description of Pattern
0, 5, 10, 15...	Increasing	20	Add 5
−8, −4, −2, −1, ...	Increasing	−0.5 or $-\frac{1}{2}$	Divide by 2
1.5, 2.75, 4, ...	Increasing	5.25	Add 1.25
$\frac{1}{8}, \frac{1}{4}, \frac{1}{2}, ...$	Increasing	1	Multiply by 2
$2, \frac{5}{4}, \frac{1}{2}, ...$	Decreasing	$-\frac{1}{4}$	Subtract $\frac{3}{4}$

ACTIVITY 1.1 *Continued*

TRY THESE A This practice gives
students an opportunity to make
sure they understand how to
identify patterns before going on
to the next questions.

15 Look for a Pattern, Work
Backward, Group Discussion,
Graphic Organizer Students
who struggle with fractions and/or
decimals may have difficulty with
some of the patterns. It may help
to encourage them to convert
some of the terms to equivalent
forms.

16 Look for a Pattern, Work Backward Students have the opportunity to review subtraction of integers and find absolute value. You may wish to have students extend the sequence, using absolute-value expressions and single numbers, by several more terms to ensure understanding and to prepare them for Item 17.

17 Look for a Pattern, Think/Pair/Share Students review operations with integers and finding absolute value. Ask students to share the order in which they performed the operations to evaluate each expression.

My Notes

SUGGESTED LEARNING STRATEGIES: Self/Peer Revision, Think/Pair/Share

> **MATH TERMS**
> The **absolute value** of a number is its distance (number of units) from 0 on a number line. Absolute value is always nonnegative.

16. Consider this sequence that uses absolute values of numerical expressions.

$$|5 - 2|, |5 - 3|, |5 - 4|, |5 - 5|, |5 - 6|, |5 - 7|$$

   a. Is this sequence increasing or decreasing? Explain.

   Answers may vary. Sample answer: If you evaluate each term, you get 3, 2, 1, 0, 1, 2. This sequence starts as a decreasing sequence but then becomes an increasing sequence.

   b. Express the next term in the sequence two ways.

   Answers may vary. Sample answer: $|5 - 8|$ and 3

17. Write the information requested in the bulleted list for each set of numerical expressions.

   a. $|-16| \times |5|, |-18 - 2|, |3 - 13|, |38| + |-2|, \left|-\frac{10}{2}\right|$

   - Evaluate each absolute-value expression.

     $|-16| \times |5| = 80, |-18 - 2| = 20, |3 - 13| = 10, |38| + |-2| = 40,$
     $\left|-\frac{10}{2}\right| = 5$

   - Order the numbers so that they form a sequence.

     Answers may vary. Sample sequence: 5, 10, 20, 40, 80

   - Describe the pattern in the sequence.

     Using the sample sequence above, each term is two times the term that comes before it.

   b. $-2|-4|, \dfrac{|-24|}{6}, |-2| \times |-5|, 40|2 \div 5|, |7| - |-9|$

   - Evaluate each absolute-value expression.

     $-8, 4, 10, 16, -2$

   - Order the numbers so that they form a sequence.

     $-8, -2, 4, 10, 16$

   - Describe the pattern in the sequence.

     6 is added each time, and the sequence is increasing.

SUGGESTED LEARNING STRATEGIES: Look for a Pattern, Discussion Group, Self/Peer Revision

The Case of the Missing Term
In the previous cases, the given patterns contained at least three terms. In this case, however, only the first two terms have been provided.

$$12, 6, \ldots$$

18. Explain how it would be possible to use any of the four mathematical operations to generate the first two numbers in the pattern. Then write the first four terms of the series based on your explanation.
   Answers may vary. See sample answers below.

   a. Addition
      Add –6; 12, 6, 0, –6

   b. Subtraction
      Subtract 6; 12, 6, 0, –6

   c. Multiplication
      Multiply by $\frac{1}{2}$; 12, 6, 3, 1.5

   d. Division
      Divide by 2; 12, 6, 3, 1.5

19. Observe and analyze your results from Question 18. Compare and contrast the patterns that were generated.
   Patterns generated by addition and subtraction are the same.
   Patterns generated by multiplication and division are the same.

My Notes

ACTIVITY 1.1 *Continued*

18 Look for a Pattern, Group Discussion, Self/Peer Revision
This exercise could be used as an introduction to the concept of inverse operations. This will be helpful when exploring division of fractions in Activity 1.4. Students who struggle with integer operations may have difficulty understanding that subtracting a number is the same as adding the opposite of the number.

19 Look for a Pattern, Group Discussion, Self/Peer Revision
The exploration of inverse operations continues as students begin to formalize their observations. Subtracting a number and adding its opposite both generate the same pattern. Dividing a number and multiplying by its reciprocal also generate the same pattern. Students should also be able to determine that addition and subtraction generate different values than multiplication and division.

ACTIVITY 1.1 Continued

TRY THESE B These short problems give students additional practice in using mathematical operations to determine possible patterns.

20 Quickwrite, Group Presentation This question combines the methods of observation students use to discover a pattern with the added component of inverse operations. Discussion of this question should include observations about multiple approaches to the same answer. In addition, students should understand that a lack of information may lead to different answers.

Suggested Assignment

CHECK YOUR UNDERSTANDING
p. 12, #1b–1e, 2b, 3, 4

UNIT 1 PRACTICE
p. 50, #1c–1d, 2–4

CHECK YOUR UNDERSTANDING

1. Descriptions may vary. Possible descriptions given:

a. Each circle has a polygon inscribed in it. Each successive polygon has one more side than the last;

b. Multiply the terms in the odd positions by 2 and add 3 to the terms in the even positions; 8, 12

c. Multiply by 0.2; 0.0016, 0.00032

d. Add 2 to the numerator and add 2 to the denominator. $\frac{7}{8}$, $\frac{9}{10}$

e. Within the absolute value symbol consecutive even integers, beginning with −2, are added to −3; 3, 5. Some students may evaluate the absolute values and consider

---

My Notes

TRY THESE B

Describe two ways to generate the next term in each of the following patterns. Answers may vary. Sample answers:

a. 9, 27, …   Multiply by 3 or add 18

b. 12, 48, …   Multiply by 4 or add 36

20. Explain why it is usually necessary to be given at least three terms in order to establish a pattern.
Answers may vary. Sample answer: A pattern is established by a series of changes. A pattern demonstrated by two terms only shows one change, and so cannot give enough information to establish a distinct pattern.

CHECK YOUR UNDERSTANDING

Write your answers on notebook paper. Show your work.

1. Describe the following patterns and determine the next two terms:

a.

b. 1, 3, 2, 6, 4, 9, …

c. 0.2, 0.04, 0.008, …

d. $\frac{1}{2}$, $\frac{3}{4}$, $\frac{5}{6}$, …

e. $|-3 + -2|$, $|-3 + 0|$, $|-3 + 2|$, $|-3 + 4|$, …

2. Come up with two different ways to represent the fourth term in each of the following patterns.

a.

b. $\frac{1}{1}$, $\frac{1}{4}$, $\frac{1}{9}$, …

3. The numbers below are known as Fibonacci numbers. Can you discover the pattern?

1, 1, 2, 3, 5, 8, …

4. **MATHEMATICAL REFLECTION** Describe the different ways that patterns can be represented as well as the process you use to discover whether a pattern exists.

---

the sequence 5,3,1,1,… They may say the sequnce doesn't have a pattern, they may think the next terms are all 1, or they may consider the sequence to be 5,3,1,1,3,5,…

2. Possible answers:

a. or 10

b. or $\frac{1}{16}$

3. Each term in the pattern is the sum of the previous two terms.

4. Answers may vary. Sample answer: Patterns can be represented as a series of numbers, shapes, or other symbols. A pattern is defined by a series of logical changes. To find a pattern given a series of terms, one must try to find the rule that reliably predicts each consecutive term.

Properties of Exponents
That's a Lot of Cats!

SUGGESTED LEARNING STRATEGIES: Discussion Group, Work Backward, Guess and Check

My Notes

As I was going to St. Ives,
I met a man with seven wives.
Every wife had seven sacks,
And every sack had seven cats.
Every cat had seven kittens
Kittens, cats, sacks, wives,
How many were going to St. Ives?

In addition to being an 18th century translation of what the *Guinness Book of World Records* claims is the oldest mathematical riddle in history, the above poem has also been the subject of great debate over the years.

CONNECT TO HISTORY

Problem 79 on the Rhind Mathematical Papyrus (circa 1650 BCE) contains the algorithm that is said to be the basis for the mathematics in this riddle.

1. Depending on the interpretation of the question, the riddle is said to have multiple answers. Determine whether or not each of the following could be considered a reasonable answer to the riddle. Justify your reasoning. Justifications may vary.

   a. 28

   Not reasonable

   b. 29

   Not reasonable

   c. 2801

   Reasonable if the man and the wives, sacks, cats, and kittens are all going to St. Ives as well.

   d. 1

   Reasonable if the narrator is the only person traveling to St. Ives.

ACTIVITY 1.2 Investigative

Properties of Exponents

Activity Focus
• Laws of exponents

Materials
• Calculator

Chunking the Activity

#1	#6	#11–12
#2	#7–9	#13–14
#3–5	#10	#15

TEACHER TO TEACHER The purpose of this activity is to allow students the opportunity to discover and verify the laws of exponents. Throughout the activity, students will be asked to generalize the rules for exponents, however, it may be necessary to convert their observations and explanations into formal rules.

1 Discussion Group, Work Backward, Guess and Check
The poem can be interpreted in several ways. The simplest explanation is that only the narrator is traveling to St. Ives, which makes the riddle's answer 1. However, if everything described in the poem is interpreted as traveling to St. Ives, the answer becomes 2801. Students who consider parts a and b to be reasonable are multiplying 7 by 4 rather than identifying each iteration as a power of 7.

2 Guess and Check, Look for a Pattern To complete the table, students may require further explanation of the concepts of expanded form, exponential form, and standard form.

3 Look for a Pattern, Simplify the Problem Students should recognize this question as an extension of the table.

4 Look for a Pattern, Simplify the Problem Students will offer various ways to group the product. While the note in the student edition defines the associative property of multiplication, it may be helpful to connect the definition of the property with the meaning of the word "associate." In some cases, student responses such as $(7 \cdot 7)(7 \cdot 7 \cdot 7)$ and $(7 \cdot 7 \cdot 7)(7 \cdot 7)$ could be used to extend the discussion to the commutative property of multiplication.

SUGGESTED LEARNING STRATEGIES: Guess and Check, Look for a Pattern, Simplify the Problem.

My Notes

MATH TERMS

An **exponent** is a number that indicates how many times a **base** is used as a factor. For example, if you have 5 factors of x, $(x \cdot x \cdot x \cdot x \cdot x)$, they can be written as x^5. In this example, x is the base, and 5 is the exponent.

MATH TERMS

The **associative property of multiplication** states that for all real numbers a, b, and c, $(a \cdot b) \cdot c = a \cdot (b \cdot c)$.

Regardless of the many interpretations of the poem, the riddle can be used to explain how **exponents** work.

2. Complete the following table.

	Number Written in…			
	Expanded Form	Exponential Form	Standard Form	Base
Wives	7	7^1	7	7
Sacks	$7 \cdot 7$	7^2	49	7
Cats	$7 \cdot 7 \cdot 7$	7^3	343	7
Kittens	$7 \cdot 7 \cdot 7 \cdot 7$	7^4	2401	7

3. If each kitten had seven stripes, we could multiply $7 \cdot 7 \cdot 7 \cdot 7 \cdot 7$ to determine the number of stripes.

   a. How would this be expressed in exponential form? 7^5

   b. What is the value in standard form?   16,807

4. You could also use the **associative property of multiplication** to group the product in various ways such as $(7) \cdot (7 \cdot 7 \cdot 7 \cdot 7)$.

   a. Determine three additional ways to regroup the product.

   Answers may vary. Sample answers: $(7 \cdot 7 \cdot 7)(7 \cdot 7)$
   $(7 \cdot 7)(7 \cdot 7 \cdot 7)$
   $(7)(7 \cdot 7)(7 \cdot 7)$

   b. Rewrite each of your responses in part a using exponents.

   $7^3 \cdot 7^2$
   $7^2 \cdot 7^3$
   $7^1 \cdot 7^2 \cdot 7^2$

SUGGESTED LEARNING STRATEGIES: Quickwrite, Look for a Pattern

My Notes

5. Describe any patterns you notice about the exponents in Question 4.

Answers may vary but should include an understanding that the final answer, in exponential form, is derived from adding the exponents.

6. Consider the product $(x \cdot x) \cdot (x \cdot x \cdot x)$

   a. Rewrite the product using exponents. $(x^2)(x^3)$

   b. Simplify the expression, and write the answer in exponential form. x^5

   c. Describe the similarities and differences between this product and the products you examined in Question 5.

   Answers may vary. Students should include that although the bases are different in the two problems, the number of times the bases are multiplied is the same. Both answers indicate base^5.

   d. Based on your observations, write a rule for multiplying terms with exponents that have the same base.

   Answers may vary. Student answers should indicate an understanding that exponents are added when the terms with the same base are multiplied.

7. If you wanted to divide the number of kittens by the number of cats, we could express this as $\frac{2401}{343} = 7$.

   a. Rewrite this equation by expressing the numerator, denominator, and the answer in exponential form.

   $\frac{7^4}{7^3} = 7^1$

   b. Describe how you could simplify the fraction.

   Answers may vary but should include some understanding of canceling terms.

ACTIVITY 1.2 *Continued*

5 Quickwrite, Look for a Pattern Students should demonstrate an understanding that regardless of how the product is grouped, the total number of sevens (5) remains the same.

6 Quickwrite, Look for a Pattern Students are asked to extend the concept of a total number of factors to a product with a variable for a base. Some students may require additional levels of questioning comparing Items 5 and 6 to lead them to the conclusion that the product of powers with the same base can be simplified by adding the exponents of the terms. While it is important for students to be able to verbalize this rule, it may be helpful to generalize the rule for them in the form $(x^n)(x^m) = x^{n+m}$.

Suggested Assignment

CHECK YOUR UNDERSTANDING
p. 18, #1–3

UNIT 1 PRACTICE
p. 50, #5–8

7 Quickwrite, Look for a Pattern This question is meant to lead students toward the procedure for dividing powers with the same base.

8 Simplify the Problem, Discussion Group It may be helpful to go back and use Self-Peer editing on 7b after Item 8 is discussed as some students may struggle with explaining how the expression could be simplified. Even as students grasp the idea of canceling common factors in the numerator and denominator they may still need help making the connection to this process and subtracting the exponents of the powers. As in Item 6, you may wish to formalize their generalized rule in the form

$$\frac{x^n}{x^m} = x^{n-m}.$$

10 Simplify the Problem, Vocabulary Organizer, Discussion Group While students should be able to explain that any number divided by itself is 1, it is important that they connect this idea to the fact that each expression, in exponential form, will simplify to 7^0.

My Notes

SUGGESTED LEARNING STRATEGIES: Simplify the Problem, Vocabulary Organizer, Discussion Group

8. Consider the expression $\frac{x^4}{x^3}$.

  a. Rewrite the expression with the numerator and denominator in expanded form.

  $$\frac{x \cdot x \cdot x \cdot x}{x \cdot x \cdot x}$$

  b. Describe how you could simplify the expression.

  Answers may vary. Sample answer: Cancel common factors
  $$\frac{x \cdot x \cdot x \cdot x}{x \cdot x \cdot x} = x$$

  c. Write a general rule for dividing terms with exponents that have the same base.
  Answers may vary. Student answers should indicate an understanding that exponents are subtracted when the terms with the same base are divided.

9. Consider the expression $\frac{x^3}{x^5}$.

  a. Rewrite the numerator and denominator in expanded form and simplify.
  $$\frac{(x \cdot x \cdot x)}{(x \cdot x \cdot x \cdot x \cdot x)} = \frac{1}{x^2}$$

  b. Now apply the general rule you found in item 8c.
  $$\frac{x^3}{x^5} = x^{3-5} = x^{-2}$$

  c. Compare your results for parts a and b, What do you notice?
  Answers may vary. Sample answer: $\frac{1}{x^2} = x^{-2}$. A power in a denominator can be written as a negative power.

  d. Write an expression for 4^{-3} without exponents. Show your work.
  $$4^{-3} = \frac{1}{4^3} = \frac{1}{64}$$

10. Although there is only one narrator in *As I was going to St. Ives*, the number 1 can be written as a **power** of 7. To see how this works, you can examine several ways to express the number 1.

  a. Explain why each of the following is equal to 1.

  $$\frac{7}{7}, \frac{49}{49}, \frac{343}{343}, \text{ and } \frac{2401}{2401}$$

  Any number divided by itself is 1.

ACADEMIC VOCABULARY

A **power** consists of two parts, a base and an exponent. For example, in the power 5^3, 5 is the base and 3 is the exponent.

SUGGESTED LEARNING STRATEGIES: Think/Pair/Share, Self/Peer Revisions

My Notes

b. Rewrite each fraction by expressing each numerator and denominator in exponential form. $\dfrac{7^1}{7^1}, \dfrac{7^2}{7^2}, \dfrac{7^3}{7^3}, \dfrac{7^4}{7^4}$

c. Explain how it is possible for the fractions in part b to simplify to 7^0.

Answer may vary. Sample answer: In each expression, subtracting the exponents yields 7^0.

11. Write a general rule that describes the outcome of raising any base to the power 0.

Any number or expression raised to the zero is always 1.

12. Use your rule to explain how the product $10{,}324^0 \cdot 8{,}576^0$ can be done using mental math.

Both terms can be simplified to 1 before multiplying. Thus, $1 \cdot 1 = 1$.

Assume each stripe on each kitten contains seven spots. The situation is becoming more complicated, and the need for using exponents has grown…uh…exponentially.

13. Determine the total number of spots on the kittens. Explain how you determined your solution.

117,649; Explanations may vary. Sample answer: I multiplied the number of stripes, 16,807, by 7.

14. In expanded form, the product could be written as

$(7 \cdot 7 \cdot 7) \cdot (7 \cdot 7 \cdot 7)$.

a. Explain why this could also be written as $(7^3)^2$.

Explanations may vary. Sample answer: $(7 \cdot 7 \cdot 7) = 7^3$, and $7^3 \cdot 7^3 = (7^3)^2$

b. Express this product in its simplest exponential form.

7^6

c. Based on this example, what operation is being performed on the exponents?

Multiplication

ACTIVITY 1.2 Continued

11 Think/Pair/Share, Self/Peer Revision Students expand on Item 10 by determining that any number or expression raised to zero is equal to 1. Students who struggle with making this connection may benefit from additional discussion or examples using different numbers.

12 Think/Pair/Share, Self/Peer Revision Students should demonstrate mastery of the concept of having zero as an exponent.

13 Think/Pair/Share, Self/Peer Revision Students will likely provide different processes for determining the spots based on their varying levels of understanding of exponents. Some may describe the process by using exponents (7^6) while others may still view the process as repeated multiplication. Still others may choose to multiply the number of stripes (16,807) by 7.

14 Think/Pair/Share, Self/Peer Revision In part a, students may not immediately recognize that the way the product is grouped represents a square. It may be helpful to lead them to making this connection by using examples such as $(3)(3) = 3^2$, $(10)(10) = 10^2$, and $(x)(x) = x^2$. You may also wish to refer back to the rule of multiplying powers with the same base and lead students in a discussion of why these two rules are different. As in previous questions, you may wish to formalize the rule in the form $(x^n)^m = x^{n \cdot m}$.

15 Graphic Organizer, Vocabulary Organizer, Self/Peer Revision, Group Presentation The table allows students to organize the concepts they have explored in this activity. If you have not done so already, you may wish to have the students add formal versions of the rules for exponents to their "My Notes" column. In addition, you may also wish to have them add a note about the rules only applying when the bases of the powers are the same.

Suggested Assignment

CHECK YOUR UNDERSTANDING
p. 18, #4–10

UNIT 1 PRACTICE
p. 50, #9–15

CHECK YOUR UNDERSTANDING

1. 3^9

2. cannot be simplified in exponential form

3. x^{17}

4. 4^1

5. 10^2

6. x^7

7. 1

8. 2^{-3}

9. $\frac{1}{8}$

10. Answers will vary but should include a connection to the concept of combining like terms.

My Notes

CONNECT TO AP

In advanced math courses, you will use the same rules to simplify and rewrite expressions in which the exponents are fractions, decimals, or negative numbers. For example, you discovered that $x^3 \cdot x^4 = x^7$. A similar problem in an advanced math course might be $x^{\frac{1}{5}} \cdot x^{\frac{2}{5}} = x^{\frac{3}{5}}$.

SUGGESTED LEARNING STRATEGIES: Graphic Organizer, Vocabulary Organizer, Self/Peer Revision, Group Presentation

15. In the table below, summarize the rules for exponents you discovered in this activity. *Examples may vary.*

Situation	Verbal Description	Numeric Example
Multiplying powers with the same base	Add the exponents to simplify the product	Sample answer: $5^2 \cdot 5^3 = 3125 = 5^5$
Dividing powers with the same base	Subtract the exponents to simplify the quotient	Sample answer: $\frac{6^5}{6^2} = 6^3 = 216$
Raising a term to an exponent of zero	Always simplifies to 1	Sample answer: $8^0 = 1$
Raising a power to another exponent	Multiply the exponents to simplify	Sample answer: $(2^4)^3 = 2^{12} = 4096$

CHECK YOUR UNDERSTANDING

Write your answers on notebook paper. Show your work.

Simplify in exponential form.

1. $3^5 \cdot 3^4$

2. $5^6 \cdot 3^2$

3. $x^{16} \cdot x^1$

4. $\frac{4^3}{4^2}$

5. $\frac{10^8}{10^6}$

6. $\frac{x^{11}}{x^4}$

7. 5^0

8. $\frac{2^4}{2^7}$

9. Write your answer to item 8 as an expression without exponents.

10. **MATHEMATICAL REFLECTION** Explain why the bases of powers must be the same in order for the rules of exponents to work.

Patterns and Exponents

CONTAGIOUS MATHEMATICS

While checking her email, Luisa stumbles across a cryptic message from someone named 5up3r H4xx0r. In the message, 5up3r 4axx0r claims to have developed a computer virus and is set to release it on the Internet. Once the virus has infected two computers, the potential exists for it to spread exponentially because each infected computer has a chance to pass it along to the next computer it connects with.

The only way for the virus to be stopped, says the hacker, is if Luisa correctly answers each of the following questions.

1. The pattern of the spread of the virus will be 1, 2, 4, 8, … Identify the next three numbers in this pattern.

2. Express the first seven numbers in the pattern as a power of 2.

3. Describe the following patterns:

   a. The pattern of the number of computers infected

   b. The pattern of the exponents of two

   c. The pattern of the difference between each term

   d. The pattern of the last digit in each term

4. Describe how the 18th term in the pattern could be determined.

5. Express each of the factors for the following products in exponential form.

   a. $32 \cdot 128$

   b. $4 \cdot 256$

   c. $16 \cdot 64$

6. Simplify each of the products in Item 5. Leave your answers in exponential form.

Assessment Focus

- Identifying and describing patterns
- Operations with exponents

Assessment Perspectives

- This embedded assessment provides students an opportunity to demonstrate understanding of identifying and describing patterns and operations with exponents. Students will also be given the opportunity to write about how well they understand each of the concepts being assessed.

Answer Key

1. Students should be able to correctly identify 16, 32, and 64 as the next three numbers in the pattern.

2. Beginning with $1 = 2^0$, students should be able to write the first seven terms of the pattern as a power of 2.

3a. Students should be able to identify that the number of computers infected doubles each time.

   b. Students should be able to determine that the exponents increase by one each time. (0, 1, 2, 3, …)

   c. Students should be able to describe the difference between consecutive terms doubles each time. Accelerated learners may also identify these differences as repeating the original pattern of numbers.

   d. Students should be able to determine that the last digit in the terms follow the pattern 2, 4, 8, 6, 2, 4, 8, …

4. Students should be able to describe the eighteenth term in the pattern as repeated multiplication or 2^{17}.

5a. Students should be able to express the product as $2^5 \cdot 2^7$.

   b. Students should be able to express the product as either $2^2 \cdot 2^8$ or $4^1 \cdot 4^4$.

   c. Students should be able to express the product as either $2^4 \cdot 2^6$ or $4^2 \cdot 4^3$.

6. Students should be able to simplify the products in Item 5 by using the rule for multiplying powers with the same base.
   a. 2^{12};
   b. 2^{10} or 4^5;
   c. 2^{10} or 4^5

Embedded Assessment 1

7a. Students should be able to simplify the expression to 2^{60}.
6

b. Students should be able to simplify the expression to 2^9.
2

8. In this item, students are given the opportunity to self-assess their strengths and weaknesses with identifying and describing patterns and the rules of exponents. Responses can be used to identify concepts that may require additional instruction or remediation.

Patterns and Exponents
CONTAGIOUS MATHEMATICS

7. Simplify each of the following expressions and determine what the last digit would be.

a. $(2^{15})^4$

b. $\dfrac{2^{12}}{2^3}$

8. Write a reply to 5up3r H4xx0r about your success in foiling the virus plan. Include in your reply a description of the problems that were difficult for you and the ones you were able to complete easily.

	Exemplary	Proficient	Emerging
Math Knowledge #1, 2, 6, 7	• Correctly identifies the next three numbers in the given pattern (1) • Correctly expresses each of the first seven terms as a power of 2 (2) • Finds correct products and quotients in exponential form and simplifies them (6, 7) • Determines the last digit of the result of the standard form (7)	Provides justification for items in questions 1, 2, 6, and 7 but only three are correct	Provides at least three justifications for questions 1, 2, 6, and 7 but they may be incorrect or incomplete
Problem Solving #4	Determines the 18th term (4)	Uses a correct method to find the 18th term but makes a computational error	Uses an incorrect method or is unable to determine the 18th term
Representation #5a, b, c	Expresses both factors of the product in exponential form (5)	Expresses most of the factors in exponential form	Is unable to express the factors in exponential form.
Communication #3a–d, 4, 8	• Correctly describes the pattern of the number of computers infected (3a), the pattern of the exponents of two (3b), the pattern of the difference between each term (3c), and the pattern of the last digit in each term (3d) • Correctly describes how the 18th pattern in the term could be determined (4) • Provides a detailed explanation about the problems solved in the EA that includes information about areas of both strength and difficulty (8)	Gives explanations for items in questions 3, 4, and 8 but only two are complete and correct	Gives at least two of the three required explanations for questions 3, 4, and 8 but they are incomplete and incorrect

Operations with Decimals
Driving for Points

SUGGESTED LEARNING STRATEGIES: Mark the Text, Think Outloud, Group Discussion

My Notes

Tony, Leilani, Chrissy, and Dale are starting a NASCAR fantasy league this season. Each team will consist of five of the top twenty drivers on the circuit. At the beginning of the season, the drivers are assigned point values based on their performances in previous years. The top twenty drivers and their point values are shown in the table below.

Driver	Point Value	Driver	Point Value
Sparky Pluggs	23.7	Victor E. Lane	18.6
Bump Ertle	23.1	Turner Wedge	18.3
Sara Wheeler	22.6	Shayla Crews	17.5
Kevin Fender	22.4	Ian Jun	16.8
Bonnie Checker	22.2	Trey Oval	16.7
Carl Burator	21.5	Camber LePointe	15.4
Chaz Errol	21.1	Stockton Carr	15.1
Ray De Ator	20.8	Tank Topov	14.9
Cam Shaffer	20.2	Forrest Gere	14.1
Monty Carlo	19.4	Roland Springs	13.8

1. The rules of the league state that the sum of the point values of the drivers on a team must not exceed 100 points. Take turns choosing teams in your groups, and complete the table below.

Team 1		Team 2		Team 3		Team 4	
Driver	Point Value	Driver	Point Value	Driver	Point Value	Driver	Point Value
Sum:		Sum:		Sum:		Sum:	

Answers may vary, but the sum of point values for each team should not exceed 100 points.

ACTIVITY 1.3 Guided

Operations with Decimals

Activity Focus
- Applying operations with decimals
- Scientific notation

Materials
- Calculator

Chunking the Activity

#1	#10
#2–3	#11, TTA
#4–6	#12–14
#7–8	#15, TTB
#9	#16, TTC

TEACHER TO TEACHER The purpose of this activity is to allow students an opportunity to explore real-world applications of decimal operations and scientific notation. The context of the activity, a fantasy sports league, may be unfamiliar to some students. It is recommended that additional time is spent making sure the students understand the concept of a fantasy league before beginning the activity. It may be helpful to compare the point values of the drivers to player ratings in sports video games like the Madden NFL series. In such games, players are rated based on their overall abilities. The driver values in this activity are determined in a similar fashion.

1 Mark the Text, Think Aloud, Group Discussion Students are asked to "draft" a team of five drivers from a list of 20. Keep in mind that some groups may struggle with the draft as they figure out how to keep each team within the 100-point limit. You may want to plan for extra time to manage this. You can encourage these groups by informing them that dealing with these issues now will benefit them as they move on to Items 2 and 3.

2-3 Guess and Check, Group Discussion, Work Backward

Students must add and subtract point values to determine total point values and remaining point values. Some students may have trouble with 2c because Bonnie Checker's point value (22.2) is exactly equal to the amount of points Leilani has left to spend in the fifth round. Since the total team value cannot exceed 100 points, choosing Checker in the fifth round would be allowed.

My Notes

SUGGESTED LEARNING STRATEGIES: Guess and Check, Group Discussion, Work Backwards

2. In the first four rounds of the draft, Leilani has chosen Sara Wheeler, Carl Burator, Turner Wedge, and Camber LePointe.

   a. How many points does Leilani have available to spend on her fifth driver?

   22.2 points

   b. Explain the process you used to determine your answer for part a.

   Find the sum of the point values for the first 4 drivers, then subtract this sum from 100.

   c. Assuming she's still available, can Leilani choose Bonnie Checker in the fifth round? Explain your reasoning.

   Yes; Explanations may vary. Sample explanation: The sum of her drivers' points would equal 100, not exceed it.

As the season progresses, the players may trade drivers as long as the total point value for each team does not exceed 100 points.

3. Tony's team consists of Sparky Pluggs, Bonnie Checker, Trey Oval, Tank Topov, and Forrest Gere. He's having second thoughts about choosing Tank Topov, however, and is considering trying to make a trade for another driver.

   a. Calculate the current point value of Tony's team.

   91.6 points

   b. How many points below the limit is Tony's current team?

   8.4 points

   c. If Tony decides to trade Topov, how many points will he have to spend on another driver?

   23.3 points

   d. Who is the highest ranked driver that Tony can trade for? Explain your reasoning.

   Bump Ertle (23.1 points); Explanations may vary. Sample explanation: Bump Ertle is the highest ranked driver with point value less or equal to 23.3.

SUGGESTED LEARNING STRATEGIES: Questioning the Text,
Group Discussion, Identify a Subtask

My Notes

After the first five races of the season, the point values of the drivers are adjusted according to how they have performed thus far. The new point values are shown below.

Driver	Point Value	Driver	Point Value
Sparky Pluggs	24.1	Kevin Fender	18.5
Carl Burator	23.9	Turner Wedge	18.2
Bonnie Checker	22.4	Trey Oval	17.9
Victor E. Lane	22.1	Forrest Gere	16.6
Sara Wheeler	21.6	Shayla Crews	16.1
Bump Ertle	21.3	Camber LePointe	15.7
Monty Carlo	20.9	Roland Springs	15.5
Tank Topov	20.1	Ray De Ator	14.8
Cam Shaffer	19.5	Ian Jun	14.3
Chaz Errol	19.2	Stockton Carr	13.2

4. Recalculate the values of the teams you chose in Item 1 based on the updated point values.
Answers will vary (some teams may now be over 100 points).

Team 1		Team 2		Team 3		Team 4	
Driver	Point Value	Driver	Point Value	Driver	Point Value	Driver	Point Value
Sum:		Sum:		Sum:		Sum:	

5. Which driver had the greatest change in point values? By how much?
Ray De Ator; He was the greatest loser and he lost 0.8 more points than the top gainer, Tank Topov, gained.

6. Which team in your group had the greatest change in total value? By how much?
Answers may vary depending on student teams.

ACTIVITY 1.3 *Continued*

4-6 Questioning the Text, Group Discussion, Identify a Subtask The point values of the driver have changed. As with most fantasy sports leagues, the initial values of the players will change throughout the course of the season based on performance. As the total team values are recalculated, some students may have total values that exceed 100.

In the context of this league (and in most fantasy leagues), this is OK as long as the driver remains on the team. If the driver is released from the team after point values are adjusted, any team wishing to add the driver to the roster would be subject to the new, adjusted value. Item 7 explores this idea further.

8 Summarize/ Paraphrase/ Retell, Quickwrite, Look for a Pattern, Group Presentation Student responses should provide informal assessments of their abilities to add and subtract fractions by hand. In questions such as this, some students may express difficulty in verbalizing the procedures they use. One method of helping them through this is to ask the students about each of the steps they took to solve a particular problem. As they answer each of your questions, have the students write down what they said. At the end of this process, the student will have compiled a suitable answer to Item 8.

My Notes

In most fantasy leagues, adjusted values only take effect when a driver is released or traded from a team. This is good news for Tony's team.

Tony's Team		
Driver	**Initial Value**	**Current Value**
Sparky Pluggs	23.7	24.1
Bonnie Checker	22.2	22.4
Trey Oval	16.7	17.9
Tank Topov	14.9	20.1
Forrest Gere	14.1	16.6
Sum:	91.6	101.1

7. If Tony had gone through with trading Tank Topov, explain why he would not be able to add him back to his team now. Justify your answer by providing specific values in the table above.

The sum of point values would exceed 100 by 1.1 points.

8. When adding and subtracting decimals by hand, explain the process you use to ensure that your calculations are done correctly.

Answers may vary but should indicate an understanding of always adding the same place value and aligning decimals.

SUGGESTED LEARNING STRATEGIES: Mark the Text, Identify a Subtask, Discussion Group

Team points are awarded each week based on where the drivers finish in the race. A driver's point value is multiplied by the number of cars he beat in the race. NASCAR races consist of 43 cars, so this formula would be used.

$$(\text{Fantasy Point Value}) \cdot (43 - \text{Finishing Position})$$

For example, the points for a driver who finished 10th in the race and had a fantasy point value of 18.4 would be calculated as follows:

$$(18.4) \cdot (43 - 10) = (18.4) \cdot (33) = 607.2 \text{ points}$$

9. The results of the sixth race are shown in the table below.

My Notes

Driver	Point Value	Finish	Points Earned	Driver	Point Value	Finish	Points Earned
Sparky Pluggs	24.1	1	1012.2	Kevin Fender	18.5	5	703
Carl Burator	23.9	12	740.9	Turner Wedge	18.2	30	236.6
Bonnie Checker	22.4	6	828.8	Trey Oval	17.9	22	375.9
Victor E. Lane	22.1	8	773.5	Forrest Gere	16.6	9	564.4
Sara Wheeler	21.6	16	583.2	Shayla Crews	16.1	28	241.5
Bump Ertle	21.3	21	468.6	Camber LePointe	15.7	30	204.1
Monty Carlo	20.9	4	815.1	Roland Springs	15.5	19	372
Tank Topov	20.1	3	804	Ray De Ator	14.8	11	473.6
Cam Shaffer	19.5	23	390	Ian Jun	14.3	32	157.3
Chaz Errol	19.2	34	172.8	Stockton Carr	13.2	41	26.4

a. Calculate the number of points earned by each driver on your team.

Answers may vary depending on student teams. Points by driver are shown in the table above.

b. Calculate the total number of points earned by your team.

Answers may vary.

c. Rank the total values of the teams in your group from greatest to least.

Answers may vary.

TEACHER TO TEACHER Fantasy sports leagues operate under the same general principal of real team sports. In other words, the object of the game is to score more points than the other team. For instance, in fantasy football leagues, teams earn points for statistics like touchdowns or rushing and receiving yards. The fictional point system in the NASCAR fantasy league is explained in the introduction to Item 9. Points are awarded based on the product of the driver value and the number of cars the driver beat in the race.

9 Mark the Text, Identify a Subtask, Discussion Group Students are given the opportunity to calculate the total points awarded to the team and compare these values against the other teams in the group. When calculating these values by hand, you may notice some student misconceptions in how the decimal point is placed in the final answer. This will be explored further in Items 10 and 11.

10 **Predict and Confirm, Work Backward** The purpose of this question is to help students understand that the digits in any product will be the same regardless of the initial placement of the decimal point. Although Dale's product is partially correct, the point value of 22.1 should have been used instead of 2.21. As students correct the error, it is important for them to understand that the digits 7, 7, 3, and 5 make up both products, and the only difference is the final placement of the decimal point. For students who have difficulty with part d, you may wish to discuss how to determine the final placement of the decimal point at this time or wait until the debrief of Item 11.

Suggested Assignment

CHECK YOUR UNDERSTANDING
p. 30, #1–2

UNIT 1 PRACTICE
p. 50, #16–22

11 **Predict and Confirm, Work Backward, Vocabulary Organizer** Now that students have hypothesized that the digits should remain the same regardless of the decimal placement, they have a chance to test the hypothesis. Students should be able to determine that the hypothesis holds true. Additional discussion may be necessary to explain the extra zero in example e (0.0625). After debriefing part d, it should be clear to students that the number of decimal places in the values being multiplied and the number of decimal places in the product are the same.

My Notes

SUGGESTED LEARNING STRATEGIES: Predict and Confirm, Work Backwards, Vocabulary Organizer

10. In the following week, Victor E. Lane finished eighth. When calculating the fantasy points, Dale multiplied the numbers as follows:

$$(2.21) \cdot (35) = 77.35 \text{ points}$$

a. Identify the error Dale made in his calculation.
The point value of 2.21 should have been 22.1.

b. Calculate the correct value of fantasy points earned by Victor E. Lane.
773.5 points

c. What do you notice about Dale's initial calculation and the one you made in part b?
The digits are the same, but the decimal is in a different position.

d. Explain why it would not have been necessary for Dale to recalculate the values.
Student explanations may vary but should include an understanding that moving the decimal one space to the right (i.e., 2.21 to 22.1) could be done with the product as well (i.e., 77.35 to 773.5).

ACADEMIC VOCABULARY

A **hypothesis** is an assumption or guess that is based on the observation of an event or series of events. The word is derived from the Greek *hypotethenai*, which means "to suppose."

11. Dale is fascinated by the observations made in Item 10 and wonders if it would work for any multiplication with decimals. He uses the following sample problems to test his **hypothesis**.

a. $25 \cdot 25$
b. $2.5 \cdot 25$
c. $2.5 \cdot 2.5$
d. $0.25 \cdot 2.5$
e. $0.25 \cdot 0.25$

a. Determine the value for each of Dale's examples.
In order: 625, 62.5, 6.25, 0.625, 0.0625

SUGGESTED LEARNING STRATEGIES: Predict and Confirm,
Guess and Check, Think/Pair/Share

b. Do you think his hypothesis was correct? Justify your
answer.

Answers may vary. Sample answer: The digits in the
product are the same regardless of the initial position
of the decimal point. The calculations show that moving
a decimal point in a factor produces a corresponding
change in the product.

c. How could you determine the final position of the
decimal point before multiplying the numbers? Explain
your reasoning.

Answers may vary. Sample answer: The total number of
decimal places in the numbers being multiplied is the
same as the number of decimal places in the product.

d. Based on your answer to part c, which of the sample
problems would have the same product as 25 · 0.25?
Explain your reasoning.

Example c; they both have the same number of total
decimal places.

TRY THESE A

a. 3.45 · 28.7
99.015

b. 88 · 2.6
228.8

c. 0.4 · 8.1
3.24

d. 40 · 0.81
32.4

e. Explain how you could have completed Item d without
calculating the values after having completed Item c.

Answers may vary. Sample answer: The digits in the product
would be the same, but the decimal would shift one space to
the right.

At the end of the season, bonus points are awarded by multiplying
the starting point value and the total earnings of each driver.
Chrissy's top driver was Ray De Ator, who earned $8,000,000 and
had a starting point value of 20.8.

12. Chrissy's calculator only displays eight digits. Explain why
displaying Ray De Ator's bonus points on her calculator
could be a problem.

166,400,000 has nine digits.

My Notes

TRY THESE A These problems
provide practice for students as a
check of their understanding of
multiplying decimals and placing
the decimal point in the product.

12 Predict and Confirm, Guess
and Check, Think/Pair/Share
Helps students understand
a common use for scientific
notation. You may wish to enrich
the discussion of this question by
asking the students to determine
the largest value able to be
displayed on an 8-digit screen.

13 Vocabulary Organizer, Look for a Pattern The scaffolding is designed for students who have never seen, or have had limited exposure to, scientific notation. While many students may see multiplying a number by 10 as "adding a zero," it is important for them to conceptualize the operation as moving the decimal point one space to the right. Students also discover the pattern which leads to negative exponents for writing numbers between 0 and 1 in scientific notation. Make sure that students see that a negative exponent does not indicate a negative value for the number in scientific notation.

14 Look for a Pattern Students apply the patterns they have discovered.

My Notes

ACADEMIC VOCABULARY

Scientific notation is a way of writing a number in terms of a decimal greater than or equal to 1 and less than 10, multiplied by a power of 10. Using symbols, a number is written in scientific notation when it is expressed in the form $a \cdot 10^n$, where $1 \le a < 10$ and n is an integer.

TECHNOLOGY TIP

Calculators use a form of scientific notation to express very large and very small numbers. For example:

8,000,000,000,000 would be expressed as 8E12. The 12 indicates that 8 is multiplied by 10 to the 12th power.

0.000000000008 would be expressed as 8E − 12. The −12 indicates that 8 is multiplied by 10 to the −12th power,

SUGGESTED LEARNING STRATEGIES: Vocabulary Organizer, Look for a Pattern

Scientific notation is used to simplify numbers that are very large or very small in order to make calculations easier. Chrissy decides that this is how she wants to calculate the bonus points, so she uses the following values:

$$(8 \cdot 10^6) \cdot (2.08 \cdot 10^1)$$

To understand how Chrissy determined these values, it is necessary to know how scientific notation works. Converting a number into scientific notation involves multiplying numbers by a factor of 10.

13. Consider the following products:

$$80,000 = 8 \cdot 10,000 = 8 \cdot 10^4$$
$$8,000 = 8 \cdot 1,000 = 8 \cdot 10^3$$
$$800 = 8 \cdot 100 = 8 \cdot 10^2$$

a. Continue the pattern.

$$80,000 = 8 \cdot 10,000 = 8 \cdot 10^4$$
$$8,000 = 8 \cdot 1,000 = 8 \cdot 10^3$$
$$800 = 8 \cdot 100 = 8 \cdot 10^2$$
$$80 = 8 \cdot 10 = \underline{\qquad} \quad 8 \cdot 10^1$$
$$8 = 8 \cdot 1 = \underline{\qquad} \quad 8 \cdot 10^0$$
$$0.8 = 8 \cdot 0.1 = \underline{\qquad} \quad 8 \cdot 10^{-1}$$
$$0.08 = 8 \cdot 0.01 = \underline{\qquad} \quad 8 \cdot 10^{-2}$$

b. Explain how Chrissy could use this pattern to express Ray De Ator's winnings in scientific notation.

She could use the pattern of increasing exponents to write 8,000,000 as $8 \cdot 1,000,000 = 8 \cdot 10^6$.

c. Why was Chrissy correct in writing 20.8 as $2.08 \cdot 10^1$?

Sample explanation: The first number in scientific notation must be greater than or equal to 1 and less than 10. She could factor out a 10 in 20.8 and write a number equivalent to 20.8 as $2.08 \cdot 10$ or $2.08 \cdot 10^1$.

14. Write these numbers in scientific notation.

a. 56, 300 $5.63 \cdot 10^4$

b. 110,000 $1.1 \cdot 10^5$

c. 6,000 $6 \cdot 10^3$

d. 0.0072 $7.2 \cdot 10^{-3}$

SUGGESTED LEARNING STRATEGIES: Identify a Subtask, Discussion Group, Quickwrite, Vocabulary Organizer

Another way to determine proper scientific notation is to count the number of places the decimal would have to be moved in order to be located to the right of the non-zero first digit in the number.

15. Consider this table.

	Numbers greater than 1	Numbers between 0 and 1
A	$89{,}200 = 8.92 \cdot 10^4$	$0.000892 = 8.92 \cdot 10^{-4}$
B	$362 = 3.62 \cdot 10^2$	$0.0362 = 3.62 \cdot 10^{-2}$
C	$52.3 = 5.23 \cdot 10^1$	$0.523 = 5.23 \cdot 10^{-1}$

a. Compare and contrast the scientific notation for the numbers in Row A.

b. Compare and contrast the scientific notation for the numbers in Row B.

c. Compare and contrast the scientific notation for the numbers in Row C.

d. Make a conjecture about the relationship between a number in scientific notation and the same number in standard form.

My Notes

a–c: Answers may vary. Sample answer: The nonzero digits are the same in each number. The powers of 10 are opposite integers. The expression with the positive exponent is greater than 1, and the expression with the negative exponent is between 0 and 1.

d: Answers may vary. Sample answer: A positive exponent in scientific notation indicates the number of places to the right to move the decimal point in order to get the number in standard form. A negative exponent in scientific notation indicates the number of places to the left to move the decimal point in order to get the number in standard form.

TRY THESE B

Express the following in scientific notation using any method.

a. 12,300
$1.23 \cdot 10^4$

b. 0.45
$4.5 \cdot 10^{-1}$

c. 23,500,000,000
$2.35 \cdot 10^{10}$

d. How many times as great as $4.25 \cdot 10^8$ is $4.25 \cdot 10^{10}$?
100 times

Now that Chrissy has converted her numbers to scientific notation, she needs to find the product to determine Ray De Ator's bonus points.

$$(8 \cdot 10^6) \cdot (2.08 \cdot 10^1)$$

Since multiplication is **commutative**, she knows that she can rearrange the product in the following manner.

$$(8 \cdot 2.08) \cdot (10^6 \cdot 10^1)$$

MATH TERMS

The **commutative property of multiplication** states that for any real numbers a and b, $ab = ba$.

15 Identify a Subtask, Discussion Group, Quickwrite Students who are able to equate multiplying or dividing multiples of ten with decimal point movement will be better equipped to conceptualize *why* scientific notation works.

TRY THESE B These problems provide practice for students as a check on their understanding of scientific notation.

16 Discussion Group, Quickwrite, Vocabulary Organizer, Self/Peer Revision Students are introduced to the commutative property of multiplication. This property will be covered in greater detail in Unit 2. When the multiples are regrouped, students will need to apply their knowledge of multiplying powers with the same base. It is important to remind students that numbers written in proper scientific notation have only one digit to the left of the decimal place as some of them may write the answer to part c as 16.64×10^7.

TRY THESE C These problems provide practice for students as a check on their understanding of scientific notation and expanded form.

Suggested Assignment

CHECK YOUR UNDERSTANDING
p. 30, #3–4

UNIT 1 PRACTICE
p. 50, #23–25

CHECK YOUR UNDERSTANDING

1. $17.45

2a. $77.48

b. $5.07

3a. 7.5×10^7

b. 1.25×10^7

4. 5×10^{-4} millimeter

5. Sample answer: When adding and subtracting, the term with the most decimal places will determine how many decimal places are in the answer. When multiplying, the number of decimal places in the answer will be the sum of the number of decimal places in the factors.

My Notes

SUGGESTED LEARNING STRATEGIES: Self/Peer Revision, Group Presentaion

16. Chrissy performs the multiplication and expresses the answer in scientific notation as $16.64 \cdot 10^6$.

 a. Explain why Chrissy's answer is incorrect.
 Answers may vary. Sample answer: The decimal point is not in the correct position, and the power should be 10^7.

 b. Describe the process she should use to correct her answer.
 The decimal point should be moved one more space to the left, and the appropriate power of 10 should be written.

 c. Write the correct amount of bonus points earned by Ray De Ator in scientific notation and in expanded form.
 Scientific notation: $1.664 \cdot 10^8$; Expanded form: 166,400,000

TRY THESE C

Express each product in scientific notation and in standard form.

 a. $(16 \cdot 3.9) \cdot (10^4 \cdot 10^3)$
 Scientific notation: $6.24 \cdot 10^8$;
 Expanded form: 624,000,000

 b. $(1.4 \cdot 32.7) \cdot (10^9 \cdot 10^{13})$
 Scientific notation: $4.578 \cdot 10^{22}$;
 Expanded form: 457,800,000,000,000,000,000,000

 c. $(7.3 \cdot 9) \cdot (10^5 \cdot 10^2)$
 Scientific notation: $6.57 \cdot 10^8$;
 Expanded form: 657,000,000

 d. $(25 \cdot 2.2) \cdot (10^2 \cdot 10^{-6})$
 $5.5 \cdot 10^{-3}$

CHECK YOUR UNDERSTANDING

Write your answers on notebook paper. Show your work.

1. Over the last four weeks, Kevin has saved $18.75, $22.30, $15.00, and $26.50. If his goal is to save $100, how much more does he need to save?

2. Kevin's sister, Olivia, has saved an average of $19.37 over the same four-week period.

 a. How much has Olivia saved?

 b. What is the difference in the amount of money Kevin and Olivia have saved?

3. The #1 pick in the NFL draft has just signed a contract that will pay him a total of $75 million over six years.

 a. Express the total amount of the contract in scientific notation.

 b. Express his yearly salary in scientific notation.

4. The thickness of a strand of hair can be about 0.0005 millimeter. What is this measurement in scientific notation?

5. MATHEMATICAL REFLECTION Explain how you can determine the number of decimal places in your final answer when adding or subtracting numbers with decimals. Explain how you can determine the number of decimal places in your final answer when multiplying numbers with decimals.

Operations with Fractions
And the Beat Goes On

SUGGESTED LEARNING STRATEGIES: Activating Prior Knowledge, Group Discussion, Create Representations

Before we get into any math, let's talk about music.

1. Take a few moments to think about the following questions and discuss them with your group.

> *What is your favorite song?*
> *Why do you like it?*
> *Why do you prefer one type of music over another?*

Believe it or not, the answers you came up with may have more to do with mathematics than you may realize. Consider the following diagrams:

2. The first circle has no divisions and is represented by the number 1.

a. Write the fractional equivalents in the portions of the other circles. See above.

b. For each of the circles, justify that the sum of each combination of fractions is 1.

Student justifications may vary but should show an understanding of adding and simplifying fractions.

c. Which circle was not like the others? Explain what made it different and the process you used to determine your answer.

Answers may vary. Sample answer: The third circle was the only one that was not divided into equivalent parts. A common denominator is required to add these fractions. Add $\frac{1}{4}$ and $\frac{1}{4}$, simplify, then add $\frac{1}{2}$ and $\frac{1}{2}$, simplify. Or, change $\frac{1}{2}$ to $\frac{2}{4}$, add $\frac{2}{4}$ and $\frac{2}{4}$, simplify.

My Notes

Operations with Fractions

Activity Focus
- Applications of fractions
  Addition
  Subtraction
  Multiplication
  Division
- Multiple representations of fractions
- Inverse operations

Materials
- Calculator

Chunking the Activity

#1	#10–11	#15
#2–3	TTA	#16
#4	#12–13	#17
#5–7	#14	TTC
#8–9	TTB	

TEACHER TO TEACHER The purpose of this activity is to help students conceptualize fractions by connecting them to visual representations, musical notes, and other equivalent forms. While it is expected that students are entering the class with a working knowledge of operations with fractions, it will be common for many students to struggle with the material. Conceptualizing the content in this activity is meant to help students move beyond their fear of fractions to a deeper understanding.

1 Activating Prior Knowledge Student responses will vary greatly. While the connection to music comes later in the activity, students may benefit from additional discussion about the beats they hear in their favorite music.

2 Group Discussion, Create Representations This activity is designed to lead students to view fractions as more than just numerators and denominators. Students who struggle with the algorithms of operations with fractions should be encouraged to create and use graphical representations to help figure out how the algorithms work.

3 Create Representations, Questioning the Text, Think/ Pair/Share Some students may have difficulty if they attempt to divide their circles into thirds, fifths, etc. In the end, students should be reminded that the goal of the question is to expand their understanding of fractions as parts of a whole.

TEACHER TO TEACHER It is recommended to take some time to discuss the context of the musical notes before allowing the students to attempt Item 4. You may wish to seek out students with music backgrounds ahead of time to allow them to help with the discussion.

4 Create Representations, Questioning the Text, Think/ Pair/Share Music theory has many connections to mathematics, but in this case, the point is to continue along with the idea of fractions being part of a whole.

TEACHER TO TEACHER It should be noted that although common time is being used in the examples, it is but one meter of music. Students with a deeper understanding of operations with fractions may benefit from extending the examples to include additional meters.

My Notes

SUGGESTED LEARNING STRATEGIES: Create Representations, Questioning the Text, Think/Pair/Share

3. Determine two additional ways to divide the circle using combinations of the same fractions from Item 1. Label each portion with the appropriate fractions, and justify that the sum of each combination of fractions is 1.

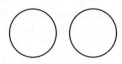

Student representations may vary but justifications should be provided similarly to those in 2b.

So what does all this have to do with music? As shown in the chart below, certain musical notes correspond to different fractional portions of a measure. In order to write sheet music, a composer must have a working knowledge of fractions.

Note	Relative Length in Common Time	Beats in Common Time	Fraction of Measure
O	Whole note	4 beats	1
♩	Half note	2 beats	$\frac{1}{2}$
♩	Quarter note	1 beat	$\frac{1}{4}$
♪	Eighth note	$\frac{1}{2}$ beat	$\frac{1}{8}$
♪	Sixteenth note	$\frac{1}{4}$ beat	$\frac{1}{16}$

4. Based on the note chart, how many of each note would it take to fill one measure in common time? Explain your reasoning.

1 whole note = 1 measure in common time
2 half notes = 1 measure in common time
4 quarter notes = 1 measure in common time
8 eighth notes = 1 measure in common time
16 sixteenth notes = 1 measure in common time

> **CONNECT TO MUSIC**
>
> In music, **common time** is also referred to as $\frac{4}{4}$ time. This means that each measure contains four beats, and a quarter note is equal to one beat. Common time is also the most frequently used beat in rock, pop, funk, country, and R & B music.

SUGGESTED LEARNING STRATEGIES: Self/Peer Revision, Discussion Group

My Notes

5. For each measure shown above, express each note as a fraction of its respective measure.

   a. Measure 1:

   Measure 1: $\frac{1}{4}, \frac{1}{4}, \frac{1}{2}$

   b. Measure 2:

   Measure 2: $\frac{1}{2}, \frac{1}{4}, \frac{1}{4}$

   c. Measure 3:

   Measure 3: $\frac{1}{4}, \frac{1}{4}, \frac{1}{4}, \frac{1}{4}$

   d. Measure 4:

   Measure 4: $\frac{1}{1}$

6. Show that the sum of the fractions in each measure is equal to 1.

   Answers may vary. Student responses should indicate the ability to add the fractions and simplify to 1.

7. Based on your observations in Item 4, explain why you think the note in the fourth measure is called a "whole note."

   A <u>whole</u> note = a <u>whole</u> measure

ACTIVITY 1.4 *Continued*

5 Self/Peer Revision, Discussion Group For the most part, the answers can be determined from the chart that appears on the previous page. The material has been scaffolded this way to ensure that students who have never seen sheet music are able to make the connection between the musical notes and the fractions of a measure they represent in common time.

6 Self/Peer Revision, Discussion Group Showing a sum of one may prove difficult for students who lack the prior knowledge of how to add fractions. It may be helpful to have the students use graphical representations like the ones in Items 2 and 3.

8-9 Graphic Organizer, Visualization, Think/Pair/Share, Quickwrite Some students may need to use graphical representations to determine the values for the first two columns in the table. For instance, the first measure could be represented by the following:

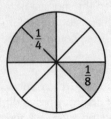

By doing so, the students can determine that $\frac{3}{8}$ of the circle is shaded and $\frac{5}{8}$ of the circle is unshaded. In addition, students can also use the representation to determine the numerous combinations of shading that will complete the measure. Encourage students to discover various combinations.

My Notes

SUGGESTED LEARNING STRATEGIES: Graphic Organizer, Visualization, Think/Pair/Share, Quickwrite

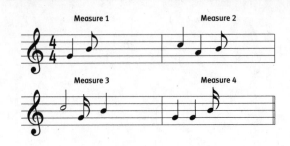

8. The measures shown above do not contain the required amount of beats. Use the table below to explore various ways to complete each measure.

Measure	Fraction of Measure Shown	Fraction of Measure Remaining	Notes to Complete Measure (Example 1)	Notes to Complete Measure (Example 2)
1	$\frac{3}{8}$	$\frac{5}{8}$	♩ ♩ ♪	♩ ♪
2	$\frac{5}{8}$	$\frac{3}{8}$	♪ ♪ ♪	♪ ♪ ♪ ♪
3	$\frac{13}{16}$	$\frac{3}{16}$	♫ ♫ ♫	♪ ♫
4	$\frac{9}{16}$	$\frac{7}{16}$	♫ ♫ ♫ ♫ ♫	♪ ♪ ♪

9. Explain the processes you used to determine the fraction of the measures shown and the fraction of the measures remaining.

Explanations may vary. Sample answer: To determine the fraction of the measures shown, add the fractions the notes represent. To determine the fraction of the measure remaining, subtract this sum from one.

SUGGESTED LEARNING STRATEGIES: Create
Representations, Predict and Confirm, Group Presentation

My Notes

10. What can you conclude about each of the following expressions? Explain your reasoning.

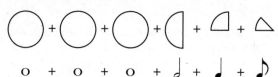

$1 + 1 + 1 + \frac{1}{2} + \frac{1}{4} + \frac{1}{8}$

All of the expressions are equal to $3\frac{7}{8}$.

11. Write the sum of the expressions in Item 10 as

   a. A mixed number. $3\frac{7}{8}$

   b. An improper fraction. $\frac{31}{8}$

   c. A decimal. 3.875

   d. A percent. 387.5%

TRY THESE A

   a. $\frac{1}{3} + \frac{1}{6}$ $\frac{1}{2}$

   b. $\frac{2}{5} + \frac{3}{8}$ $\frac{31}{40}$

   c. $\frac{5}{12} - \frac{5}{6}$ $-\frac{5}{12}$

   d. $4\frac{1}{4} + 2\frac{1}{2}$ $6\frac{3}{4}$

   e. $6\frac{3}{5} - 2\frac{2}{3}$ $3\frac{14}{15}$ or $\frac{59}{15}$

   f. Create graphical representations of Items a and d. Use the My Notes space.
      Student representations may vary.

10-11 Create Representations, Predict and Confirm, Group Presentations Allow for further exploration of expressing equivalent forms of rational numbers. It may be helpful to provide additional examples and a review of how to convert rational numbers into various equivalent forms.

TRY THESE A These problems provide an opportunity for students to practice adding and subtracting fractions.

Suggested Assignment

CHECK YOUR UNDERSTANDING
p. 40, #1–2

UNIT 1 PRACTICE
p. 50–51, #26–30

12 Questioning the Text, Predict and Confirm Students who struggle with this question may benefit from describing the product as $\frac{3}{4}$ of $\frac{1}{2}$. Since $\frac{3}{4}$ is less than a whole, they should be able to conclude that the product will be less than $\frac{1}{2}$.

13 Create Representations You may wish to preface this question using visual aids. Show students an unshaded diagram first, and ask them to describe how $\frac{1}{2}$ of the diagram could be represented. Once they determine that shading 4 of the 8 sectors would represent $\frac{1}{2}$ of the circle, they can better understand that shading only 3 of the four sectors would represent $\frac{3}{4}$ of $\frac{1}{2}$, or $\frac{3}{8}$, of the circle.

My Notes

SUGGESTED LEARNING STRATEGIES: Questioning the Text, Predict and Confirm, Create Representations

When multiplying fractions such as $\frac{3}{4} \cdot \frac{1}{2}$, it is helpful to think of the multiplication symbol • as the word "of." So you read, "Find $\frac{3}{4}$ of $\frac{1}{2}$."

12. Without completing the problem, do you think the answer will be greater than or less than $\frac{1}{2}$? Explain your reasoning.

Answers may vary. Sample answer: The product will be less than one half because $\frac{3}{4}$ of a half is less than a whole half.

13. Consider the picture below.

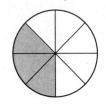

a. Explain how this picture could be used to represent $\frac{3}{4}$ of $\frac{1}{2}$.

Answers may vary. Sample answer: If you focus on just one half of the circle, 3 of its fourths are shaded.

b. Express the shaded portion of the circle as a single fraction.

$\frac{3}{8}$

SUGGESTED LEARNING STRATEGIES: Visualization,
Simplify Think/Pair/Share

My Notes

The problem $\frac{2}{3} \cdot \frac{3}{4}$ could be modeled in the same way. This problem is asking you to find $\frac{2}{3}$ of $\frac{3}{4}$.

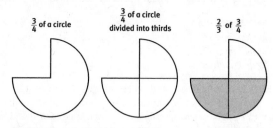

$\frac{3}{4}$ of a circle $\frac{3}{4}$ of a circle divided into thirds $\frac{2}{3}$ of $\frac{3}{4}$

Depending on how the problem is completed, several "different" answers could be given. Using the diagrams above, the answer could be expressed as $\frac{2}{4}$ or $\frac{1}{2}$.

By simply multiplying the numerators and denominators, the answer could be shown as $\frac{2}{3} \cdot \frac{3}{4} = \frac{2 \cdot 3}{3 \cdot 4} = \frac{6}{12}$.

14. Explain why $\frac{1}{2}$, $\frac{2}{4}$, and $\frac{6}{12}$ are the same number.

Each fraction simplifies to $\frac{1}{2}$.

TRY THESE B

a. $\frac{4}{5} \cdot \frac{1}{3}$ b. $\frac{6}{7} \cdot \frac{3}{10}$

   $\frac{4}{15}$ $\frac{9}{35}$

c. $\frac{8}{3} \cdot \frac{13}{15}$ d. $\frac{4}{12} \cdot \frac{6}{8}$

   $\frac{104}{45}$ or $2\frac{14}{45}$ $\frac{1}{4}$

e. Create a graphical representation of Item a.

   Student representations may vary.

TEACHER TO TEACHER   The explanation at the top of the page is meant to expand upon the concepts explored in Item 13. While most students may already have a solid understanding of how to multiply fractions, struggling students will benefit from extended discussion of this example.

14 Visualization, Simplify the Problem, Think/Pair/Share
When discussing this question, it may be helpful to refer back to the diagram at the top of the page. In the diagram, half of a whole circle is shaded. Another way to describe the diagram is that 2 of the 4 sectors of a whole circle are shaded.

Challenge students by asking them how the diagram could be altered to show how $\frac{6}{12}$ is also equivalent to the other values.

Example

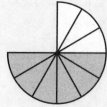

TRY THESE B These problems provide practice for students as a check of their understanding of multiplying fractions.

TEACHER TO TEACHER The information at the top of the page is designed to introduce a method for dividing fractions that goes beyond the simple algorithm of "invert and multiply." While the concept may appear simple to master, the problems are meant to help students understand *why* the mathematics works instead of just *how* it works.

15 Vocabulary Organizer, Mark the Text Remind students that the mixed number in part d must be changed to an improper fraction before its reciprocal can be determined.

TEACHER TO TEACHER In addition to moving past the algorithm, students will explore the idea that multiplication and division are inverse operations of one another. Eventually, students may move on to the algorithm of "invert and multiply," but may benefit from being able to connect the concept of "inverting" to "inverse operations."

16 Self/Peer Revision Extends the discussion of multiplication and division as inverse operations of one another. Once again, the purpose of this exploration is to allow students to understand that dividing by a number is the same as multiplying by its inverse (reciprocal). Further discussion should focus on the connection between the phrases "invert and multiply" and "multiplying by the inverse." In other words, *why* the algorithm works as opposed to *how* it works.

SUGGESTED LEARNING STRATEGIES: Vocabulary Organizer, Mark the Text, Self/Peer Revision

My Notes

MATH TIP

You can gain a greater understanding of a concept by learning about "why" something works as opposed to memorizing "how" something works.

ACADEMIC VOCABULARY

The **reciprocal** of a number is its multiplicative inverse.

A common strategy used to divide fractions uses the directions "invert and multiply." The problem, however, is that the phrase can often raise more questions than answers. For example:

What does invert mean?
What do I invert?
Why do I invert?
Why do I multiply?

These are all valid questions that deserve equally valid answers.

The first two questions are easy to answer. To invert something is to turn it upside down. In mathematics, this is referred to as finding the **reciprocal** of a number. In other words, inverting the fraction $\frac{2}{3}$ would give us the reciprocal, or $\frac{3}{2}$. When dividing fractions such as in the problem $\frac{2}{5} \div \frac{2}{3}$, the second fraction is inverted to produce $\frac{2}{5} \cdot \frac{3}{2}$.

15. Determine the reciprocal of the following:

  a. $\frac{4}{3}$ $\frac{3}{4}$

  b. $\frac{5}{18}$ $\frac{18}{5}$

  c. 15 $\frac{1}{15}$

  d. $5\frac{3}{5}$ $\frac{5}{28}$

As for the last two questions concerning *why* this works, it's important to understand the concept of inverse operations.

16. Consider the problem $10 \div 2$.

  a. Without using the words "divided by," explain what this problem is asking you to do.
  Answer may vary. Sample answer: Find half of 10.

SUGGESTED LEARNING STRATEGIES: Predict and Confirm, Discussion Group, Activating Prior Knowledge, Group Presentation

My Notes

b. What number could be multiplied by 10 to reach the same solution?

$\frac{1}{2}$

c. What do you notice about the number 2 and your answer to part b?

2 and $\frac{1}{2}$ are reciprocals.

d. Use your answer to part b to rewrite the problem using multiplication.

$10 \cdot \frac{1}{2}$

e. Based on your observation, explain what is meant by describing multiplication and division as inverse operations of one another.

Answers may vary. Student explanations should indicate an understanding that dividing by a number or multiplying by its reciprocal (inverse) produces the same value.

Background music in movies and television shows is not chosen at random. In fact, the music is often chosen so that it directly relates to the emotions being portrayed on the screen.

17. The following table lists the average beats per minute of music meant to express various emotions.

Emotion	Beats per Minute
Joy and Triumph	120
Mystery and Suspense	115
Comfort and Peace	100
Loneliness and Regret	120

a. Describe a scene from a movie or television show that would parallel each of the four categories in the table.

Answers may vary.

17 Predict and Confirm, Discussion Group, Activating Prior Knowledge, Group Presentation In solving this problem, students are able to apply the concept of inverse operations to a real-world situation.

TRY THESE C These problems provide practice in dividing fractions.

Suggested Assignment

CHECK YOUR UNDERSTANDING
p. 40, #3–5

UNIT 1 PRACTICE
p. 51, #31–35

CHECK YOUR UNDERSTANDING

1. Answers may vary. Sample answers:
   a. $\frac{19}{15}$ or $1\frac{4}{15}$
   b. $\frac{7}{24}$ or $\frac{14}{48}$
   c. $\frac{7}{30}$ or $\frac{14}{60}$
   d. 3 or $\frac{36}{12}$

2. Students may choose to convert the mixed numbers to improper fractions or express the mixed numbers in decimal form before performing their calculations.
   Answer: $1\frac{11}{12}$, graphical representations will vary.

3. $\frac{3}{5} \div \frac{4}{7}$ is greater. Answers may vary. Sample answer: Since $\frac{4}{7}$ is less than 1, the product $\frac{3}{5} \cdot \frac{4}{7}$ will give an answer that is less than a whole $\frac{3}{5}$. The quotient $\frac{3}{5} \div \frac{7}{4}$ can be rewritten as $\frac{3}{5} \cdot \frac{7}{4}$. Since $\frac{7}{4}$ is greater than 1, $\frac{7}{4}$ of $\frac{3}{5}$ will be greater than $\frac{3}{5}$.

4. The answer could be determined by multiplying 36 by $\frac{1}{4}$ or dividing 36 by 4.

5. Answers may vary. Sample answer: Adding and subtracting fractions are similar because you must have a common denominator in order to operate. Multiplying and dividing fractions does not require this. In order to divide fractions, it is usually easier to find the reciprocal and multiply.

My Notes

SUGGESTED LEARNING STRATEGIES: Quickwrite

b. Explain how you could use multiplication or division to determine the number of beats in a three-minute song.
Answers may vary. Sample answer: Multiplying the number of beats per minute by 3 or dividing the beats per minute by $\frac{1}{3}$ will both produce the correct number of beats in a three-minute song.

TRY THESE C

a. $\frac{4}{5} \div \frac{3}{7}$ $\frac{28}{15}$ or $1\frac{13}{15}$

b. $\frac{6}{15} \div \frac{2}{9}$ $\frac{9}{5}$ or $1\frac{4}{5}$

c. $\frac{14}{3} \div 4$ $\frac{7}{6}$ or $1\frac{1}{6}$

CHECK YOUR UNDERSTANDING

Write your answers on notebook paper. Show your work.

1. Express the solutions to the following problems in two different forms.
   a. $\frac{3}{5} + \frac{4}{6}$ b. $\frac{5}{8} - \frac{1}{3}$
   c. $\frac{2}{5} \cdot \frac{7}{12}$ d. $\frac{4}{3} \div \frac{4}{9}$

2. Describe the process you would use to find the solution to the problem below. Express your answer numerically and with a graphical representation.
$$3\frac{1}{4} - 1\frac{1}{3}$$

3. Without performing any calculations, determine which of the following problems will produce the greatest answer. Explain your reasoning.
$$\frac{3}{5} \cdot \frac{4}{7} \quad \text{or} \quad \frac{3}{5} \div \frac{4}{7}$$

4. Tony has 36 pages left in the book he is reading. He plans to read $\frac{1}{4}$ of the pages tonight before going to bed. Explain how you can determine the number of pages Tony will read by using either multiplication or division.

5. **MATHEMATICAL REFLECTION** Explain the similarities and differences between adding, subtracting, multiplying, and dividing fractions.

Rational and Irrational Numbers
Know When to Fold 'Em

A popular urban myth is that it is impossible to fold a piece of paper in half more than seven times.

1. Remove a sheet of paper from your notebook, and try it for yourself. You may fold the paper in any direction you wish as long as you fold the paper in half each time. When you have finished experimenting, share your results with your group members.

While the validity of the myth itself is not relevant to this activity, folding the paper in half repeatedly presents some interesting theories about numbers.

2. Complete the following table based on the first six folds you made in your paper.

Folds	Number of Regions on Paper	Each Region's Fraction of the Original Paper	Sketch of Unfolded Paper Showing Folds
0	1	1	
1	2	$\frac{1}{2}$	
2	4	$\frac{1}{4}$	
3	8	$\frac{1}{8}$	
4	16	$\frac{1}{16}$	
5	32	$\frac{1}{32}$	
6	64	$\frac{1}{64}$	

My Notes

Rational and Irrational Numbers

Activity Focus
- Rational and Irrational numbers
- Estimating square roots

Materials
- Calculator
- Plain paper (for folding)

Chunking the Activity

#1	#5–6
#2–3	#7
#4	#8

TEACHER TO TEACHER This activity is designed to allow students to conceptualize the difference between rational and irrational numbers. In addition, students will explore methods for estimating square roots and will be able to explain why it's only possible to *estimate* irrational numbers with rational values.

1 Use Manipulatives, Graphic Organizer, Discussion Group The myth in the introduction to Item 1 is difficult to disprove, but it has been done. On an episode of the television show, Mythbusters, the hosts used very long, thin paper and a steamroller to fold a sheet 11 times! Encourage students to experiment with various folding techniques to see how many times they can fold their papers, however, don't let them become frustrated if they can't disprove the myth.

2 Use Manipulatives, Graphic Organizer, Discussion Group Although students may manage to fold their papers more, they only need to be able to fold them 6 times to complete the table in Item 2. This question is intended to allow the students to generate an initial set of fractions between 0 and 1.

3 Think/Pair/Share, Predict and Confirm, Use Manipulatives, Graphic Organizer This activity provides a very basic approach to the concept of limits. As the paper is folded, the dimensions of the resulting quadrilateral become smaller and smaller. As the number of folds approaches infinity, the dimensions of the folded resulting quadrilateral approach zero. While it is not intended for the students to end up with a fundamental understanding of limits and infinity, they should be able to understand that there are an infinite amount of numbers between 0 and 1.

4 Use Manipulatives, Graphic Organizer Students begin with a paper folded into thirds. Folding the paper in half over and over again produces another set of rational numbers between 0 and 1. They should discover that these values are all different from the ones generated in Item 2.

My Notes

SUGGESTED LEARNING STRATEGIES: Think/Pair/Share, Predict and Confirm, Use Manipulatives, Graphic Organizer

3. Consider the dimensions of the resulting quadrilateral each time the paper is folded.

a. What is happening to the dimensions of the paper?

The dimensions of the folded quadrilateral are getting smaller.

b. In theory, what size is the resulting quadrilateral approaching as you keep folding?

In theory, the dimensions of the quadrilateral are approaching zero.

c. Is it possible for a resulting quadrilateral to actually reach this size? Explain your answer.

No. Answers may vary. Sample answer: At some point, it will be impossible to physically fold the paper in half again.

4. Fold your paper into thirds as shown below.

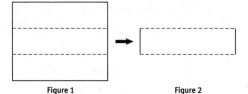

Figure 1   Figure 2

a. Beginning with your paper folded into a third as shown in Figure 2 above. Then fold the paper in half repeatedly and complete the table below.

	Figure 2	Figure 3	Figure 4	Figure 5	Figure 6	Figure 7
Each Region's Fraction of Original Paper	$\frac{1}{3}$	$\frac{1}{6}$	$\frac{1}{12}$	$\frac{1}{24}$	$\frac{1}{48}$	$\frac{1}{96}$

Rational and Irrational Numbers
Know When to Fold 'Em

SUGGESTED LEARNING STRATEGIES: Use Manipulatives, Create Representations, Self/Peer Revision, Discussion Group

b. Are any of these fractions the same as those from the table in Item 2? Explain why this might be true.

None of the fractions are equivalent to the fractions in Item 2. Answers may vary. Possible answer: The second table records folds that start with a region that is $\frac{1}{3}$ of a whole sheet. The values in the second table are $\frac{1}{3}$ the values in the first table, which started with a whole sheet.

5. Use another piece of paper to show how you could find other fractional values between 0 and 1. Discuss your results with your group.

Student examples may vary.

6. Fill in the missing values in the following table.

Representations may vary. Sample graphical representations are shown in the table.

Fraction in simplest terms	Decimal Form	Percent	Graphical Representation
$\frac{1}{10}$	0.1	10%	
$\frac{1}{5}$	0.2	20%	
$\frac{1}{3}$	$0.\overline{3}$	$33.\overline{3}\%$	
$\frac{2}{5}$	0.4	40%	
$\frac{3}{5}$	0.6	60%	
$\frac{2}{3}$	$0.\overline{6}$	$66.\overline{6}\%$	
$\frac{3}{4}$	0.75	75%	
$\frac{4}{5}$	0.8	80%	
$\frac{9}{10}$	0.9	90%	

My Notes

5 Use Manipulatives, Create Representations, Self/Peer Revision, Discussion Group Some students may struggle as they attempt to fold their papers into fifths, sixths, etc. This question is not meant to confuse students but to reiterate that an infinite amount of rational numbers can be generated between 0 and 1.

TEACHER TO TEACHER If some students still cannot grasp the idea, ask them if it is possible to name the largest real number. If they respond by saying it's impossible because 1 can always be added to make an even larger number, explain that the same concept applies here. No matter what number can be found between zero and one, it can always be divided by another integer (2, 3, 4, etc.). This is what the students were modeling by folding the paper over and over.

6 Create Representations Filling in the table breaks away from the theoretical aspects of rational numbers and moves to some practice with equivalent forms. The table allows students to demonstrate their levels of understanding for converting between fractions, decimals, and percents. It also provides an opportunity for conceptualization of these values in the form of graphical representations. A major connection to be made with these values is that every number in the table, regardless of the form in which it is written, is considered to be rational.

TEACHER TO TEACHER Now that the students have a better understanding of rational numbers, the concept of irrational numbers is introduced. You may wish to enrich the discussion of irrational numbers by talking about the transcendental numbers π and e.

As students work through Item 7, some may have difficulty with the concept of perfect squares and square roots. It may be necessary to review these topics before proceeding.

7 Vocabulary Organizer, Mark the Text, Identify a Subtask, Predict and Confirm Once students determine that $\sqrt{43}$ should be somewhere between 6 and 7, they will square 6.5 to see if it gives them a value greater than or less than 43. Since 42.25 is less than 43, the students should be able to determine that the estimate must be greater than 6.5. You may have them square 6.6 (43.56) as well to help them determine the value must be between 6.5 and 6.6. Results are then compared to a calculator estimate of $\sqrt{43}$.

SUGGESTED LEARNING STRATEGIES: Vocabulary Organizer, Mark the Text, Identify a Subtask, Predict and Confirm

My Notes

MATH TERMS

A **rational number** is any number that can be written as the ratio of two integers where the divisor is not zero. All of the fractions and percents in this unit so far have been *rational* numbers.

An **irrational number** cannot be expressed as the ratio of two integers. Nor can it be expressed as a terminating or repeating decimal. *Pi* is an irrational number.

READING MATH

The number $\sqrt{43}$ is read "the square root of 43."

MATH TERMS

The rational numbers together with the irrational numbers form the set of **real numbers**.

Many early mathematicians believed that all numbers were **rational**; that is, they could be written as a quotient of two integers. However, as early as the 7th century BC, mathematicians from India were aware of numbers that could not be expressed as the quotient of two integers. Eventually, it became accepted that the square roots of most real numbers could not be expressed rationally. Not only that, but **irrational** numbers cannot be expressed as terminating or repeating decimals.

It is possible, however, to determine reasonable estimates for these numbers. To do so, it's helpful to become familiar with the relative size of some common rational numbers.

7. Consider the number $\sqrt{43}$.

a. Between which two perfect squares is the integer 43?
36 and 49

b. Between which two integers is $\sqrt{43}$? Explain your reasoning.
$\sqrt{43}$ is between 6 and 7.
Answers may vary. Sample answer: Because $\sqrt{36} = 6$ and $\sqrt{49} = 7$.

c. What rational number is exactly halfway between the integers you determined in part b?
6.5

d. Square the rational number you found in part c. Is this number greater than or less than 43?
42.25 is less than 43.

e. Use the information discovered in parts a to d to estimate $\sqrt{43}$ to the nearest hundredth. Explain your reasoning.
Student estimations may vary but should range from 6.51 and 6.99.

SUGGESTED LEARNING STRATEGIES: Predict and Confirm, Quickwrite, Group Presentation

TRY THESE A These problems provide practice for students as a check of their understanding of estimating square roots.

My Notes

f. Use a calculator to determine $\sqrt{43}$, and compare it to your estimate.

$\sqrt{43} \approx 6.5574385$. Student comparisons will vary.

TRY THESE A

Estimate the following square roots to the hundredths place without using a calculator. · Estimated values should range from:

a. $\sqrt{10}$ 3.01 and 3.50

b. $\sqrt{28}$ 5.01 and 5.50

c. $\sqrt{94}$ 9.50 and 9.99

d. Give the approximate location of each irrational number on the number line below.

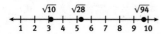

8. Using a calculator, $\sqrt{3}$ is shown to be 1.7320508....

a. Explain how you know this is between the estimates of $1\frac{7}{10}$ and $1\frac{4}{5}$.

In decimal form, $1\frac{7}{10} = 1.7$ and $1\frac{4}{5} = 1.8$. The value given for $\sqrt{3}$ is between these numbers.

b. Explain the connection between these estimates and the actual value with rational and irrational numbers.

Student explanations may vary but should include an understanding that their estimates were rational numbers and can only serve as approximations of irrational numbers.

> **CONNECT TO AP**
>
> In the branch of mathematics known as calculus, you will learn how to estimate the square root of a number using a linear equation.

8 Predict and Confirm, Quickwrite, Group Presentation By converting the mixed numbers to decimals, students should recognize that $\sqrt{3}$ is, in fact, between these values.

Connect to AP

In Calculus AB, students will learn how to estimate the square root of a number using a linear equation. In Calculus BC, this notion will be extended to estimating the square root of a number using a polynomial of degree *n*. As the number of terms of the polynomial increases, the estimation becomes more accurate. In AP Statistics, students will learn to use the mean of a simple random sample to estimate the mean of a population.

Suggested Assignment

CHECK YOUR UNDERSTANDING
p. 46, #1–18

UNIT 1 PRACTICE
p. 51, #36–39

CHECK YOUR UNDERSTANDING

Answers may vary.

1. Sample answers: $\frac{62}{5}$ and $\sqrt{150}$

2. Sample answers: $\frac{43}{9}$ and $\sqrt{22}$

3. Sample answers: $\frac{3}{4}$ and $\frac{\sqrt{2}}{2}$

4. Sample answers: $100\frac{9}{12}$ and $\sqrt{10,165}$

5. Rational; all addends are rational.

6. Irrational; $\sqrt{27}$ is irrational.

7. Rational; all addends are rational.

8. Irrational; π and $\frac{\pi}{3}$ are irrational.

9. Rational; all addends are rational.

10. Reasonable estimates should range from 4.01 to 4.49.

11. Reasonable estimates should range from 11.01 to 11.49.

12. Reasonable estimates should range from 1.01 to 1.49.

13. Reasonable estimates should range from 9.01 to 9.49.

14. 9

15. 12

16. 2

17. 5

18. Sample answer: Because it is always possible to calculate a number that is halfway between two numbers. To do this, you find the difference between the numbers, divide it in half, and add the result to the smaller number.

When you cube a number, you raise the number to the third power. For example, 4 cubed = $4^3 = 4 \cdot 4 \cdot 4 = 64$.

The cube root of a number n is the number that when used as a factor three times gives a product of n. The symbol for cube root is $\sqrt[3]{}$. The expression $\sqrt[3]{64} = 4$ because $4 \cdot 4 \cdot 4 = 64$.

9. Is $\sqrt[3]{64}$ rational or irrational? Explain.

Rational. Since $\sqrt[3]{64} = 4$ and 4 is a rational number, $\sqrt[3]{64}$ must be rational.

A cube root that cannot be simplified to a rational number is irrational.

10. Is $\sqrt[3]{12}$ rational or irrational? Explain.

Irrational. Since there is no rational number that can be used as a factor three times to get 12, $\sqrt[3]{12}$ is irrational.

CHECK YOUR UNDERSTANDING

Write your answers on notebook paper. Show your work.

Determine a rational and an irrational number between each of the following pairs of numbers.

1. $12\frac{1}{10}$ and $12\frac{3}{5}$

2. $4\frac{2}{3}$ and $4\frac{8}{9}$

3. $\frac{1}{2}$ and 1

4. $100\frac{2}{3}$ and $100\frac{5}{6}$

Tell if each of the following sums is rational or irrational. Explain your reasoning.

5. $\frac{3}{4} + 0.8 + 12\%$

6. $2\frac{1}{5} + 0.75 + \sqrt{27}$

7. $24\% + \sqrt{16} + 0.3$

8. $\frac{33}{8} + \pi + \frac{\pi}{3}$

9. $0.\overline{77} + 4 + 5\frac{1}{3}$

Determine a reasonable estimate to the hundredths place for each of the following. Then give their approximate location on a number line.

10. $\sqrt{18}$ 11. $\sqrt{130}$

12. $\sqrt{2}$ 13. $\sqrt{86}$

14. $\sqrt{81}$ 15. $\sqrt{144}$

16. $\sqrt[3]{8}$ 17. $\sqrt[3]{125}$

18. MATHEMATICAL REFLECTION Explain why it is always possible to find another number (rational or irrational) between any two numbers.

10.–13.
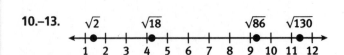

Rational Numbers

A RECIPE FOR SUCCESS

On May 15, 2005, a group of volunteers met in Las Vegas to create what would become the world's largest cake. In order for the cake to qualify for the *Guinness Book of World Records*, it had to meet the following qualifications:

- contain traditional ingredients in the correct proportions,
- be prepared in the same manner as a normal-sized cake,
- be prepared according to appropriate hygiene standards, and
- be totally edible and safe to eat.

To create the world's largest cake, the organizers had to begin with a recipe for one cake and scale the ingredients accordingly. A sample recipe for one cake is shown below.

2 cups flour

$1\frac{1}{3}$ tablespoon baking powder

$\frac{1}{4}$ teaspoon salt

$\frac{2}{3}$ cup sugar

2 eggs

$\frac{3}{4}$ cup milk

$\frac{1}{2}$ teaspoon vanilla

1. If a volunteer prepared for 15 cakes, determine the following:

   a. The sum of the needed cups of sugar and milk.

   b. The difference between the number of teaspoons of vanilla needed and the number of teaspoons of salt needed.

   c. Describe the step-by-step process you used to determine your answer for part a.

Embedded Assessment 2

Assessment Focus

- Operations with fractions
- Equivalent forms of numbers
- Rational and Irrational numbers
- Scientific notation
- Inverse operations

Assessment Perspectives

This embedded assessment provides students an opportunity to demonstrate understanding of operations with fractions, scientific notation, and the difference between rational and irrational numbers. This activity does not assess the students' ability to estimate the value of a square root.

Answer Key

1a. $15 \cdot \frac{2}{3} + 15 \cdot \frac{3}{4} = \frac{30}{3} + \frac{45}{4}$
$= 10 + 11\frac{1}{4} = 21\frac{1}{4}$ Cups

b. $15 \cdot \frac{1}{2} - 15 \cdot \frac{1}{4} = \frac{15}{2} - \frac{15}{4}$
$= \frac{30}{4} - \frac{15}{4} = \frac{15}{4} = 3\frac{3}{4}$ tsp

c. Students should be able to explain their processes verbally or with graphical representations.

2a. $\frac{4}{3}$

  b. 1.33…

  c. $133\frac{1}{3}\%$

  d. Graphic representations may vary. Sample representation:

3. This item points out that just because it is possible to find a particular value, it does not mean that the value will yield any useful information.

4. Students should be able to identify the amounts as rational numbers because each can be written as a quotient of two integers.

5. Students should be able to convert the numbers to scientific notation and explain the process they would use to determine the product in scientific notation. 1.3×10^5; 1.28×10^5

6. about 20

7. Students should be able to express their understanding of multiplication and division being inverse operations of one another.

2. Express the amount of baking powder needed for one cake as each of the following:

  a. An improper fraction.

  b. A decimal.

  c. A percent.

  d. A graphical representation.

3. Does it make sense, in the real world, to convert the amount of baking powder used to a percent? Explain why or why not.

4. Are the amounts of the ingredients used rational or irrational numbers? Explain your reasoning.

5. The finished cake weighed in at 130,000 pounds, breaking the world record of 128,000 pounds.

  a. Express each of these values in scientific notation.

  b. Explain the process you would use to find the product of the numbers in scientific notation.

6. If cake A weighs $3 \cdot 10^6$ ounces and cake B weighs $7 \cdot 10^7$ ounces, how many times as heavy as cake A is cake B?

7. The world record cake used approximately 60,000 eggs. If the previous world record cake was $\frac{8}{9}$ the size of the Las Vegas cake, explain why you could multiply 60,000 by $\frac{8}{9}$ or divide 60,000 by $\frac{9}{8}$ to determine the number of eggs used in the smaller cake.

Rational Numbers

A RECIPE FOR SUCCESS

	Exemplary	Proficient	Emerging
Math Knowledge 1a, b, 2a, b, c, 4, 5a	• Correctly determines the sum of the measurements of sugar and milk (1a) and the difference between measurements of vanilla and salt (1b) • Correctly converts a mixed number to an improper fraction (2a), a decimal (2b), a percent (2c) • Correctly determines numbers as rational or irrational (4) • Correctly expresses the weight of the cakes in scientific notation (5a)	• Attempts both calculations but is able to correctly determine only the sum or the difference • Converts the mixed number into two of the three required forms • Determines four of the seven measurements as rational or irrational • Expresses the weight of one of the cakes in scientific notation correctly	• Attempts both calculations but is unable to find the sum or the difference. • Provides one correct conversion of the mixed number • Determines fewer than four of the measurements as rational or irrational • Does not express the weight of the cakes in scientific notation correctly
Representation 2d	Represents the measurement of baking powder as a visual model (2d)		Is unable to represent the baking powder measurement using a visual model.
Communication 1c, 3, 4, 5b, 7	• Correctly describes the step-by-step process used to find the answer (1c) • Correctly explains why a percent is not an appropriate form of measurement in a recipe (3) • Correctly explains whether the measurements are rational or irrational (4) • Correctly explains a process for finding the product of two numbers written in scientific notation.(5b) • Correctly explains why multiplying 60,000 by $\frac{8}{9}$ or dividing 60,000 by $\frac{9}{8}$ produces the same value. (7)	Communicates four of the five explanations clearly and accurately.	Communicates three of the five explanations clearly and accurately.

Embedded Assessment 2

TEACHER TO TEACHER You may wish to read through the rubric with students and discuss the differences in the expectation levels. Make sure students understand the meanings of any terms used.

Activity 1.1

1a.

b. $1, \dfrac{4}{3}$

c. $4, -1$

d. $1, \dfrac{1}{4}$

2. Possible answers include multiple representations of $\dfrac{4}{25}$.

3. add -3, subtract 3, multiply by 4, divide by $\dfrac{1}{4}$

4. The first letter of each word follows the order of the alphabet. The number of letters in each word increases by 1.

Activity 1.2

5. 6^7

6. 12^{15}

7. x^{19}

8. x^{13}

9. 8^4

10. 15

11. x^9

12. 1

13. 1

14. $\dfrac{1}{x^4}$ or x^{-4}

15. $\dfrac{1}{x^2}$ or x^{-2}

Activity 1.3

16. 60.3

17. 26.23

18. 131.38

19. 27.86

20. 29.26

21. 187.2

22. 98.7

23a. 2.34×10^5

   b. 8.7×10^7

   c. 3.03×10^2

   d. 7.0620102×10^6

ACTIVITY 1.1

1. Determine the next two terms in the following patterns.

a.

b. $0, \dfrac{1}{3}, \dfrac{2}{3}, \ldots$

c. $14, 13, 11, 8, \ldots$

d. $64, 16, 4, \ldots$

2. Express the fifth term in the pattern in two different ways: $100, 20, 4, \ldots$

3. Explain how you could use either addition, subtraction, multiplication, or division to generate the next term in the pattern $-1, -4, \ldots$

4. Describe the following pattern, and continue it as long as you can:

   a, by, cat, dove, early, …

ACTIVITY 1.2

5. $6^4 \cdot 6^3$

6. $12^6 \cdot 12^9$

7. $x^{14} \cdot x^5$

8. $x^1 \cdot x^5 \cdot x^7$

9. $\dfrac{8^7}{8^3}$

10. $\dfrac{15^6}{15^5}$

11. $\dfrac{x^{19}}{x^{10}}$

12. 150^0

13. $x^0 \cdot 8^0$

14. $\dfrac{x^2}{x^6}$

15. $\dfrac{x}{x^3}$

ACTIVITY 1.3

16. $25.7 + 34.6$

17. $12.2 + 14.03$

18. $155.68 - 24.3$

19. $46 - 18.14$

20. $2.8 \cdot 10.45$

21. $18 \cdot 10.4$

22. $100 - 3(2.3) + 5.6$

23. Express in scientific notation:

   a. 234,000

   b. Eighty-seven million

   c. 303

   d. 7,062,010.2

24. Express in standard form:

   a. $3.5 \cdot 10^8$

   b. $4.62 \cdot 10^{-4}$

   c. $3.5 \cdot 10^{-5}$

   d. $4.62 \cdot 10^3$

25. Express your answer in scientific notation:
   $(1.35 \cdot 10^6) \cdot (8.1 \cdot 10^5)$

ACTIVITY 1.4

 +

26.

27. $\dfrac{4}{3} + \dfrac{3}{4}$

28. $5\dfrac{2}{5} + \dfrac{4}{5}$

24a. 350,000,000

   b. 0.000462

   c. 0.000035

   d. 4,620

   25. 1.0935×10^{12}

29. $\frac{8}{9} - \frac{7}{12}$

30. $8 - \frac{7}{12}$

31. $\frac{4}{9} \cdot \frac{6}{11}$

32. $\frac{14}{20} \cdot \frac{1}{6}$

33. $\frac{10}{11} \div \frac{1}{3}$

34. $14 \div \frac{3}{2}$

35. A roll of quarters contains ten dollars. Explain how you could determine the number of quarters in a roll by using either multiplication or division.

ACTIVITY 1.5

36. Express each of the following as a quotient of two integers.
   a. 38%
   b. 0.074
   c. 2.9
   d. 6
   e. $5\frac{3}{8}$

37. Identify each of the following as either rational or irrational.
   a. 5
   b. $\frac{3}{10}$
   c. 0.85
   d. $2.\overline{3}$
   e. 140%
   f. $\sqrt{49}$
   g. $\sqrt{120}$

38. Determine a reasonable estimate for the following and give the approximate location of each on a number line.
   a. $\sqrt{14}$
   b. $\sqrt{27}$
   c. $\sqrt{118}$
   d. $\sqrt{97}$

39. If *Pi* is considered an irrational number, explain why using 3.14 or $\frac{22}{7}$ to find the area of a circle would only give you an estimate of the actual answer.

38a-d.

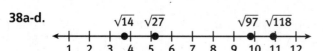

UNIT 1 PRACTICE Continued

Activity 1.4

26. $\frac{7}{8}$ or equivalent representation

27. $\frac{25}{12}$ or $2\frac{1}{12}$

28. $\frac{31}{5}$ or $6\frac{1}{5}$

29. $\frac{11}{36}$

30. $\frac{89}{12}$ or $7\frac{5}{12}$

31. $\frac{24}{99}$

32. $\frac{7}{60}$

33. $\frac{30}{11}$ or $2\frac{8}{11}$

34. $\frac{28}{3}$ or $9\frac{1}{3}$

35. Multiply 10 by 4 or divide 10 by $\frac{1}{4}$.

Activity 1.5

36. Possible answers:
   a. $\frac{38}{100}$ or $\frac{19}{50}$
   b. $\frac{74}{1000}$ or $\frac{37}{500}$
   c. $\frac{29}{10}$
   d. $\frac{6}{1}$
   e. $\frac{43}{8}$

37a. rational
   b. rational
   c. rational
   d. rational
   e. rational
   f. rational
   g. irrational

38a. Reasonable estimates should range from 3.51 to 3.99.
   b. Reasonable estimates should range from 5.01 to 5.49.
   c. Reasonable estimates should range from 10.51 to 10.99.
   d. Reasonable estimates should range from 9.51 to 9.99.

39. The values given for *Pi* are rational numbers. Since π is an irrational number, the given values must be estimates.

Reflection

Student Reflection

Discuss the essential questions with students. Have them share how their understanding of the questions has changed through studying the concepts in the unit.

Review the academic vocabulary. You may want students to revisit the graphic organizers they have completed for academic vocabulary terms and add other notes about their understanding of terms.

Encourage students to evaluate their own learning and to recognize the strategies that work best for them. Help them identify key concepts in the unit and to set goals for addressing their weaknesses and acquiring effective learning strategies.

Teacher Reflection

1. Of the key concepts in the unit, did any present special challenges for students?

2. How will you adjust your future instruction for students/activities?

3. Which strategies were most effective for facilitating student learning?

4. When you teach this unit again, what will you do differently?

Reflection

An important aspect of growing as a learner is to take the time to reflect on your learning. It is important to think about where you started, what you have accomplished, what helped you learn, and how you will apply your new knowledge in the future. Use notebook paper to record your thinking on the following topics and to identify evidence of your learning.

Essential Questions

1. Review the mathematical concepts and your work in this unit before you write thoughtful responses to the questions below. Support your responses with specific examples from concepts and activities in the unit.

   - How are fractions, decimals, and percents related?
   - Why is it important to understand the procedures for working with different kinds of numbers?

Academic Vocabulary

2. Look at the following academic vocabulary words:
   - hypothesis
   - reciprocal
   - power
   - scientific notation

   Choose three words and explain your understanding of each word and why each is important in your study of math.

Self-Evaluation

3. Look through the activities and Embedded Assessments in this unit. Use a table similar to the one below to list three major concepts in this unit and to rate your understanding of each.

Unit Concepts	Is Your Understanding Strong (S) or Weak (W)?
Concept 1	
Concept 2	
Concept 3	

   a. What will you do to address each weakness?

   b. What strategies or class activities were particularly helpful in learning the concepts you identified as strengths? Give examples to explain.

4. How do the concepts you learned in this unit relate to other math concepts and to the use of mathematics in the real world?

1. When pouring concrete for a rectangular patio, a contractor will make a "diagonal check" to make sure that the corners are right angles. One contractor wrote down the four common diagonal measurements she uses on a regular basis. Which list below represents the measurements ordered from **least to greatest**?

$$2\sqrt{10}, 10\sqrt{5}, 12\sqrt{2}, 2\sqrt{41}$$

A. $2\sqrt{10}, 2\sqrt{41}, 10\sqrt{5}, 12\sqrt{2}$

B. $2\sqrt{10}, 2\sqrt{41}, 12\sqrt{2}, 10\sqrt{5}$

C. $12\sqrt{2}, 10\sqrt{5}, 2\sqrt{10}, 2\sqrt{41}$

D. $2\sqrt{41}, 10\sqrt{5}, 2\sqrt{41}, 12\sqrt{2}$

1. Ⓐ Ⓑ Ⓒ Ⓓ

2. There is evidence that some microscopic life forms existed as long as 3,700 to 3,800 million years ago. This evidence was found in Isua greenstone in Greenland. What power of ten would you use when naming these two numbers using scientific notation?

2.

Read
Solve
Explain

3. ABC Cellular offers a plan to purchase international text messages. The basic plan is to pay $0.25 per text message. Upgrade 1 allows you to send 100 text messages a month for $9.95 with additional messages charged at $0.15 each. Upgrade 2 allows unlimited international texting for $29.25 a month. In one month Evyn sent 150 text messages to her friend in Costa Rica.

Part A: Calculate Evyn's charge for each plan. Which plan would be the best for Evyn? Justify your answer.

Answer and Explain

Basic Plan: 150 × 0.25 = $37.50

Upgrade 1: (50 × 0.15) + 9.95 = $17.45

Upgrade 2: $29.25; Upgrade 1 is the best plan since it is

cheaper then either of the other plans.

Part B: The following month, Evyn makes 240 calls to Costa Rica. Does this change the plan that should be selected? Justify your answer.

Answer and Explain

Yes, the best plan for making 240 calls is the unlimited

plan which costs $29.25. The basic plan would cost $60;

Upgrade I plan would cost $30.95.

UNIT 1 Math Standards Review

These two pages provide practice with four standardized test question formats that are used in many national and state high-stakes tests:

- Multiple choice
- Gridded response
- Short response
- Extended response

These items also provide practice with the mathematics content of this unit.

1 Multiple choice
- Order Irrational Numbers

2 Gridded response
- Use scientific Notation

3 Short Response
- Perform operations with Decimals

4 Extended response
- Use formulas
- Perform operations with rational numbers

TEACHER TO TEACHER: You might read through the extended-response item with students and discuss your expectation levels. Make sure students understand the meanings of any terms used.

Read
Solve
Explain

4. The formula $t = \frac{\sqrt{h}}{4}$ represents the time (t) in seconds that it takes an object to fall from a height of h feet.

Part A: If a ball is dropped from a height of 200 ft, calculate how long it will take to reach the ground to the nearest tenth.

Answer and Explain

$t = \frac{\sqrt{200}}{4}$

$t \approx 3.5$ seconds

Part B: If $t = 1\frac{1}{4}$ seconds, find h. Explain what the number you calculated represents.

Answer and Explain

$1.25 = \frac{\sqrt{h}}{4}$

$5 = \sqrt{h}$

$25 = h$; 25 ft is the height an object must fall from to reach the ground in 1.25 seconds

Part C: What is the height from which an object must be dropped to land on the ground after one second?

Answer and Explain

$1 = \frac{\sqrt{h}}{4}$

$4 = \sqrt{h}$

16 ft $= h$

This unit builds on students' knowledge of linear patterns and expressions. Students solve equations using a variety of methods, solve inequalities, and evaluate expressions. The properties of real numbers, equality, and inequality are used to justify student solution steps in a variety of problems. Students apply their knowledge to write algebraic models for a variety of verbal models and situations.

Academic Vocabulary

Blackline masters for use in developing students' vocabulary skills are located at the back of this Teacher's Edition. Encourage students to explore the meanings of the academic vocabulary words in this unit, using graphic organizers and class discussions to help students understand the key concepts related to the terms. Encourage students to place their vocabulary organizers in their math notebooks and to revisit these pages to make notes as their understanding of concepts increases.

Embedded Assessments

The two Embedded Assessments for this unit follow Activities 2.3 and 2.5.

CollegeBoard
inspiring minds™

Algebra/AP/College Readiness

Unit 2 teaches students to write expressions, equations, and inequalities from verbal and physical models, an important pre-AP skill. Students hone their ability to solve equations and inequalities and simplify expressions by:

- Writing algebraic models from a variety physical, numeric, and verbal descriptions.
- Learning a variety of solution methods and making decisions about the best way to solve a problem.
- Justifying their answers using the algebraic properties and principles.
- Communicating their understanding in both verbally and in writing.
- Understanding constant rate of change and relating it to verbal, physical, and algebraic models.

Embedded Assessment 1   A Penny for Your Thoughts

- Linear patterns
- Multiple representations
- Solving equations
- Evaluating expressions
- Properties of real numbers
- Literal equations

Embedded Assessment 2   A Gold Medal Appetite

- Writing and solving equations
- Writing, graphing, and solving inequalities
- Using formulas
- Solving literal equations

Suggested Pacing

The following table provides suggestions for pacing either a 45-minute period or a block schedule class of 90 minutes. Space is left for you to write your own pacing guidelines based on your experiences in using the materials.

	45-Minute Period	90-Minute Period	Your Comments on Pacing
Unit Overview	$\frac{1}{2}$	$\frac{1}{4}$	
Activity 2.1	4	2	
Activity 2.2	7	$3\frac{1}{2}$	
Activity 2.3	4	2	
Embedded Assessment 1	1	$\frac{1}{2}$	
Activity 2.4	2	1	
Activity 2.5	4	2	
Embedded Assessment 2	1	$\frac{1}{2}$	
Total	$23\frac{1}{2}$	$11\frac{3}{4}$	

Unit Practice

Practice Problems for each activity in the unit appear at the end of the unit.

Math Standards Review

To help accustom students to the formats and types of questions they may encounter on high stakes tests, additional problems are provided at the end of the unit. These problems are constructed for multiple choice, short response, extended response, and gridded responses.

Expressions, Equations, and Inequalities

Unit 2

Unit Overview
In this unit you will write expressions representing patterns and sentences and you will study several ways to solve equations and inequalities.

Academic Vocabulary
Add these words to and others you encounter in this unit to your vocabulary notebook.

- equation
- expression
- inequality
- inverse operation
- literal equation
- n^{th}
- property
- sequence
- solution

Essential Questions

? How are the properties of real numbers useful when solving equations and simplifying expressions?

? What are the similarities and differences in the procedures for solving and expressing the solutions of equations and inequalities?

EMBEDDED ASSESSMENTS

This unit has two Embedded Assessments, one following Activity 2.3 and the other following Activity 2.5. These Embedded Assessments allow you to demonstrate your understanding of writing, solving, and graphing equations and inequalities as well as evaluating expressions and using formulas.

Embedded Assessment 1

Patterns, Expressions, Equations, Formulas   p. 89

Embedded Assessment 2

Equations and Inequalities   p. 107

55

UNIT 2 OVERVIEW

Unit Overview
Have students read the unit overview and ask them to recall patterns they have worked with in mathematics and patterns they see in the real world.

Essential Questions
Read the essential questions with students. Ask them to recall types of numbers they have studied and properties associated with those numbers.

Materials
- Beans, counters or other small round objects to represent pebbles
- Chart paper and markers for posters
- Algebra tiles
- Algebra tiles equation mat
- Scissors
- Glue or tape
- A balance (optional)
- Small paper cups and centimeter cubes

Academic Vocabulary
Read through the vocabulary list with students. Assess prior knowledge by asking students if they can define any of the terms. Discuss with students the importance of precise language in mathematics. Remind students that they will be adding these and other words to their vocabulary notebooks.

UNIT 2 GETTING READY

You may wish to assign some or all of these exercises to gauge students' readiness for Unit 2 topics.

Prerequisite Skills
- Writing expressions (Items 1, 2)
- Evaluating expressions (Item 3)
- Plotting on a number line (Items 4, 5)
- Solving one step equations (Item 6)
- Patterns (Item 7)
- Area and Perimeter (Item 8)

Answer Key

1. Answers may vary. Sample answer: An expression has numbers and symbols. An equation has numbers and symbols, and also expresses equality.

2a. $2x + 1$

b. $x - 6$

c. $\frac{2}{3}x$

3a. 11.2

b. 4.5

c. 6.4

4. D can be anywhere between -5 and 1. See art below.

5. Drawings will vary.

  a. Answers may vary. Sample answer: Students will put a point on 3 and draw a line from there to the right to 8 and put a point.

  b. Answers may vary. Sample answer: Students will put a point on 10 and "scallop" back to the left 6 times (to 9, 8, 7, 6, 5, 4) and put a point on 4.

6a. 6

b. 4.5

c. $\frac{5}{10}$ or $\frac{1}{2}$

d. 12.7

Write your answers on notebook paper. Show your work.

1. What is the difference between an expression and an equation?

2. Write an expression for the following:
   a. one more than twice a number.
   b. a number decreased by six.
   c. two-thirds of a number.

3. Evaluate the following expressions if $x = 4.1$ and $y = 2.3$.
   a. $2x + 3$
   b. $16 - 5y$
   c. $x + y$

4. Place the following points on the number line and label each point.
   A is 3.
   B is 6.
   C is -7.
   D is a number between -5 and 1.

5. Use the number lines to show the following:
   a. $3 + 5$

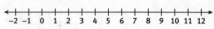

   b. $10 - 6$

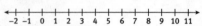

6. Solve the following equations.
   a. $x + 3 = 9$
   b. $2x = 9$
   c. $x + \frac{1}{10} = \frac{3}{5}$
   d. $x - 4.6 = 8.1$

7. Use the following numbers.
   $$3, 7, 11, 15, 19, 23, 27$$
   a. Tell the second, fourth, and seventh term.
   b. Describe how to find the next two numbers keeping the pattern the same.

8. Find the perimeter and area of the triangle and rectangle shown below.

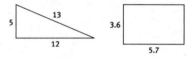

7a. second is 7; fourth is 15; seventh is 27.

b. Answers may vary. Sample answer: To get the next number two numbers add 4 and then add 4 again. 31 and 35

8. triangle: $A = 30$ square units, $P = 30$ units rectangle: $A = 20.52$ square units. $P = 18.6$ units

4.

Writing Expressions for Patterns
Pebbles in the Sand

ACTIVITY 2.1

SUGGESTED LEARNING STRATEGIES: Activating Prior Knowledge, Think/Pair/Share, Create Representations, Look for Patterns

People have been investigating number patterns for thousands of years. Legend has it that Pythagoras and his students arranged pebbles in the sand to represent number patterns. One pattern they studied is shown below.

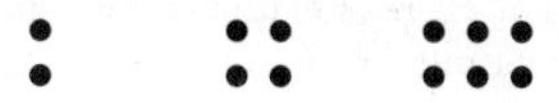

Figure 1 Figure 2 Figure 3

1. Draw the fourth, fifth, and sixth figures.

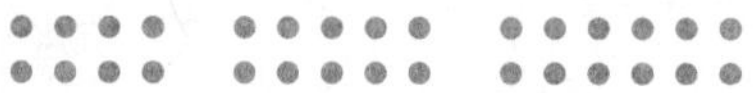

2. Organize the number of pebbles in each figure into a table.

Figure Number	Number of Pebbles
1	2
2	4
3	6
4	8
5	10
6	12
7	14

3. Extend the pattern to determine how many pebbles are in the 10th figure.
20 pebbles

4. Describe the patterns you observe in the pebble drawings and the table in words.
Answers may vary. Sample answer: Each figure has two more pebbles than the previous one.

My Notes

CONNECT TO HISTORY

The Pythagoreans led a strict, secretive life around 500 BCE. They were vegetarians and wore simple clothing. Men and women were considered as equals. They believed that all things in the universe had a unique numerical attribute, and that numbers had mystical properties.

WRITING MATH

The word *figure* may be used to name drawings in a mathematical pattern. For example, Figure 3 refers to the third drawing in the pebble pattern on this page.

TEACHER TO TEACHER Use your word wall and a vocabulary organizer or notebook to reinforce new vocabulary that appears throughout this unit.

The word "figure" is used repeatedly in this and other activities. The figure number will be used repeatedly in this activity as the input value when organizing information into tables. Later in this unit, students will see the term "*n*th figure." It refers to the general expression for figure number *n*.

A concept map will help students make connections between several words such as "pattern," "table," "figure," "figure number," "input," "expression," "variable," "substitute," "evaluate," "sequence," "term," "n^{th} figure."

ACTIVITY 2.1 Investigative

Writing Expressions for Patterns

Activity Focus

- Patterns (linear and non–linear)
- Multiple representations
- Writing expressions
- Problem solving

Materials

- Beans, counters, or other small round objects to represent pebbles
- Chart paper and markers for posters

Chunking the Activity

#1–5	#11–12	#17	#21
#6–8	#13	#18	#22
#9	#14–15	#19	
#10	#16	#20	

TEACHER TO TEACHER The theme of patterns and representations is continued and expanded in this initial activity in Unit 2. Students explore and model patterns using manipulatives, tables and rules. By the end of the lesson, students should be able to organize information into a table and generalize a rule for a given number pattern. Many of the patterns in this unit have a constant difference.

1 Think/Pair/Share, Create Representations Start this activity by asking students to recall some of the patterns they studied in Activity 1.1. Pass out manipulatives for students to use in forming the 4th, 5th, and 6th figures, if needed.

2-3 Create Representations, Look for Patterns Students may choose to extend the pattern by drawing additional figures or by adding rows to the table they created.

4 Quickwrite Most students will notice that the number of pebbles increases by 2 each time. Some might say that the numbers of pebbles are the even numbers. Students that notice the number of pebbles is twice the figure number are ready to generalize a rule for this pattern.

ACTIVITY 2.1 *Continued*

5 Look for Patterns, Quickwrite, Debriefing When you debrief the groups ask which strategy is better for arriving at the number of pebbles in the 53rd figure, multiplying 53 by 2 or extending the table to the 53rd row.

6-8 Create Representations, Look for Patterns, Guess and Check, Group Presentation Your class may work quickly through Items 6 and 7 depending on how well they made the connection to multiplication. Use these questions as an opportunity to reinforce the meaning of the word expression, the difference between a numeric and algebraic expression, and how we evaluate an expression. Item 8c emphasizes the importance of checking the rules you generalize from a pattern.

My Notes

ACADEMIC VOCABULARY

An **expression** is a mathematical phrase using numbers or variables or both. $1 + 1$ and $3x + 5$ are examples of expressions.

MATH TERMS

You do not solve an expression; you **evaluate** it for a specific value. To do this, substitute a value for the variable and simplify.

5. How many pebbles are in the 53rd figure? How do you know?
106. Answers may vary. Sample answer: I multiplied the figure number by 2.

6. Write a numeric **expression** using the number 3 for the number of pebbles in the third figure.
$2 \cdot 3$

7. Write a similar numeric expression using the number 7 for the number of pebbles in the seventh figure.
$2 \cdot 7$

8. Let n stand for the figure number.

a. Write an expression using the variable n to represent the number of pebbles in figure n.
$2 \cdot n$ or $2n$

b. What value would you substitute for n if you wanted to find the number of pebbles in the third figure?
I would substitute 3 into the expression.

c. Check to see that your expression in part (a) is correct by **evaluating** it when $n = 3$.
$2(3) = 6$

d. Use your expression to determine the number of pebbles in the 100th figure.
$2(100) = 200$; 200 pebbles

MINI-LESSON: Evaluating Expressions

Ongoing practice on evaluating algebraic expressions can occur throughout this activity. Activity 2.3 builds this skill to mastery. Some simple practice problems are shown below. Having students evaluate an expression for different values of the same variable helps to develop the concept of a function as a set of related input and output values.

Evaluate each expression for $n = 2, 5,$ and 10.

1. $4n$ 8, 20, 40
2. $3n - 5$ 1, 10, 25
3. $8 - n$ 6, 3, −2

ACTIVITY 2.1 *Continued*

9. Patterns can be written as **sequences**.

 a. Write the pebble pattern as a sequence.

  {2, 4, 6, 8, . . . }

 b. How would you describe this sequence of numbers?

  Answers will vary. Sample answer: The sequence is the even
  numbers greater than or equal to 2; or multiples of 2.

10. Another pebble arrangement is shown below.

  Figure 1 Figure 2 Figure 3

 a. Draw the fourth, fifth, and sixth figures.

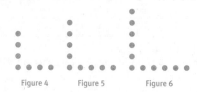

  Figure 4 Figure 5 Figure 6

My Notes

ACADEMIC VOCABULARY

A **sequence** is an ordered list of numbers, and each number is called a term of the sequence. {0, 1, 2, 3, . . .} is a sequence.

9 Create Representations, Quickwrite, Debriefing Make sure students understand that the number of pebbles in Figure 1 is first in the sequence, the number in Figure 2 is second, etc. If it has not been expressed before, students will name this sequence as the set of even numbers.

TEACHER TO TEACHER Students explore several different pebble patterns. Make sure you have manipulatives available for groups that need them to build their pebble patterns. One of the main goals is for students to connect the constant difference observed in the tables to the coefficient of n in the rules they formulate.

10 Think/Pair/Share, Create Representations, Look for Patterns, Quickwrite, Group Presentation After giving students a few minutes to work this activity alone, have them collaborate with their group members. As you circulate, check to see how individual students are doing on their own to see if they are able to replicate the process from the previous day's lesson. Have groups present their results on white boards. If any groups discovered an algebraic rule for the number of pebbles in figure n, have them present last.

TEACHER TO TEACHER Spend time during group presentations making connections between the numbers in the table, the arrangement of pebbles and the patterns that students described. Some groups might relate the addition of 2 each time to the placing of a pebble on the end of each row. Other groups might see the pattern as the sum of n, the number of pebbles along the bottom, and $n - 1$, the number of pebbles on the side, or as two times n, subtracting 1 so as not to double-count the corner pebble. If groups do not come up with multiple ways to see the pattern you may wish to demonstrate alternate methods.

11 Create Representations
Students can look to the **Math Terms** box for a model on how to complete the third column in their table.

12 Quickwrite, Debriefing
Make a connection to the figures. Each figure has two more pebbles than the previous one.

Connect to AP

Observing patterns of change is a great way for students to begin to understand and describe different types of functions. It is also a natural pre-cursor to understanding rate of change in calculus. Only linear patterns exhibit a constant difference between consecutive terms of a sequence. In calculus, the derivative (rate of change) of a linear function is the constant difference. Other types of sequences have patterns in their differences as well, and they are all implicitly tied to the derivative of the related function.

For example, the sequence $a_n = n^2$ is related to the quadratic function $y = x^2$. Notice that the sequence of differences is a *linear* pattern. The derivative (rate of change) of a quadratic function is a linear function.

N	Term	Difference
1	1	--
2	4	3
3	9	5
4	16	7
5	25	9

My Notes

CONNECT TO AP

The ability to identify patterns allows you to understand and describe different types of functions and provides a foundation for understanding rate of change in calculus.

b. Organize the number of pebbles in each figure in the first two columns of the table below.

Figure Number	Pebbles	Difference in Number of Pebbles (Question 11)
1	1	2
2	3	2
3	5	2
4	7	2
5	9	2
6	11	2
7	13	2
8	15	2
9	17	2
10	19	

c. Extend the table to determine the number of pebbles in the 10th figure.
See above. There are 19 pebbles in the 10th figure.

d. Look back at the pebble patterns in Question 10, then describe the pattern you observe in the pebble drawings and in the table above in words.
Sample answer: The number of pebbles in each figure is 1 less than 2 times the figure number.

11. Subtract **consecutive terms** in the table and record this information in the column on the right side of the table.
See above.

MATH TERMS

Consecutive terms follow each other directly in a sequence. In the table below, 5 and 8 are consecutive terms. There is a **constant difference** between the terms in the table that is equal to 3.

n	term	
1	5	3
2	8	3
3	11	3
4	14	

12. How does the **constant difference** in the new column relate to the patterns you observed?
Answers may vary. Sample answer: The constant difference is a fundamental part of the pattern. Each consecutive figure increases by 2 pebbles. This consistency can allow us to observe that the number of pebbles in each figure is one less than the figure number multiplied by two.

SUGGESTED LEARNING STRATEGIES: Summarize/Paraphrase/
Retell, Look for Patterns, Create Representations, Guess and
Check, Group Presentation, Think/Pair/Share, Quickwrite

My Notes

13. The number of pebbles in the fourth and fifth figures can be written using repeated additions of the constant difference, 2. For example, the third figure is $1 + 2 + 2$ or $1 + 2(2)$.

   a. Write the number of pebbles in the fourth and fifth figure using repeated addition of the constant difference.
   Fourth figure: $1 + 2 + 2 + 2$ or $1 + 2(3)$
   Fifth figure: $1 + 2 + 2 + 2 + 2$ or $1 + 2(4)$

   b. Let n stand for the figure number. Write an expression using the variable n to represent the number of pebbles in Figure n.
   $1 + 2(n - 1)$ or $2n - 1$

   c. Check to see that your expression in part (b) is correct by evaluating it when $n = 5$.
   $2(5 - 1) + 1 = 9$

   d. Use your expression to determine the number of pebbles in the 100th figure.
   $2(100 - 1) + 1 = 199$; there are 199 pebbles in the 100th figure.

14. Patterns can be written as sequences.

   a. Write the pebble pattern from Question 10 as a sequence.
   $\{1, 3, 5, 7, \ldots\}$

   b. How would you describe this sequence of numbers?
   Answers may vary. Sample answer: The sequence of odd numbers greater than or equal to 1.

15. What do you observe about the constant difference in the sequence of consecutive even numbers compared to the sequence of consecutive odd numbers?
   Both sequences have a constant difference of 2.

ACTIVITY 2.1 *Continued*

13 Summarize/Paraphrase/ Retell, Look for Patterns, Create Representations, Guess and Check, Group Presentation, Debriefing Using repeated addition, students generalize a rule for the number of pebbles in figure n. Students may struggle with writing $2(n - 1)$ in the expression for the number of pebbles in figure n. Remind them that we always add 2 one less time than the figure number.

If time permits, show how expressions for other patterns observed by groups are equivalent to $2(n - 1) + 1$:

Groups that saw a row of n and a column of $n - 1$ will have $n + n - 1$.

Groups that saw a row and column of n with 1 subtracted so as not to double-count the corner will have $2n - 1$.

Some groups might physically try to rearrange their pebbles into 2 by n rectangles similar to the pattern in Items 1 to 9, and notice that they are always 1 pebble short of having a full rectangle.

Some groups might use guess and check in order to understand that they have a $2n$ pattern but need to reduce the total by 1 to get the correct values for this pattern.

14-15 Think/Pair/Share, Create Representations, Quickwrite, Debriefing Ask students to write this pattern as a sequence, name it as the odd numbers but notice that the constant difference is still 2.

Suggested Assignment

CHECK YOUR UNDERSTANDING
p. 66, #1–4, 5–7 Pattern A

UNIT 2 PRACTICE
p. 109, #1–2

TEACHER TO TEACHER Much of the work in Items 16–18 will focus on student groups exploring different patterns, describing them in words, writing an expression for the nth figure, and then using that expression to answer questions.

Each group should be assigned one of the four pebble patterns. Patterns A and D have the same general expression. All of the patterns are linear. All groups should present their results to the class.

16 Create Representations, Look for Patterns, Work Backwards, Guess and Check, Group Presentation To start this Item, have students recall the process they went through identifying previous patterns. They should recall drawing a few additional figures, organizing the information in a table, describing the pattern in words, writing a general expression, and then using the expression to determine the number of pebbles given a figure number.

As a new challenge, in Item 16e, groups will need to determine whether or not it is possible to have a figure with 100 pebbles. Honor all solution methods but make sure groups clearly justify their thinking. It is not expected that all groups will write and solve an equation.

The following questions could be used when debriefing the group presentations.

- How did you see the pattern?
- How do you know your pattern works?
- How can two different pebble patterns have the same rule?
- How did you decide on whether a figure could have 100 pebbles?

My Notes

SUGGESTED LEARNING STRATEGIES: Create Representations, Look for Patterns, Work Backwards, Group Presentation

16. Four different pebble patterns are shown below. Choose one with your group. Use your selected pattern to answer the questions below, and then prepare a group presentation of your results.

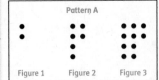

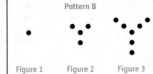

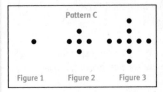

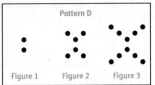

Figure Number	Pattern A	Pattern B
1	2	1
2	6	4
3	10	7
4	14	10
5	18	13
6	22	16

Figure Number	Pattern C	Pattern D
1	1	2
2	5	6
3	9	10
4	13	14
5	17	18
6	21	22

a. Draw a few additional figures and then organize the information into a table.

The next figure in each pattern is shown below.

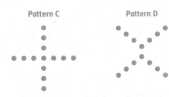

- Does anyone see the pattern differently?
- How are all these pattern problems alike?
- How are they different?

Writing Expressions for Patterns
Pebbles in the Sand

SUGGESTED LEARNING STRATEGIES: Create Representations, Quickwrite, Look for Patterns, Work Backwards, Guess and Check, Group Presentation, Pre-Writing, Visualization, Use Manipulatives, Identify a Subtask

My Notes

b. Describe the pattern in words.

Patterns A and D: Start with 2 pebbles and increase by 4 each time.
Pattern B: Start with 1 pebble and increase by 3 each time.
Pattern C: Start with 1 pebble and increase by 4 each time.

c. Write an expression using the variable n to represent the number of pebbles in Figure n.

Pattern A and D: $4(n-1) + 2$ or $4n - 2$
Pattern B: $3(n-1) + 1$ or $3n - 2$
Pattern C: $4(n-1) + 1$ or $4n - 3$

d. Use your expression to determine the number of pebbles in the 10th, 53rd, and 200th figures.

	10th	53rd	200th
Patterns A and D:	38	210	798
Pattern B:	28	157	598
Pattern C:	37	209	797

e. For the pattern you selected, is it possible to have a figure with 100 pebbles? Explain your thinking.

For Pattern B, it is possible. For Patterns A, C, and D it is not possible. Explanations may vary.

17. Based on the class's work for Question 16, how does the constant difference in a pebble pattern relate to the algebraic expression?

The constant difference is the coefficient of n in the expression.

18. With your group, design your own pebble pattern using the constant difference and first term provided by your teacher. Write an expression for the number of pebbles in Figure n and use your expression to determine the number of pebbles in the 100th figure.

Answers may vary.

Suggested Values for Item 18

Give each group a first term and constant difference. They will come up with a pebble pattern and the expression.

First Term	Constant Difference	Expression
3	2	$2n + 1$ or $2(n-1) + 3$
1	5	$5n - 4$ or $5(n-1) + 1$
4	2	$2n + 2$ or $2(n-1) + 4$
2	3	$3n - 1$ or $3(n-1) + 2$
4	3	$3n + 1$ or $3(n-1) + 4$
3	3	$3n$ or $3(n-1) + 3$
5	2	$2n + 3$ or $2(n-1) + 5$

---

17 Look for Patterns, Graphic Organizer If students have not already made the connection between the constant difference and the coefficient of n in their rule, now is the time to make it clear to students.

Figure	Table
Explanation	Rule

A graphic organizer could be used to help students make this connection. Students can fill in their sample problem and identify the constant difference in each representation.

18 Prewriting, Visualization, Create Representations, Use Manipulatives, Look for Patterns, Identify a Subtask, Group Presentation Provide each group with a constant difference and a first term. Some suggested values are listed below. They will need to think of a pebble pattern arrangement. Students will be using multiple strategies to accomplish this complex task. One challenge will be to make sure that the added pebbles are placed in a consistent fashion. Have students prepare a poster displaying their pattern. As you circulate around the room, make sure that the figures they draw and the expressions they write are consistent with the information given.

Another common mistake groups could make is using the starting number of pebbles as the constant in their expression. Given a starting number of 3 and a constant difference of 2, the correct expression would be $2(n-1) + 3$ or $2n + 1$, not $2n + 3$.

Suggested Assignment

CHECK YOUR UNDERSTANDING
p. 66, #5–7 Pattern B, #8

UNIT 2 PRACTICE
p. 109, #3

TEACHER TO TEACHER   In Items 19–21, students explore the non-linear patterns represented by the figurate numbers. Students will observe that while the differences have a pattern, it is not constant. The quadratic patterns come from relating the figure number to the dimensions of the pebble shape and considering the total number of pebbles as an array. For example, in Item 19, the pebbles are arranged in an *n* by *n* square.

19 Look for Patterns, Quickwrite, Create Representations, Debriefing, Interactive Word Wall, Vocabulary Organizer Students should quickly notice that the difference is not constant but that there is a pattern. Rather than having them extend the pattern of adding the next odd number all the way to the 10th figure, groups should be looking for a way to relate the figure number to the total number of pebbles. If a group is stuck you might ask them what shape is formed by each pebble arrangement. Alternatively, ask them how many pebbles are in each row and column. As you debrief the question, make sure students notice that you are multiplying two variables together rather than just multiplying the variable by a constant.

My Notes

SUGGESTED LEARNING STRATEGIES: Look for Patterns, Quickwrite, Create Representations

19. Here is another pebble pattern studied by the Pythagoreans.

Figure 1   Figure 2   Figure 3

a. Does this pattern have a constant difference? Explain.
No. The difference between the number of pebbles in each figure is different.

b. How many pebbles are there in the fourth, fifth and sixth figures?
fourth: 16 pebbles; fifth: 25 pebbles; sixth: 36 pebbles

c. How many pebbles are there in the 10th figure? How did you determine your answer?
100 pebbles. Sample answer: The number of pebbles in each figure is the square of the figure number.

ACADEMIC VOCABULARY

The ***n***th figure is figure number *n* in a sequence.

d. How many pebbles are there in the 40th figure? In the ***n***th figure?
40th: 1600, *n*th: $n \cdot n$ or n^2

e. Write the number of pebbles as a sequence {first term, second term, third term, . . .}.
{1, 4, 9, 16, . . .}

f. The Pythagoreans called the numbers in the sequence the square numbers. Why do you think they gave them this name?
Sample answer: Each number is the square of a counting number, and each figure forms a square.

Writing Expressions for Patterns
Pebbles in the Sand

SUGGESTED LEARNING STRATEGIES: Mark the Text, Look for Patterns, Create Representations, Guess and Check, Quickwrite

My Notes

20. The numbers in the pebble pattern shown below are called the rectangular numbers.

Figure 1   Figure 2   Figure 3

a. How many pebbles are in the fourth, fifth, and sixth figures?
fourth: 20 pebbles; fifth: 30 pebbles; sixth: 42 pebbles

b. How many pebbles are there in the 10th figure? How did you determine your answer? There are 110 pebbles. Answers may vary. Sample answer: The base and height of each consecutive rectangle both increase by 1 pebble. So the 10th figure will have a base of 10, and a height of 11.

c. How many pebbles are there in the 40th figure? In the nth figure?
40th: 1640; n^{th}: $n(n+1)$

21. The Pythagoreans called the numbers in this pebble pattern the triangular numbers.

Figure 1   Figure 2   Figure 3

a. Why do you think the Pythagoreans called these numbers triangular?
Sample answer: They are arranged in a triangular shape.

b. How is the triangular number pebble pattern related to the pebble pattern of the rectangular numbers?
If you cut the rectangle in half along the diagonal, you get two of the same triangular number.

c. Use your answer to part b to write an algebraic expression for the number of pebbles in the nth triangular number.
$\frac{n(n+1)}{2}$

---

20 Mark the Text, Look for Patterns, Create Representations, Guess and Check, Debriefing Students see a rectangular array of pebbles. If students made the connection that the figure number was the length of each side of the squares in the previous problem, then this problem should be fairly easy for them. Some students may struggle with representing the two consecutive numbers as n and $n + 1$ when writing the expression for this pattern.

21 Mark the Text, Look for Patterns, Create Representations, Quickwrite, Debriefing The pattern for the triangular numbers can be challenging for students. After groups have struggled with this problem, you may need to direct them back to the previous question. Ask them if they can "see" the triangular numbers in the rectangular number pattern. A line might help as well.

Once students can verbalize that any triangular number is half of the corresponding rectangular number, they will be ready to write the expression.

21 d–e Guess and Check, Predict and Confirm, Debriefing Students verify that their rule works by drawing the fourth triangular number and then checking to see if their expression gives the correct value.

22 Guess and Check, Work Backwards, Quickwrite, Debriefing A culminating question where students look back at the patterns for square, rectangular and triangular numbers. Students may try a variety of strategies from extending tables, to considering the factors of 42, to drawing a figure with 42 pebbles in it. All of these solution methods are valid as long as students are able to explain their reasoning.

Suggested Assignment

CHECK YOUR UNDERSTANDING
p. 66, #9

UNIT 2 PRACTICE
p. 109, #4

CHECK YOUR UNDERSTANDING

1. Fig 1: 4; Fig 2: 6; Fig 3: 8

2. Fig 4: 10; Fig 5: 12; Fig 6: 14

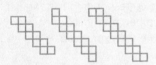

3. There are 22 small squares in the tenth figure. You begin with the 4 squares in figure 1 and add 2 nine times.

4. {4, 6, 8, 10, ...}

5. Pattern A: 4; Pattern B: 5

6. Pattern A: $4n - 1$
   Pattern B: $5n - 3$

7. Pattern A: 199; Pattern B: 247

8. No; Explanations may vary. Sample answer: Pattern B increases by 5 pebbles in each additional figure so it will always have more pebbles for a given figure number than Pattern A which increases by 4 pebbles.

My Notes

SUGGESTED LEARNING STRATEGIES: Guess and Check, Predicting and Confirming, Work Backwards, Quickwrite

d. Verify your answer to part c by substituting $n = 4$ into the expression. Do you get the number of pebbles in the fourth triangular number? $\dfrac{n(n+1)}{2} = \dfrac{4(4+1)}{2} = 10$

e. Use your expression to predict the number of pebbles in the 30th triangular number. $\dfrac{30(30+1)}{2} = 465$ pebbles

22. Is the number 42 a square number, rectangular number or triangular number? Explain your reasoning.
Rectangular. Answers may vary. Sample answer: It would be the sixth rectangular figure. This would give it a base of 6 and a height of 7: $6(7) = 42$.

CHECK YOUR UNDERSTANDING

Write your answers on notebook paper. Show your work.
A pattern of small squares is shown below. Use this pattern for questions 1 to 4.

Figure 1   Figure 2   Figure 3

1. How many small squares are in each figure?

2. Draw the fourth, fifth and sixth figures and determine the number of small squares in each figure.

3. How many squares would be in the 10th figure? Explain your reasoning.

4. Write the number of small squares in each figure as a sequence.

5. What is the constant difference for each pebble pattern shown in the tables at the bottom of the first column?

6. For each pebble pattern, write an expression for the nth figure using the variable n.

7. How many pebbles are in the 50th figure for each pebble pattern?

8. Both pebble patterns have 7 pebbles in figure 2. If the patterns continue, will they ever have the same number of pebbles for another figure? Explain your reasoning.

9. **MATHEMATICAL REFLECTION** How does representing patterns in multiple ways help you to solve problems?

Pebble Pattern A

Figure	1	2	3	4	5
Pebbles	3	7	11	15	19

Pebble Pattern B

Figure	1	2	3	4	5
Pebbles	2	7	12	17	22

9. Answer may vary. Sample answer: Representing a pattern in multiple ways helps you identify the pattern and confirm that your description of the pattern is correct.

Solving Equations
Which Way Do I Choose?

SUGGESTED LEARNING STRATEGIES: Quickwrite

My Notes

Your school is challenging teachers to "be smarter than an 8th grader" at a school pep rally. The teachers who participate ask the 8th grade experts for help. One of the problems given to the teachers is listed below.

The Shelf Problem

Mr. Jacobson used a 14-ft board to make four shelves of equal length for the living room. He had 2 feet of board left over when he was finished. How long was each shelf?

The students solved the problem four different ways.

Emma's Solution:

$14 - 2 = 12$

$\dfrac{12}{4} = 3$

Each shelf is 3 feet long.

Kayla's Solution:

Let x = the length of each shelf

$$4x + 2 = 14$$
$$4x + 2 - 2 = 14 - 2$$
$$4x = 12$$
$$\dfrac{4x}{4} = \dfrac{12}{4}$$
$$x = 3$$

Each shelf is 3 feet long.

MATH TIP

Algebra tiles are manipulatives used to solve equations.

Each small square is 1 unit and each rectangle represents an unknown quantity, $1x$.

Dan's Solution:

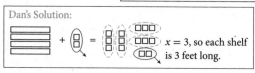 $x = 3$, so each shelf is 3 feet long.

Joe's Solution:

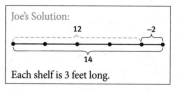

Each shelf is 3 feet long.

For problems 1–5, answers may vary.

1. Describe how Emma solved the problem.

Sample answer: Emma subtracted 2 from 14 because there were two feet of board left over. Then she divided by 4 to get the length of each of the four shelves.

Solving Equations

Activity Focus
- One- and two-step equations
- Equation solving strategies
- Multiple representations
- Combining like terms
- Problem solving

Materials
- Algebra tiles
- Chart paper and markers for posters
- Algebra tiles equation mat

Chunking the Activity

#1–6	#14	#21–23
#7	#15	#24–26
#8–9	#16	#27
#10	#17	
#11–12	#18–19	
#13	#20	

TEACHER TO TEACHER — A game-show setting is used to review, re-teach and extend strategies for solving one- and two-step equations. Typical word problems motivate discussion on multiple solution methods.

1 Quickwrite The problem provides a chance for students to hone their mathematical communication skills. Observe their use of mathematical vocabulary to see how familiar they are with words for the different mathematical operations.

MINI-LESSON: Algebra Tiles

Algebra tiles use a geometric model to represent variable and numeric quantities. The names of the tiles correspond to their area. The tiles are different colors on either side (one color represents the opposite of the other color). A unit tile is a 1 by 1 square. An x tile is a 1 by x rectangle. An x^2 tile is an x by x square. The tiles are purposely created so the x length on the x tiles are not commensurate with the unit tiles, allowing x to represent an unknown quantity. The expression $x^2 + 3x + 2$ is shown to the right.

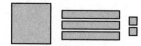

Commercially produced sets of algebra tiles usually come with instructions and a short lesson book to help teachers and students learn to use them.

2-4 Quickwrite The four student solutions from the first page represent the four ways of solving equations covered in this activity. It may be helpful for students to refer back to these solutions throughout the activity.

5 Think/Pair/Share, Quickwrite Students should recognize that all four methods have not only the solution in common, but also the division by 4 and the taking away of 2 from 14.

6 Prewriting, Create Representations, Guess and Check, Use Manipulatives, Debriefing Do not spend an excessive amount of time on this question if students cannot think of a different way to solve this problem. However, be sure to recognize their creative efforts when they do find an alternative solution method. You may also learn valuable information about the way they were taught to solve equations in previous classes on this question.

Suggested Assignment

CHECK YOUR UNDERSTANDING
p. 78, #1–3

UNIT 2 PRACTICE
p. 110, #5

My Notes

SUGGESTED LEARNING STRATEGIES: Quickwrite, Think/ Pair/Share, Pre-Writing, Create Representations, Guess and Check, Use Manipulatives

2. Describe how Kayla solved the problem.

Sample answer: Kayla represented the value she wanted to find with a variable. Then she used the information from the word problem to solve for the variable.

3. Describe how Dan solved the problem.

Sample answer: Dan represented the problem with manipulatives. He took 14 algebra tiles, subtracted 2, and split the remaining twelve into equal groups.

4. Describe how Joe solved the problem.

Sample answer: Joe represented the problem graphically. He set a number line equal to 14, and divided it into segments based on information from the problem.

5. Do these methods have anything in common? Explain.

Sample answer: They all have the same solution. Each problem involves subtracting 2 from 14 and dividing the result by 4.

6. Can you think of another way to solve this problem? If so, show your method below.

Answers will vary.

ACADEMIC VOCABULARY

An **equation** is a mathematical statement that makes two expressions equal. The **solution** to an equation is a value of a variable that makes the equation a true statement.

Many **equations** contain a variable like the one Kayla used to solve the shelf problem, but they do not have to.

$$\text{Emma's solution: } \frac{14-2}{4} = 3$$
$$\text{Kayla's solution: } 4x + 2 = 14$$

The **solution** to this equation is a value of the variable that makes the equation a true statement. For example, $4x + 2 = 14$ has the solution $x = 3$ because $4(3) + 2 = 14$.

This activity will teach you different methods for solving equations and how to determine which method is best to use in different situations. Remember that there is not always one "right" method for solving a problem, and many problems can be solved more than one way.

Solving Equations
Which Way Do I Choose?

SUGGESTED LEARNING STRATEGIES: Think/Pair/Share, Guess and Check, Mark the Text, Create Representations

Simple equations can often be solved using *mental math*. Sometimes this method is known as guess and check.

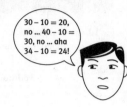

30 − 10 = 20, no ... 40 − 10 = 30, no ... aha 34 − 10 = 24!

My Notes

EXAMPLE 1

Solve the equation $x - 10 = 24$.

Step 1: Think about numbers that would make the equation true. Or, restate the equation as a question: "What number minus 10 is 24?"

Solution: Since $34 - 10 = 24$, x must equal 34.

TRY THESE A

Solve these problems using mental math.

a. Fifteen more than a number is 23. What is the number? 8

b. One-half of a number is 70. What is the number? 140

c. Four more than twice a number is 24. What is the number? 10

> **READING MATH**
>
> Equations in mathematics are like sentences in language arts, and an expression is like a phrase.
>
> The equation, $2 + x = 10$, means "Two more than a number is 10."
>
> The expression $2 + x$, means "Two more than a number."

7. Translate each sentence into an equation. Let the variable n represent the number.

a. Fifteen more than a number is 23. $n + 15 = 23$

b. One-half of a number is 70. $\frac{n}{2} = 70$

c. Four more than twice a number is 24. What is the number?

   $4 + 2n = 24$

8. Translate these words into an equation and solve it using mental math: The sum of a number and 5 is 30. What is the number?

   $n + 5 = 30; n = 25$

9. Translate this equation into words and solve for x using mental math: $\frac{x}{7} = 5$.

   A number divided by 7 is 5. The number is 35.

ACTIVITY 2.2 *Continued*

TEACHER TO TEACHER This portion of the activity focuses on solving equations using mental math and on translating sentences into equations, and concludes with students creating a graphic organizer of familiar words that stand for the four operations (addition, subtraction, multiplication, and addition).

Try These A These problems provide practice in solving problems using mental math.

7-9 Marking the Text Think/Pair/Share, Create Representations, Guess and Check, Debriefing These exercises can be used as a formative assessment. Students should do these independently at first and then share their results with their group.

If students need additional practice here are some other equations to have them solve using mental math.

$n - 8 = 12$ $n = 20$

$3n = 21$ $n = 7$

$6 + n = 7$ $n = 1$

$2n + 5 = 25$ $n = 10$

Some more challenging problems are listed below.

$8n = 128$ $n = 16$

$17 + n = 9$ $n = -8$

$8 - n = 10$ $n = -2$

$0.5n + 2 = 12$ $n = 20$

10 Graphic Organizer, Vocabulary Organizer, Discussion Group, Debriefing Have each group fill in as many words as they can think of for the 4 operations. Then each group will share their results. Compile all of the words onto a sheet of chart paper and post it in the classroom for the rest of this unit.

11-12 Marking the Text, Summarize/Paraphrase/Retell, Create Representations, Guess and Check, Quickwrite This is a slightly more complicated problem but students are likely to be able to solve it using mental math.

Suggested Assignment

CHECK YOUR UNDERSTANDING
p. 78, #4–5

UNIT 2 PRACTICE
p. 110, #6

SUGGESTED LEARNING STRATEGIES: Graphic Organizer, Vocabulary Organizer, Discussion Group, Mark the Text, Summarize/Paraphrase/Retell, Creating Representations, Guess and Check, Quickwrite

My Notes

10. Create a graphic organizer of words and phrases that stand for each operation shown below. A few have been filled in for you.

Sample answers:

Addition	Subtraction
more than add sum increased by in addition plus more	minus difference less than less fewer take away decreased by
Multiplication	**Division**
twice product of half of (one-third of, etc.)	the quotient of divide per divided by

11. Try solving the following problem using one of the methods shown on the first page of this activity. Explain how you solved the problem.

The Peach Problem
Mindie was packing peaches into baskets for the farmer's market. She had 50 peaches and 6 baskets. If she wants to have an equal number of peaches in each basket and 2 left over to cut up for samples, how many peaches will be in each basket?

8 peaches. Explanations may vary. Sample answer: By setting up an equation with a variable and solving for the variable.

12. Write an equation that could be used to solve the peach problem. Let n stand for the number of peaches in one basket.

$6n + 2 = 50$

SUGGESTED LEARNING STRATEGIES: Graphic Organizers,
Work Backwards, Group Presentation, Think/Pair/Share,
Create Representations

One way to solve an equation like the one from Question 12 is
by using the *undoing method*. Think about the operations applied
to the variable. Then use **inverse operations** to undo them. The
solution to $5n + 3 = 48$ is shown in the flow chart below.

$$n \xrightarrow{\cdot 5} 5n \xrightarrow{+3} 5n+3$$
$$9 \xleftarrow{\div 5} 45 \xleftarrow{-3} 48$$

13. Make a flow chart graphic organizer like the one above to
represent and solve each equation.

a. $4x - 10 = 50$

$$n \xrightarrow{\cdot 4} 4n \xrightarrow{-10} 4n-10$$
$$15 \xleftarrow{\div 4} 60 \xleftarrow{+10} 50$$

b. $5 + \frac{x}{2} = 8$

$$x \xrightarrow{\div 2} \frac{x}{2} \xrightarrow{+5} \frac{x}{2}+5$$
$$6 \xleftarrow{\cdot 2} 3 \xleftarrow{-5} 8$$

c. $\frac{2}{3}x + 5 = 17$

$$x \xrightarrow{\cdot \frac{2}{3}} \frac{2}{3}x \xrightarrow{+5} \frac{2}{3}x+5$$
$$18 \xleftarrow{\cdot \frac{3}{2}} 12 \xleftarrow{-5} 17$$

14. Solve the equation you wrote in Question 12 using the
undoing method.

Answers may vary. Sample answer:
$$6n + 2 = 50$$
$$-2 \quad -2$$
$$6n = 48$$
$$n = 8$$

My Notes

ACADEMIC VOCABULARY

The **inverse operations**
undo each other. Adding
and subtracting are inverse
operations. Multiplying and
dividing are inverse operations.

ACTIVITY 2.2 Continued

TEACHER TO TEACHER The class will learn to
solve equations using a
graphic organizer that illustrates
inverse operations. It helps to
emphasize applying the inverse
operations in the reverse order
that they were applied to the
variable to solve the equation.

13 Graphic Organizers,
Work Backwards, Group
Presentation, Debriefing
Students apply the model to
solve equations using a graphic
organizer. Each group should
work collaboratively to solve
these problems and then
prepare a group presentation.
You might have each group
present one equation only. On
part c, stop they class if they
need assistance on how to
undo fraction multiplication.
You can demonstrate that
multiplication by the reciprocal is
the inverse operation for fraction
multiplication.

Differentiating Instruction
You may want to provide a blank
template (with only the squares,
arrow and equals signs) of the
graphic organizer for struggling
students to use on Item 13.
This will allow them to spend
more time processing the math
and less time drawing the
diagram.

14 Think/Pair/Share,
Graphic Organizer, Create
Representations, Work
Backwards, Debriefing This
item applies the method from
Item 13 to the equation for the
peach problem.

Suggested Assignment

CHECK YOUR UNDERSTANDING
p. 78, #6–8

UNIT 2 PRACTICE
p. 110, #7

ACTIVITY 2.2 *Continued*

TEACHER TO TEACHER This page covers an equation solving technique called the number line method. The method will most likely be unfamiliar to students. Refer to Joe's solution on the first page of this activity (p. 67).

15 Visualization, Create Representations, Group Presentation, Debriefing
Expect some struggles as students grapple with this new way to solve equations. The questions become increasingly difficult. If your class is not making progress on part c, you may need to lead a whole class discussion to help them move forward. On c they will need to combine making multiple copies of *x* with adding on 5 more units. The critical step in part c is realizing that the two *x* segments must be 10 units long.

Debrief all of the questions as a whole group, having different groups share their results and look for different approaches to drawing the number lines.

Suggested Assignment

CHECK YOUR UNDERSTANDING
p. 78, #9–11

UNIT 2 PRACTICE
p. 110, #8–9

My Notes

The *number line method* can also be used to solve equations. Look back at Joe's solution using a number line on the first page of this activity.

EXAMPLE 2

Solve $3x = 18$.

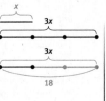

Step 1: Draw a line. The length will be x.
Step 2: Draw another line that is 3x lengths.
Step 3: Label the total length 18.
Solution: Use the lines to find the length of one *x*. 18 divided into 3 equal parts is 6, so one *x* must equal 6.

15. Solve these problems using the number line method.

a. $x - 14 = 15$

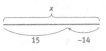

$x = 29$

b. $\frac{x}{5} = 12$

$x = 60$

c. $2x + 5 = 15$

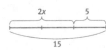

$x = 5$

Solving Equations
Which Way Do I Choose?

SUGGESTED LEARNING STRATEGIES: Use Manipulatives, Create Representations, Guess and Check, Group Presentation, Quickwrite

My Notes

Algebra tiles are also helpful when solving equations.

EXAMPLE 3

Use algebra tiles to model and solve this equation: $5x - 8 = 7$

Step 1: Record a picture of the equation.

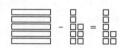

Step 2: Add or remove an equal numbers of unit tiles from both sides to isolate the x tiles on one side.

Step 3: Divide the remaining unit tiles evenly among the x-tiles that remain. Draw a picture of the results.

Solution: $x = 3$. The remaining unit tiles can be divided into five groups of three.

16. Use algebra tiles to model and solve each equation. Draw a picture to illustrate your solution method. Use the My Notes space.

   a. $18 = 3x$ $x = 6$

   b. $5 + 4x = 21$ $x = 4$

   c. $15 = 4x + 3$ $x = 3$

   d. $2x + 8 = 13$ $x = 2.5$

17. How was using algebra tiles to solve the last equation in Question 16 different from the others?   Answers may vary. Sample answer: The solution to 16d was not a whole number.

TEACHER TO TEACHER Pairs can share a set of algebra tiles and an equation mat. Students should still work in groups of 4 so pairs can check their work as they progress. You may choose to do the first problem as a class. Make sure students are building the equations, not just drawing the pictures.

16 Use Manipulatives, Create Representations, Guess and Check, Group Presentation, Debriefing The activity gives the class an opportunity to practice solving equations using algebra tiles. They should build the equations on their mat and then record pictures showing the solution process. As a class, work towards devising a consistent system for showing the different solving steps on the pictures. For example, circle the zero pairs, draw arrows coming off the mat to indicate removing equal numbers of tiles. Draw arrows coming into the mat to show adding equal numbers of tiles.

In part d of Item 16, the solution is not a whole number so students will need to decide how to "divide" up the left over unit tile. It is OK if students are not sure what to do. You can address this when debriefing the whole group.

Finally, encourage groups to check their solutions by substituting their answer into the original equation to see if it makes a true statement.

17 Quickwrite, Debriefing Focuses students on the fact that not all equations have integer solutions. Even though we cannot physically divide a unit tile in half, we can still think about dividing it evenly among the 2 piles.

Suggested Assignment

CHECK YOUR UNDERSTANDING
p. 78, #12–14

MINI-LESSON on Algebra Tiles

Students can build their equations on a mat like the one shown below. Key ideas when solving equations using algebra tiles are

1. Removing zeros (a positive and negative of the same tile make 0),

2. Adding the same quantity to both sides,

3. Removing the same quantity from both sides, and

4. Dividing the remaining unit tiles on one side evenly among the remaining x tiles on the other.

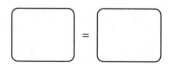

TEACHER TO TEACHER At this point, students should be weaned off of using manipulatives and graphic organizers to help them model and solve equations. This portion of the activity focuses on representing the solution process algebraically and providing a reason for each step. The properties of real numbers and properties of equality will be used to justify equation solving steps in Activity 2.3. For this portion of the activity, we want students to explain their thinking by saying things like "add 2 to both sides."

18-19 Graphic Organizer, Create Representations, Identify a Subtask, Use Manipulatives, Note Taking, Debriefing These items are designed to be completed as a whole class. Students will fill in the picture. They could do this on their own. Then, lead them through recording the solution steps and describing the process.

My Notes

SUGGESTED LEARNING STRATEGIES: Graphic Organizer, Create Representations, Identify a Subtask, Use Manipulatives, Notetaking

Using manipulatives and drawing pictures can be a time-consuming process when solving equations, and some equations cannot be solved using these methods. Symbols and words can be used to solve equations, which is referred to as solving an equation algebraically.

18. Fill in the table below based on the given equation. Illustrate the equation, solve it, and describe each step involved.

Picture	Equation	Description
	$5x + 3 = 18$ $-3 \quad -3$ $5x = 15$ $\dfrac{5x}{5} = \dfrac{15}{5}$ $x = 3$	original equation remove 3 tiles (subtract 3 from each side) divide into 5 equal groups (divide each side by 5)

19. Solve the equation $3x - 10 = 11$. Describe each step that is required.

Equation	Description
$3x - 10 = 11$ $+10 \quad +10$ $3x = 21$ $\dfrac{3x}{3} = \dfrac{21}{3}$ $x = 7$	original equation add 10 to both sides divide both sides by 3 solution

SUGGESTED LEARNING STRATEGIES: Think/Pair/Share,
Create Representations, Guess and Check, Identify a Subtask,
Quickwrite, Mark the Text, Visualization

My Notes

20. Solve each equation algebraically showing each step and
describing your work.

a. $5x + 8 = 23$ $x = 3$

b. $\frac{2}{3}x - 5 = 7$ $x = 18$

c. $6 + 3x = 25$ $x = 6\frac{1}{3}$

d. $12 = 6x - 18$ $x = 5$

Using variables to represent unknown quantities helps to solve
more complicated problems. Using manipulatives or a number
line can also help. Emma used mental math to solve the shelf
problem, but Katie wrote and then solved an equation by balancing
both sides.

21. Do you think Emma could have used mental math to solve
the following problem? Explain your reasoning.

> **The Bead Problem**
> Veronica loves to make jewelry. She picked out some yellow,
> red, and green glass beads at the local bead shop. She bought
> a total of 28 beads. There were twice as many red beads as
> yellow beads and 8 more green beads than yellow beads. How
> many beads of each color did Veronica buy?

Sample answer: This problem has too many different quantities
to solve using mental math.

MATH TIP

To "undo" multiplication by a
fraction, divide by the fraction,
which is the same as multiplying
by the reciprocal.

$$\frac{3}{4}x = 12$$

$$\left(\frac{4}{3}\right)\frac{3}{4}x = \left(\frac{4}{3}\right) \cdot \frac{12}{1}$$

$$1x = \frac{48}{3}$$

$$x = 16$$

ACTIVITY 2.2 *Continued*

20 Think/Pair/Share, Create
Representations, Guess and
Check, Identify a Subtask,
Debriefing Students can work
these problems independently
and then check their work with
the group. Student work should
reflect correct algebraic steps and
a short explanation of what they
did to isolate the variable.

As students transition into
working on the bead problem,
have them reflect back on the
different methods that they have
learned. Are some easier than
others? Are some better than
others?

21 Quickwrite, Marking the
Text, Visualization This
problem is more complicated.
The equation will have multiple
variable terms on one side.
Algebra tiles will be used to model
and solve this problem.

Suggested Assignment

CHECK YOUR UNDERSTANDING
p. 78, #15–18

UNIT 2 PRACTICE
p. 110, #10–12

22 Create Representations, Debriefing This item is scaffolded so students can develop the equation more easily.

23 Think/Pair/Share, Create Representations, Simplify the Problem, Debriefing Ask students to convert their visual equation to an algebraic one. Students will probably write their equation as $4x + 8 = 28$ rather than writing each x term separately.

As you debrief this question remind students that using manipulatives or other tools that make equations concrete will help them solve problems as they become increasingly complicated.

Suggested Assignment

CHECK YOUR UNDERSTANDING
p. 78, #19–21

UNIT 2 PRACTICE
p. 110, #13–14

My Notes

SUGGESTED LEARNING STRATEGIES: Create Representations, Think/Pair/Share, Simplify the Problem

22. Let 1 x tile represent the number of yellow beads.

   a. Use algebra tiles to represent the number of red beads.

   b. Use algebra tiles to represent the number of green beads.

   c. Use algebra tiles to represent the verbal equation shown below.

YELLOW BEADS	+	RED BEADS	+	GREEN BEADS	=	TOTAL BEADS

23. Write an equation to represent the bead problem. Solve the equation. Describe your work in the space below. How many beads of each color did Veronica buy?

Equation	Description
$x + 2x + x + 8 = 28$	original equation
$4x + 8 = 28$	group x terms
$-8 \quad -8$	subtract 8 from both sides
$4x = 20$	
$\dfrac{4x}{4} = \dfrac{20}{4}$	divide both sides by 4
$x = 5$	solution

Veronica bought 5 yellow beads, 10 red beads and 13 green beads.

Solving Equations
Which Way Do I Choose?

SUGGESTED LEARNING STRATEGIES: Use Manipulatives, Create Repesentations, Simplify the Problem, Quickwrite, Graphic Organizer, Discussion Group

Collecting all of the like tiles together as you did in the Bead Problem is known as *combining like terms*.

24. Simplify the following expressions by combining like terms.

   a. $3x - 2 + 4x + 8$ $7x + 6$

   b. $5x - 2x + 4 + 3x - 6$ $6x - 2$

   c. $4 + 2x - 10 + 3x - 6x + 1$ $-x - 5$

25. Are the original expression and the simplified result equivalent expressions? Explain.
   Yes. Answers may vary. Sample answer: Only zero pairs were removed so the simplified expression is equal to the original one.

26. You have learned several different strategies for solving equations. Each method is listed below. Go back through this activity and find an example of each way to solve an equation and record it below. Write a short explanation of each method as well.

MENTAL MATH   INVERSE OPERATIONS
Answers may vary.

NUMBER LINE   ALGEBRA TILES

SOLVING ALGEBRAICALLY

My Notes

MATH TIP
Flip over algebra tiles to represent a negative quantity. A positive tile and a negative tile of the same shape form a zero pair.

TEACHER TO TEACHER This activity closes with some practice on combining like terms, a final reflection on the different equation solving methods and one last word problem to challenge students.

24 Use Manipulatives, Create Repesentations, Simplify the Problem, Debriefing Students will use Algebra tiles to build each expression, remove any zeros and then combine the results.

25 Quickwrite As you debrief this question make sure students are clear that the expressions are indeed equivalent.

26 Graphic Organizer, Quickwrite, Discussion Group, Debriefing Have students look back through their work and reflect on the different solution methods. They should create a graphic organizer that summarizes the key points of each equation solving technique. Have them pick an appropriate example for each method.

27 Summarize/Paraphrase/ Retell, Use Manipulatives, Create Representations, Guess and Check, Simplify the Problem, Quickwrite, Group Presentation After students work on this problem in their groups for about 5 minutes, check to see if they are making progress. If not, you might suggest that students let x represent the number of $5 tickets that were sold. This way, students can avoid fractions in their equation. You might also suggest that they try solving this one using the number line method.

Suggested Assignment

CHECK YOUR UNDERSTANDING
p. 78, #22–24

UNIT 2 PRACTICE
p. 110, #15–16

CHECK YOUR UNDERSTANDING

1. $x = 47$
2. $x = 20$
3. $x = 40$
4. $4 + n = -11, n = -15$
5. $5n = 200, n = 40$
6. $x = 16.5$
7. $x = 5$
8. $x = 36$
9. $x = 9$
10. $x = 15$
11. $x = 8$
12. $x = 12.5$
13. $x = 2$
14. $x = 1$
15. $x = 22$
16. $x = 5.4$
17. $x = 12.5$
18. $x = 24$
19. $x = -9$
20. $x = \frac{16}{3}$
21. $x = 6$

My Notes

Solutions may vary. A possible equation is $10x + 10x + 5x = 850$ where x represents $\frac{1}{3}$ the tickets sold. The solution is $x = 34$. That means 34 $5 tickets were sold and 68 $10 tickets were sold.

SUGGESTED LEARNING STRATEGIES: Summarize/ Paraphrase/Retell, Use Manipulatives, Create Representations, Guess and Check, Simplify the Problem, Quickwrite, Group Presentation

27. One last problem for teachers during the "smarter than an 8th grader" rally is listed below. Write an equation and solve it to answer this problem. Clearly explain your work. Prepare a poster showing your solution.

> **The Ticket Problem**
> Two-thirds of the people bought $10 tickets and the rest bought $5 tickets to see the school play. Ticket sales totaled $850, how many tickets were sold at each price?

CHECK YOUR UNDERSTANDING

Write your answers on notebook paper. Show your work.

Solve each equation using mental math.

1. $x - 15 = 32$
2. $8x = 160$
3. $\frac{x}{2} + 1 = 21$

Write and solve an equation for each sentence.

4. Four more than a number is -11.
5. The product of a 5 and a number is 200.

Solve each equation using the inverse operations.

6. $2x - 9 = 24$
7. $5 + 3x = 20$
8. $\frac{2}{3}x + 6 = 30$

Solve each equation using the number line method.

9. $3x = 27$
10. $3x + 5 = 50$
11. $38 - 2x = 22$

Solve each equation using algebra tiles.

12. $25 + 2x = 50$
13. $16 = 4x + 8$
14. $2x + 5 + 3x = 10$

Solve each equation algebraically.

15. $11 + x = 33$
16. $2x - 4.6 = 6.2$
17. $25 + 2x = 50$
18. $\frac{3}{4}x - 11 = 7$

Solve each equation using the method of your choice.

19. $8x = -72$
20. $5 + 3x = 21$
21. $6x + 3 - 2x = 27$

Solve the word problems using a method of your choice. Write an equation for each problem.

22. Sophie bought a total of 27 guppies and angel fish. She bought twice as many guppies as angel fish. How many of each kind of fish did Sophie purchase?

23. Thomas used 100 feet of rope to make 3 swings, one for each of his children. He had 13 feet left over when he was finished. How much rope did he use on each swing?

24. **MATHEMATICAL REFLECTION** What have you learned about solving equations as a result of this activity?

22.–24. Methods may vary. Sample answers are given.

22. Sample answer: $2x + x = 27$. Sophie bought 9 angel fish and 18 guppies.

23. Sample answer: $3x + 13 = 100$. Each swing used 29 feet of rope.

24. Sample answer: I learned about inverse operations and how they "undo" operations in an equation so that I can isolate the variable.

Properties, Expressions, and Formulas
What's in a Name?

SUGGESTED LEARNING STRATEGIES: Look for Patterns, Think/ Pair/Share, Guess and Check, Quickwrite

Words that have the property of being spelled the same forwards and backwards are called *palindromes*. The names Hannah and Otto are two examples of names that are palindromes.

1. Can you think of some other names or words that are palindromes?

   Answers may vary. Sample answers: Anna, radar, level

Numbers and operations have interesting **properties** as well.

2. Classify each statement below as true or false. Rewrite any false statements to make them true.

   $3 + 5 = 5 + 3$ True $3 \cdot 5 = 5 \cdot 3$ True

   $2 + (-2) = 0$ True $10 \div 2 = 2 \div 10$ False; $10(2) = 2(10)$

   $6 - 3 = 3 - 6$ False $2(5 \cdot 3) = (2 \cdot 5)(3)$ True
   $6 + 3 = 3 + 6$

   $5 + 0 = 0$ False $2\left(\frac{1}{2}\right) = 0$ False; $2\left(\frac{1}{2}\right) = 1$
   $5 + 0 = 5$

   $2 + (4 + 5) = (2 + 4) + 5$ True $1 \cdot 3 = 3$ True

3. Which statements above are similar to a palindrome?

   $3 + 5 = 5 + 3$, $6 - 3 = 3 - 6$, and $3 \cdot 5 = 5 \cdot 3$

4. Explain how you corrected the false statements.

   Answers may vary. Sample answer: I either changed the operation to its inverse, or I modified the answer to fit the operation shown.

My Notes

ACADEMIC VOCABULARY

A **property** in mathematics is a rule or statement that is always true.

TEACHER TO TEACHER: As you go through this activity, add new vocabulary words to your interactive word wall. Depending on your students' familiarity with the properties of real numbers and properties of equality, you may or may not add all of those terms to your word wall.

You can also use a vocabulary organizer or mathematics notebook to help students record and review key terms.

Properties, Expressions, Formulas

Activity Focus
- Properties of real numbers
- Evaluating expressions
- Solutions to equations
- Literal equations and formulas
- Justifying solution steps

Materials
- Scissors
- Glue or tape

Chunking the Activity

#1	#7	#17
#2–4	#8–12	#18
#5	#13–15	#19–20
#6	#16	#21

TEACHER TO TEACHER: Expressions, equations, properties, formulas: Naming and identifying mathematical terms can be as challenging for our students as understanding, manipulating and applying them. Names, naming and the use of names is a theme that threads throughout this activity.

1 Look for Patterns This question connects to language arts and helps students understand what it means when we say something exhibits a certain property.

2-4 Think/Pair/Share, Guess and Check Working in groups, students verify, correct, and explain their thinking. Have students share the different ways they corrected the false statements. Make sure that students have made appropriate corrections to the false statements. While some students might begin to name the properties illustrated by the statements in Item 2, it is not expected that all students will remember them.

5 Look for Patterns, Quickwrite, Interactive Word Wall, Vocabulary Organizer Asks students to describe the properties of real numbers in words. Take the time to observe how well students are able to articulate these properties. At this point they should be fairly familiar with them. However, if you notice some students are struggling, you may want to provide a few more additional examples to help them understand the different properties. Add terms as needed to your word wall and ask students to record them in their vocabulary organizer as well.

6 Quickwrite, Debriefing, Notetaking As students complete the Quickwrite on this question, make sure they are providing numerical examples to support their reasoning. Emphasize use of proper vocabulary. You might point out that a single counterexample can be used to prove that a property is false. Take time after debriefing this question for students to take notes in their mathematics journal. A graphic organizer could be set up to compare and contrast the various properties.

My Notes

SUGGESTED LEARNING STRATEGIES: Look for a Pattern, Quickwrite, Interactive Word Wall, Vocabulary Organizer, Note Taking

The properties of real numbers are listed below for your reference. These properties are true for all real numbers.

5. Describe each property in your own words in the space provided.

Descriptions may vary. Sample answers:

Name	Property	Description
Commutative Property of Addition	$a + b = b + a$	You can change the order when you add two numbers and still get the same result.
Commutative Property of Multiplication	$a \cdot b = b \cdot a$	You can change the order when you multiply two numbers and still get the same result.
Associative Property of Addition	$a + (b + c) = (a + b) + c$	When you add, you can change how you group numbers and still get the same result.
Associative Property of Multiplication	$a \cdot (b \cdot c) = (a \cdot b) \cdot c$	When you multiply, you can change how you group numbers and still get the same result.
Additive Inverse Property	$a + (-a) = 0$	A number plus its opposite equals 0.
Multiplicative Inverse Property	$a\left(\dfrac{1}{a}\right) = 1, a \neq 0$	A number multiplied by its reciprocal equals 1.
Additive Identity Property	$a + 0 = a$	A number plus 0 is the number.
Multiplicative Identity Property	$a \cdot 1 = a$	A number times 1 is the number.
Distributive Property of Multiplication Over Addition	$a(b + c) = a \cdot b + a \cdot c$	The product of a number and a sum is the sum of two products.

6. Do the commutative and associative properties apply for the operations of subtraction and division? Explain why or why not.

No; Explanations may vary. Sample explanation: Here are examples that prove the properties do not apply:

$10 - 6 = 4$ but $6 - 10 = -4$

$\dfrac{10}{2} = 5$ but $\dfrac{2}{10} = 0.2$.

$10 - (5 + 3) = 2$ but $(10 - 5) + 3 = 8$.

$(3 \div 2) \cdot 2 = 3$ but $3 \div (2 \cdot 2) = 0.75$.

SUGGESTED LEARNING STRATEGIES: Think/Pair/Share,
Look for a Pattern, Activate Prior Knowledge, Create
Representations, Guess and Check

7. Name the property of real numbers illustrated by each statement.

a. $x \cdot 4y = 4x \cdot y$
Additive Identity Property

b. $100 \cdot 1 = 100$
Multiplicative Identity Property

c. $x(3 \cdot 2x) = (x \cdot 3) \cdot 2x$
Associative Property of Multiplication

d. $3(1 + x) = 3(1) + 3x$
Distributive Property

e. $(-8)\left(-\frac{1}{8}\right) = 1$
Multiplicative Inverse Property

Amy likes to play games with names and writes an *algebraic expression* using the letters in her name. Her expression is shown below.

$$am + y$$

8. Which operations (addition, subtraction, multiplication, division) did Amy use in her name expression?
multiplication and addition

9. Which operation do you perform first in a problem that contains both of these operations? Explain.
multiplication before addition due to the order of operations

10. Write Amy's name expression using words.
Answers may vary. Sample answer: The product of *a* and *m* plus *y*

11. What values could you pick for *a*, *m*, and *y* so the value of the expression is Amy's current age, 13 years old?
Answers may vary. Sample answer: $a = 2$, $m = 5$, $y = 3$

12. Use the letters of your name to write an algebraic expression that uses at least 2 operations. Figure out values for each letter so the expression is equal to your age.
Answers will vary.

My Notes

> **MATH TERMS**
> An **algebraic expression** is a mathematical phrase that contains a variable. You can **evaluate** and **simplify** expressions.

ACTIVITY 2.3 *Continued*

7 Think/Pair/Share, Look for a Pattern, Debriefing All of these statements include variables. You might want to alert your students to the fact that the properties will still apply for any variable (as long as it is a real number). Make sure students work this problem independently at first. As you circulate around the room, pay attention to how many students are able to complete this question accurately on their own.

Suggested Assignment

CHECK YOUR UNDERSTANDING
p. 88, #1–5

UNIT 2 PRACTICE
p. 110, #17

TEACHER TO TEACHER This portion of the activity focuses on evaluating expressions and verifying solutions to equations. Students will use their own names to form expressions and equations. Have students with a long first name use a nickname, their last name (if it is short), their initials, or their pet's name. Names longer than 6 or 7 letters are probably not feasible for this activity. Two-letter first names should not be used either.

By the end of this lesson, make sure students understand the difference between an expression and an equation. They should see that expressions are *evaluated* and equations are *solved*.

8-10 Activate Prior Knowledge, Create Representations Reinforce the idea that the multiplication symbol does not need to be explicitly written when one or more factors is a variable. The term *am* means "the product of *a* and *m*." Also, reinforce that according to the rules for order of operations multiplication occurs before addition.

---

11 Guess and Check Multiple solutions are possible. Struggling students may try to use values such as 1 for *a*, 0 for *m*, and 3 for *y*, thinking that *a* is the ten's digit and *m* is the one's digit of a two-digit number. If so, you will need to re-emphasize that *am* is a product. Differentiate this lesson for more advanced students by asking for 3 fractions or 3 negative numbers that make the value equal 13.

12 Create Representations, Guess and Check, Debriefing Have students work in their groups to verify that their name expressions work for the selected values. You can extend this lesson by asking groups to pass their expression to another student to come up with a different set of values that makes the expression equal to the age.

EXAMPLE 1/Try These A
Students can record these in their notebooks and practice on more typical problems like those they might see on a standards-based assessment.

TRY THESE A These problems provide practice for students as a check on their understanding of using the order of operations and evaluating expressions.

13-14 Create Representations, Guess and Check Introduces a literal equation using another name. Students should notice that an equation contains an equals sign while an expression does not. Encourage students to use the words "is equal to" for the equal symbol.

SUGGESTED LEARNING STRATEGIES: Create Representations, Guess and Check

My Notes

To *evaluate an expression*, substitute the given values of each variable into the expression. Then use the order of operations to evaluate each expression.

EXAMPLE 1
Evaluate each expression if $a = 8$, $b = 1$, $c = -2$, and $d = \frac{1}{2}$.

a. $3a + bc$

Step 1:   Substitute.
$$3(8) + (1)(-2)$$
Step 2:   Simplify.
$$3(8) + (1)(-2) = 24 + (1)(-2) = 24 - 2$$
Subtraction is done last because of the order of operations.
$$24 - 2 = 22$$
Solution: 22

b. $4bd - 5c^2$

Step 1:   Substitute.
$$4(1)\left(\frac{1}{2}\right) - 5(-2)^2$$
Step 2:   Simplify.
$$4(1)\left(\frac{1}{2}\right) - 5(4) = 2 - 5(4) = 2 - 20$$
Multiplication and division are always done before addition and subtraction.
$$2 - 20 = -18$$
Solution: -18

TRY THESE A
Evaluate each expression if $x = 3$, $y = -2$, and $z = 4$. Justify each step using the order of operations.
a. $4xy + z$ -20 **b.** $2y^2 + 3x - z$ 13 **c.** $\dfrac{5xy}{z + 1}$ -6

> **MATH TERMS**
> An **equation** relates two expressions with an equals sign. You can *solve* an equation for a variable.

An *equation* is a mathematical statement that equates two expressions. Amy's friend Juan wrote his name as an equation.
$$ju = a + n$$

13. What operations are used in Juan's name equation?
multiplication and addition

14. Write Juan's name equation in words.   Answers may vary.
Sample answer: The product of *j* and *u* is equal to *a* plus *n*.

MINI-LESSON: Evaluating an Expression
Additional practice problems are provided below. Be sure to emphasize the order of operations with your students as they work through these additional problems.
Let $x = 2$, $y = -5$, and $z = 4$.

1. $3x + y$ 1
2. $xz - y$ 13
3. $2y + 3x - 3z$ -16
4. $3y^2$ 75
5. $\dfrac{(x + z)}{(y + 7)}$ 3
6. $0.5xy + \dfrac{z}{2}$ -3

Evaluate each expression for the given value of the variable.

7. $2x - 3$ for $x = -4$ -11
8. $a^2 + b^2$ for $a = 5$ and $b = 12$ 169
9. $\dfrac{2x}{3} + 5$ for $x = 12$ 13
10. $-2(x - (-4)) + 3x$ for $x = -2$ -10

Properties, Expressions, and Formulas
What's in a Name?

SUGGESTED LEARNING STRATEGIES: Create Representations, Guess and Check, Identify A Subtask, Work Backwards

My Notes

Recall that an equation is *true* when both sides have the same numerical value.

15. Find values for *j*, *u*, *a*, and *n* that will make Juan's name equation true. Each letter should have a different numerical value.
Answers may vary. Sample answer: $j = 5$, $a = 4$, $u = 2$, $n = 6$

16. Use the letters in your name to write a name equation and then find values for each letter to make your name equation true.
Answers will vary.

Juan's name equation is an example of a **literal equation**. Literal equations can be solved using the same procedures as equations containing one variable.

ACADEMIC VOCABULARY

A **literal equation** has more than one variable, and the equation can be solved for a specific variable. Formulas are examples of literal equations. For example, the distance formula ($D = rt$) is a literal equation, and it can be solved for *D*, *r*, or *t*.

$D: D = rt$

$r: r = \dfrac{D}{t}$

$t: t = \dfrac{D}{r}$

EXAMPLE 2

Solve the equation $ju = a + n$ for *a*.

Step 1: Isolate the variable by subtracting n from both sides.
$$ju - n = a + n - n$$

Step 2: Simplify.
$$ju - n = a$$

Solution: Rearrange the equation in terms of the variable solved for.
$$a = ju - n$$

TRY THESE B

Solve each name equation for the vowel.

a. $br = ad$ $\quad a = \dfrac{(br)}{d}$ $\quad$ **b.** $n + ic = k$ $\quad i = \dfrac{(k - n)}{c}$ $\quad$ **c.** $j = \dfrac{e}{n}$ $\quad e = jn$

17. Solve your name equation for a letter of your choice.
Answers will vary.

ACTIVITY 2.3 Continued

15 Create Representations, Guess and Check, Debriefing Emphasizes what it means for an equation to be true. It may surprise students to see multiple sets of variables that make this equation true, as many of them might think that equations are supposed to have only one solution. Ask them why this equation has many solutions where previous equations only had one. Hopefully they will recognize that using more than one variable leads to multiple solution possibilities.

TEACHER TO TEACHER One of the most common uses of literal equations are as formulas for various mathematics, science, and business applications. This portion of the activity exposes students to solving formulas for a particular variable.

16 Create Representations, Guess and Check, Debriefing Encourage creativity when creating a name equation. You might see how many different equations students can create. Students whose names have a repeated letter (e.g. Pete) should use the same value for all occurrences of the variable.

TRY THESE B Additional examples are provided in the Mini-Lesson below if your class is struggling with the Try These problems.

17 Identify A Subtask, Work Backwards, Debriefing Make sure students solve for a variable that only appears once in their name equation. You might demonstrate how like variables would simplify using this equation $pe = te$ and solving for *t*.

Suggested Assignment

CHECK YOUR UNDERSTANDING
p. 88, #6–10

UNIT 2 PRACTICE
p. 110, #18

MINI-LESSON: Literal Equations

Some additional name equations are provided below for extra practice. Find values for the variables that make each equation true.

1. *tom* = *my* possible answer $t = 2$, $o = 3$, $m = -2$, $y = 6$
2. $e + th = \dfrac{a}{n}$ possible answer $e = 6$, $t = 4$, $h = 1$, $a = 20$, $n = 2$
3. $a + s = ia$ possible answer $a = 6$, $s = 0$, $i = 1$

Solve each equation for the indicated variable.

4. $j + o + n = ah$, solve for *n* $n = ah - j - o$
5. $k = ia$, solve for *a* $a = \dfrac{k}{i}$
6. $ha + n = na$, solve for *h* $h = \dfrac{(na - n)}{a}$
7. $ri + l = ey$, solve for *y* $y = \dfrac{(ri + l)}{e}$

TRY THESE C These problems provide practice for students as a check on their understanding of solving equations for a variable.

18 Quickwrite Most of these problems require only one step to isolate the given variable. Students may not be familiar with Euler's formula that relates the number of vertices, faces and edges of a solid. Using process of elimination, they should be able to match the name with this formula. A quick internet search will provide you with some additional resources to explain this unique relationship.

Suggested Assignment

CHECK YOUR UNDERSTANDING
p. 88, #11–13

UNIT 2 PRACTICE
p. 110, #19

My Notes

MATH TERMS
A **formula** is an equation written using symbols that describes the relationship between different quantities.

CONNECT TO AP
Using formulas and solving literal equations for one of the variables are important skills in both calculus and statistics.

Formulas are a type of literal equation. You can solve for any variable in a formula.

EXAMPLE 3

Solve the equation $2\ell + 2w = p$ for w.

$2\ell + 2w = p$	isolate the variable being solved for
$2\ell - 2\ell + 2w = p - 2\ell$	subtract 2ℓ from each side
$2w = p - 2\ell$	
$w = \dfrac{p - 2\ell}{2}$	divide both sides by 2

TRY THESE C

Solve each equation for the indicated variable.

a. $m = 2q + 4u$, for q

$q = \left(\dfrac{1}{2}\right)m - 2u$

b. $8s = 6z + 2n$, for n

$n = 4s - 3z$

18. Solve for the indicated variable in each formula.

Name	Formula	Solve for	
Circumference of a Circle	$C = 2\pi r$	r	$r = \dfrac{C}{2\pi}$
Simple Interest	$I = prt$	p	$p = \dfrac{I}{rt}$
Euler's Formula	$F + V = E + 2$	V	$V = E + 2 - F$
Area of a triangle	$A = \frac{1}{2}bh$	B	$b = \dfrac{2A}{h}$
Area of a trapezoid	$A = \frac{1}{2}h(b_1 + b_2)$	b_1	$b_1 = \dfrac{2A}{h} - b_2$
Temperature (Degrees Celsius)	$C = \frac{5}{9}(F - 32)$	F	$F = \dfrac{9}{5}C + 32$
Temperature (Degrees Fahrenheit)	$F = \frac{9}{5}C + 32$	C	$C = \dfrac{5}{9}(F - 32)$

SUGGESTED LEARNING STRATEGIES: Quickwrite, Look for Patterns, Discussion Group

When solving an equation, each step can be justified by using *properties*. Earlier in this activity you learned several properties of real numbers. Three properties of equality are listed below.

Properties of Equality for Real Numbers *a*, *b*, and *c*	
Addition Property	if $a = b$, then $a + c = b + c$
Multiplication Property	if $a = b$, then $ca = cb$
Symmetric Property	if $a = b$, then $b = a$

My Notes

READING MATH
Property names often describe the mathematics used in the property itself.

19. Write a description of each property of equality in your own words.

Answers may vary. Sample answers:

a. Addition Property

You can add the same number to both sides of an equation without changing the solution.

b. Multiplication Property

You can multiply both sides of an equation by the same number without changing the solution (as long as the number isn't 0).

c. Symmetric Property

You can exchange sides on an equation without changing the solution.

20. Do you think there are subtraction and division properties of equality? Explain why or why not.

Yes; Answers may vary. Sample answer: As long as you perform the same operation to both sides, equality will be maintained. However, the subtraction and division properties of equality would be essentially the same as the addition and multiplication properties of equality.

EXAMPLE 4

Solve the equation $2x - 8 = 4$ and justify each step.

Equation	Justification
$2x - 8 = 4$	original equation
$2x - 8 + \underline{8} = 4 + \underline{8}$	Addition Property of Equality
$2x + \underline{0} = 12$	Additive Inverse Property
$\underline{2x} = 12$	Additive Identity Property
$\dfrac{2x}{2} = \dfrac{12}{2}$	Division Property of Equality
$\underline{1}x = 6$	Multiplicative Inverse
$\underline{x} = 6$	Mulitplicative Identity

Unit 2 • Expressions, Equations, and Inequalities **85**

ACTIVITY 2.3 *Continued*

TEACHER TO TEACHER In the final portion of this activity, students name the solution steps in an equation using the properties of real numbers and the properties of equality.

Students are introduced to the properties of equality and then they will work through several exercises where they have to state the property that justifies each solution step. Students should record these properties in their notes or vocabulary organizer. These properties can be added to your word wall. If it is not already there, the word "justify" can also be added to your word wall.

19 Quickwrite, Debriefing Check to see whether or not students can verbalize the properties listed above.

20 Look for a Pattern, Discussion Group This item should provoke some interesting discussion. Subtraction and division properties of equality are certainly valid (as long as the divisor is not zero), but they are not necessary as subtraction is defined as addition of the additive inverse and division as multiplication by the multiplicative inverse.

TRY THESE D These problems provide practice for students as a check on their understanding of the properties of equality.

SUGGESTED LEARNING STRATEGIES: Think/Pair/Share

My Notes

TRY THESE D

Use the properties of equality and properties of real numbers to justify each step shown below.

a.

Equation	Justification
$8.25 = 0.75x + 3$	Original equation
$8.25 - 3 = 0.75x + 3 - 3$	Subtraction Property of Equality
$5.25 = 0.75x + 0$	Additive Inverse Property
$5.25 = 0.75x$	Additive Identity Property
$\frac{5.25}{0.75} = \frac{0.75x}{0.75}$	Division Property of Equality
$7 = \frac{1x}{1}$	Multiplicative Inverse Property
$7 = x$	Multiplicative Identity Property
$x = 7$	Symmetric Property of Equality

b.

Equation	Justification
$6.25 = 0.25x + 4$	Original equation
$6.25 - 4 = 0.25x + 4 - 4$	Subtraction Property of Equality
$2.25 = 0.25x + 0$	Additive Inverse Property
$2.25 = 0.25x$	Additive Identity Property
$\frac{2.25}{0.25} = \frac{0.25x}{0.25}$	Division Property of Equality
$9 = \frac{1x}{1}$	Multiplicative Inverse Property
$9 = x$	Multiplicative Identity Property
$x = 9$	Symmetric Property of Equality

Properties, Expressions, and Formulas
What's in a Name?

SUGGESTED LEARNING STRATEGIES: Think/Pair/Share

ACTIVITY 2.3 *Continued*

21 Think/Pair/Share, Debriefing
Debrief after this question to
make sure students are correctly
justifying each step.

Suggested Assignment
CHECK YOUR UNDERSTANDING
p. 88, #14–16

UNIT 2 PRACTICE
p. 110, #20

My Notes

c.

Equation	Justification
$3(x + 3) = 18$	original equation
$3x + 9 = 18$	Distributive Property
$3x + 9 - 9 = 18 - 9$	Subtraction Property of Equality
$3x + 0 = 9$	Additive Inverse Property
$3x = 9$	Additive Identity Property
$\frac{3x}{3} = \frac{9}{3}$	Division Property of Equality
$1x = 3$	Multiplicative Inverse Property
$x = 3$	Multiplicative Identity Property

21. The literal equation below has been solved for the variable y.
Use the properties to justify each step.

Equation	Justification
$x = 3y + 6$	original equation
$x - 6 = 3y + 6 - 6$	Subtraction Property of Equality
$x - 6 = 3y + 0$	Additive Inverse Property
$x - 6 = 3y$	Additive Identity Property
$\frac{x - 6}{3} = \frac{3y}{3}$	Division Property of Equality
$\frac{x - 6}{3} = 1y$	Multiplicative Inverse Property
$\frac{x - 6}{3} = y$	Multiplicative Identity Property
$y = \frac{x - 6}{3}$	Symmetric Property of Equality

CHECK YOUR UNDERSTANDING

1. Additive Identity Property
2. Associative Property of Multiplication
3. Distributive Property
4. Multiplicative Inverse Property
5. Commutative Property of Multiplication
6. 36
7. 13
8. 1
9. no
10. yes
11. $w = \dfrac{A}{l}$
12. $m = \dfrac{F}{a}$
13. $y = \dfrac{-c - ax}{b}$
14. In order: original equation, Addition Property of Equality, Additive Inverse Property, Additive Identity Property, Division Property of Equality, Multiplicative Inverse Property, Multiplicative Identity Property
15. 15°
16. Answers may very. Sample answer: An equation is a mathematical statement that says that two expressions are equal. A formula is a literal equation that states a general mathematical rule. The properties of numbers and equality tell you why an equation in a given step can be derived from the equation in the previous step.

CHECK YOUR UNDERSTANDING

Write your answers on notebook paper. Show your work.

Name the property illustrated by each statement.

1. $2x + 0 = 2x$
2. $2(5 \cdot 11) = (2 \cdot 5)11$
3. $6(x + 4) = 6x + 6 \cdot 4$
4. $3\left(\dfrac{1}{3}\right) = 1$
5. $5(x + 3) = (x + 3)5$

Evaluate each expression if $x = 2$, $y = -3$ and $z = 4$.

6. $2xy^2$
7. $3x - 5y - 2z$
8. $\dfrac{4x + 2y}{z - 2}$

Is the equation true for the given values?

9. $2x - 3 = 5x + 12$, $x = -3$
10. $3x - 2y = 8$, $x = 4$, $y = 2$

Solve each equation for the indicated variable.

11. $A = lw$, for w
12. $F = ma$, for m
13. $ax + by + c = 0$, for y
14. Justify the steps in the solution below using the properties of real numbers and of equality.

$$12x - 7 = 29$$
$$12x - 7 + 7 = 29 + 7$$
$$12x + 0 = 36$$
$$12x = 36$$
$$\dfrac{12x}{12} = \dfrac{36}{12}$$
$$1x = 3$$
$$x = 3$$

15. If a thermometer shows a reading of 59°F, what is the temperature in degrees Celsius?
16. **MATHEMATICAL REFLECTION** What is the difference between an expression, an equation, and a formula? How do the properties of numbers and equality explain steps in a mathematics problem?

Patterns, Expressions, Equations, Formulas

A PENNY FOR YOUR THOUGHTS

1. A penny pattern is shown below.

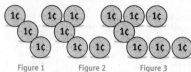

Figure 1   Figure 2   Figure 3

a. How many pennies are in the 5th, 10th, and 100th figure? Explain your thinking using pictures, tables or expressions.

b. Is it possible for a figure in this pattern to contain 85 pennies? Explain your thinking.

2. Explain how to solve the following equation using mental math.

$$4x + 1 = 13$$

3. Solve the equation below using a method of your own choice. Explain your method.

$$2x + 5 + 4x = 8$$

4. What property is illustrated by each expression?

a. $5 \cdot p = p \cdot 5$

b. $p + (5p + 10p) = (p + 5p) + 10p$

c. $5(p + 10) = 5p + 5 \cdot 10$

5. Given $pen = ny$.

a. Solve this literal equation for y.

b. What is the value of y if $p = 5$, $e = 10$, and $n = 15$?

c. Could you have determined the value of y without knowing the value of n? Which property of numbers helps to justify your answer?

Answer Key

1a. fifth: 11, tenth: 21, one hundredth: 201. Sample answer: The number of pennies in the nth figure is $2n + 1$.

b. Yes; Sample answer: $2n + 1 = 85$. $n = 42$. Figure 42 has 85 pennies.

2. $x = 3$; Sample answer: Four times a number has to be 12 since $12 + 1$ equals 13. So the number must be 3.

3. $x = \frac{1}{2}$

4a. Commutative property of multiplication

b. Associative property of addition

c. Distributive property of multiplication over addition

5a. $y = \frac{pen}{n}$ or $y = pe$

b. $y = 50$.

c. yes; multiplicative inverse property.

Embedded Assessment 1

Assessment Focus
- Linear patterns
- Multiple representations
- Solving equations
- Evaluating expressions
- Properties of real numbers
- Literal equations

Materials
- None

TEACHER TO TEACHER This activity asks students to solve a pattern involving arrangements of pennies similar to the work they did in Activity 2.1. They then give their thoughts on solving equations and naming properties or real numbers. Finally, they solve a literal equation formed from the letters in the word penny.

1 Students that answer this problem by drawing additional figures or making and extending a table of values or using a guess and check strategy may need review on how to derive a general expression from a visual or numerical pattern.

2 This question emphasizes communication. Check to see that students are using appropriate vocabulary.

3 Students could solve this equation in a variety of ways. However, those students who approach this problem algebraically and do not make mistakes have mastered an important goal of the first part of this unit. Student explanations should focus on the method they chose and an explanation of the solving steps.

4 This item reviews the properties of addition and multiplication.

5 This item asks students to solve a literal equation and then evaluate it for given values for the variables. Part c challenges them to extend their thinking and recognize an application of the multiplicative inverse property.

Embedded Assessment 1
Use after Activity 2.3.

Patterns, Expressions, Equations, Formulas

A PENNY FOR YOUR THOUGHTS

	Exemplary	Proficient	Emerging
Math Knowledge #4a–c, 5a–c	The student: • Gives the correct property for each equation. (4a–c) • Solves the literal equation for *y*. (5a) • Finds the value of *y* from the given information. (5b) • Determines whether *y* can be found without *n* and the property to justify the conclusion. (5c)	The student attempts all six items but is able to answer only four of them correctly and completely.	The student attempts at least four of the items but is able to answer only two of them correctly and completely.
Problem Solving #1a, 1b, 3	The student: • Finds the number of pennies in the 5th, 10th, 100th figures. (1a) • Determines if a figure can contain 85 pennies. (1b) • Solves the equation. (3)	The student attempts all three items but is able to answer only two of them correctly and completely.	The student attempts at least two of the items but is able to answer only one of them correctly and completely.
Representation #1a	The student uses pictures, tables, expressions to support answer. (1a)	The student's response is incomplete but contains no mathematical errors.	The student's response contains mathematical errors.
Communication #1b, 2, 3	The student: • Gives a complete explanation about whether a figure can contain 85 pennies. (1b) • Explains how to solve the equation using mental math. (2) • Explains the selected method used to solve the equation. (3)	The student attempts all three items but is able to answer only two of them correctly and completely.	The student attempts at least two of the items but is able to answer only one of them correctly and completely.

Modeling and Solving Multi-Step Equations
Cups and Cubes

SUGGESTED LEARNING STRATEGIES: Think Aloud, Use Manipulatives, Quickwrite, Create Representations

My Notes

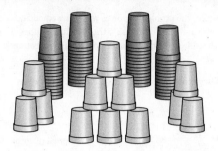

Creating a model of a problem can help you break the problem down into parts that you can visualize.

Some small paper cups contain an equal number of centimeter cubes. They are placed on a balance scale with some additional cubes.

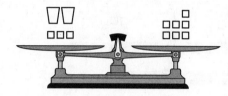

1. If the scale is balanced, how many cubes must be in each cup?

Each cup must contain 2 cubes.

2. Explain how you solved this problem.

Answers may vary. Sample answer: I thought: 3 plus what equals 7? $3 + 4 = 7$. And 4 divided by 2 is 2.

3. Write an equation to represent the diagram shown above. Let x represent the number of cubes in a cup.

$2x + 3 = 7$

MINI-LESSON: Cups and Cubes Model

You will need enough small paper cups and centimeter cubes so each group can model the equations. Ten paper cups and 30 cubes per group are suggested.

In this model, each cup represents an x. So 3 cups represent $3x$. Each cube represents a 1, so 5 cubes is the number 5.

Explain to students that you will be ignoring the weight of the paper cups in this scenario.

The goal is to figure out how many cubes would have to be placed in each cup to maintain the balance.

Modeling and Solving Multi-Step Equations

Activity Focus
- Multi-step equations, including variables on both sides
- Modeling equations with manipulatives
- Justifying solution steps

Materials
- A balance (optional)
- Small paper cups and centimeter cubes

Chunking the Activity

#1	#4–5	#8–9	#12–13
#2	#6	#10	#14
#3	#7	#11	#15–18

Differentiating Instruction

This activity provides another hands-on model for solving equations. Struggling learners will benefit from a concrete representation of the variable quantities. An actual balance could be brought into class to use as a model.

1-2 Think Aloud, Use Manipulatives, Quickwrite, Debriefing Give students time to discuss and solve this problem in their groups. Carefully observe how they approach the problem. Do they naturally remove cubes from both sides of their imaginary balance? Do they use a guess and check strategy? Do they understand that there must be the same amount of cubes in each cup?

3 Create Representations

ACTIVITY 2.4 Continued

4-5 **Visualization, Quickwrite, Debriefing, Note Taking, Group Presentation** This item helps students understand both the process of solving an equation using this model and how to represent it on their papers. Have groups report their explanations, and then come to a consensus as a class on an efficient way to explain each move.

ACTIVITY 2.4
continued

Modeling and Solving Multi-Step Equations
Cups and Cubes

My Notes

SUGGESTED LEARNING STRATEGIES: Visualization, Quickwrite, Note Taking

4. One way to solve the problem involves removing equal amounts from both sides and then regrouping the remaining cubes. The diagrams below illustrate this process. Write an explanation for the second and third diagram.

Diagram	Explanation

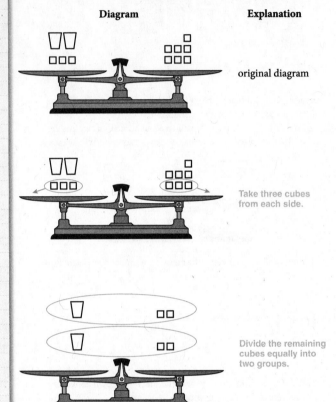

original diagram

Take three cubes from each side.

Divide the remaining cubes equally into two groups.

5. From the diagrams shown above, how many cubes are in each cup?

There are two cubes in each cup.

92 SpringBoard™ Mathematics with Meaning™ **Level 3**

SUGGESTED LEARNING STRATEGIES: Mark the Text, Use Manipulatives, Create Representations, Quickwrite

6. Model each of the following problems using cups and cubes, then determine how many cubes are in a cup. Record your work using a diagram like the one above. Write an explanation for each step, an equation for the original problem, and the solution. Let x be the number of cubes in a cup.

a. If 3 cups are on one side of the scale and 12 cubes on the other, how many cubes must be in each cup to maintain the balance?

Diagram   **Explanation**

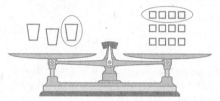

Divide the cubes evenly among the three cups. Each cup has 4 cubes.

Equation: $3x = 12$ Solution: $x = 4$

b. If 3 cups and 10 cubes are on one side of the scale and 16 cubes are on the other side, how many cubes must be in each cup to maintain the balance?

Diagram   **Explanation**

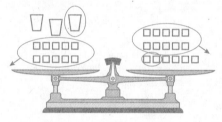

Remove 10 cubes from each side and divide the remaining 6 cubes evenly among the 3 cups.

Equation: $3x + 10 = 16$ Solution: $x = 2$

My Notes

6 **c–e** Marking the Text, Use Manipulatives, Create Representations, Quickwrite, Group Presentation, Debriefing

Part c is a model where students have cups (variables) on both sides of the balance. Students should remove equal numbers of cups just like they removed equal numbers of cubes in the earlier problems. This problem sets the stage for one of the major focuses of this activity: solving equations with variables on both sides.

Select groups to present their solutions to each part of Item 6. Have students edit and correct their work as needed before continuing.

TEACHER TO TEACHER | When students are finishing these problems they may try to divide the cubes up into the remaining cups. While this helps them understand the process of division, it actually makes the model inaccurate.

In order for the original equation to be balanced, each cup would already contain the appropriate number of cubes. As they solve these problems, the students are trying to discover this number without "peeking" into the cups.

Suggested Assignment

CHECK YOUR UNDERSTANDING
p. 98, #1–2

UNIT 2 PRACTICE
p. 111, #23–24

My Notes

c. If there are 3 cups and 8 cubes on one side of the scale and 7 cups and 4 cubes on the other side, how many cubes must be in each cup to maintain the balance?

Diagram   **Explanation**

Remove 4 cubes from each side and 3 cups from each side. Divide the remaining cubes evenly among the four cups.

Equation: $3x + 8 = 7x + 4$ Solution: $x = 1$

d. If there are 7 cups and 3 cubes on one side of the scale and 2 cups and 23 cubes on the other side, how many cubes must be in each cup to maintain the balance?

Diagram   **Explanation**

Remove 3 cubes from each side and 2 cups from each side. Divide the remaining cubes evenly among the 5 cups.

Equation: $7x + 3 = 2x + 23$ Solution: $x = 4$

e. If there are 8 cups and 2 cubes on one side of the scale and 4 cups and 6 cubes on the other side, how many cubes must be in each cup to maintain the balance?

Diagram   **Explanation**

Remove 2 cubes and 4 cups from each side. Divide the remaining cubes among the 4 cups.

Equation: $8x + 2 = 4x + 6$ Solution: $x = 1$

Modeling and Solving Multi-Step Equations
Cups and Cubes

SUGGESTED LEARNING STRATEGIES: Use Manipulatives, Create Representations, Simplify the Problem, Work Backwards, Group Presentation

My Notes

7. Model each equation on the balance diagram shown below. Then solve the equation and explain each step. Let x equal the number of cubes in a cup.

a. $14 = 3x + 2$

Explanation: Remove 2 cubes from each side and divide the remaining 12 cubes evenly among the three cups.

Solution: $x = 4$

b. $6x + 5 = 4x + 9$

Explanation: Remove 4 cups and 5 cubes from each side. Divide the remaining 4 cubes evenly among 2 cups.

Solution: $x = 2$

c. $3(x + 2) = 15$

Explanation: Remove 6 cubes from each side. Divide the remaining 9 cubes evenly among 3 cups.

Solution: $x = 3$

ACTIVITY 2.4 *Continued*

7 Use Manipulatives, Create Representations, Simplify the Problem, Work Backwards, Group Presentation, Debriefing
Students go from equations to pictorial representations. If needed, they can build each model with cups and cubes as well. At this point, students should be coming up with a solution and explaining their steps according to the model. Later in the activity, they will write the solution algebraically and give a reason for each step.

Students may need some guidance with $3(x + 2) = 15$. If they are stuck, explain to them that they need 3 sets of 1 cup and 2 cubes. Others might apply the distributive property and put down 3 cups and 6 cubes. If so, this provides a good opportunity to make the distributive property concrete.

8 Quickwrite Have students study the example and try to relate it back to the cubes and cups model.

9 Quickwrite, Debriefing Students should recognize that manipulatives may be difficult to use.

10 Think/Pair/Share, Create Representations, Identify a Subtask, Simplify the Problem, Debriefing The first two equations in Item 6 should be relatively easy for students as they solved equations like this in Activity 2.2. They will need to follow the example at the top of this page when solving 6c–e.

Suggested Assignment

CHECK YOUR UNDERSTANDING
p. 98, #3–5

UNIT 2 PRACTICE
p. 111, #23–24

SUGGESTED LEARNING STRATEGIES: Quickwrite, Think/ Pair/Share, Create Representations, Identify a Subtask, Simplify the Problem

My Notes

The solution to a cups and cubes equation can be represented algebraically. Each step can be given an explanation.

EXAMPLE

Solve the equation and provide an explanation for each step.

$$12x + 5 = 6x + 17$$

Step 1: Subtract 6x from each side. $\quad -6x \qquad -6x$

$$6x + 5 = 17$$

Step 2: Subtract 5 from each side. $\quad -5 \quad -5$

$$6x = 12$$

Step 3: Divide both sides by 6. $\quad \dfrac{6x}{6} = \dfrac{12}{6}$

Solution: $x = 2$

8. How do the steps in the example represent the cups and cubes process from previous questions?

Answers may vary. Sample answer: We are still "balancing" the equation. Subtracting 6x is like taking 6 cups away from each side of the balance. Subtracting 5 is like taking away 5 cubes from each side. Dividing 12 by 6 is like dividing the remaining cubes evenly into the 6 remaining cups.

9. Could the equation solving methods you learned in question 7 be used to solve an equation like the one in the example shown above? Explain why or why not.

Yes. Explanations may vary.

10. Solve each equation you wrote in Question 6 like the one shown above. Give an explanation for each step.

10. a.	$3x = 12$	original equation				
	$\dfrac{3x}{3} = \dfrac{12}{3}$	divide by 3				
	$x = 4$	solution				

b. $3x + 10 = 16$ original equation
$\quad -10 \quad -10$ subtract 10
$3x = 6$
$\dfrac{3x}{3} = \dfrac{6}{3}$ divide by 3
$x = 2$ solution

c. $3x + 8 = 7x + 4$ original equation
$\quad -3x \qquad -3x$ subtract 3x
$8 = 4x + 4$
$\quad -4 \qquad -4$ subtract 4
$4 = 4x$
$\dfrac{4}{4} = \dfrac{4x}{4}$ divide by 4
$1 = x$ solution

d. $7x + 3 = 2x + 23$ original equation
$\quad -2x \qquad -2x$ subtract 2x
$5x + 3 = 23$
$\quad -3 \quad -3$ subtract 3
$5x = 20$
$\dfrac{5x}{5} = \dfrac{20}{5}$ divide by 5
$x = 4$ solution

e. $8x + 2 = 4x + 6$ original equation
$\quad -4x \qquad -4x$ subtract 4x
$4x + 2 = 6$
$\quad -2 \quad -2$ subtract 2
$4x = 4$
$\dfrac{4x}{4} = \dfrac{4}{4}$ divide by 4
$x = 1$ solution

Modeling and Solving Multi-Step Equations
Cups and Cubes

SUGGESTED LEARNING STRATEGIES: Quickwrite, Note Taking, Identify a Subtask, Simplify the Problem, Think/Pair/Share, Create Representations, Group Presentation

My Notes

11. Could you model the equation $3x - 10 = -2x + 5$ using cups and cubes? Explain.

Explanations may vary. Sample answer: You can't model it because there is no way to represent negative numbers with cups and cubes.

12. Write a reason for each step of the equation $3(x - 2) = 8$, which has been solved below.

$3(x - 2) = 8$	original equation
$3x - 6 = 8$	Distributive Property
$+6 \quad +6$	add 6 to both sides
$3x = 14$	
$\dfrac{3x}{3} = \dfrac{14}{3}$	divide by 3
$x = 4\dfrac{2}{3}$	solution

13. Write a reason for each step of the equation $-8x - 4 + 5x = 17$, which has been solved below.

$-8x - 4 + 5x = 17$	original equation
$-3x - 4 = 17$	combine like terms
$+4 \quad +4$	add 4 to both sides
$-3x = 21$	
$\dfrac{-3x}{-3} = \dfrac{21}{-3}$	divide by -3
$x = -7$	solution

TRY THESE A

Solve each equation and provide an explanation for each step.

a. $7x + 11 - 10x = 26$

b. $2 - 3(x + 1) = 6x - 9$

c. $2(x + 7) = 6(x - 8)$

d. $2x - 10 = 3(x - 9)$

e. $8 - x = 3x + 2(x - 4)$

f. $\frac{1}{2}(18x - 8) = 6x - \frac{7}{2}$

TEACHER TO TEACHER The model used yesterday can prove unwieldy when dealing with negative quantities. From this point on, the lesson focuses on solving equations with variables on both sides algebraically.

11 Quickwrite, Think/Pair/Share, Debriefing Students may have some creative ideas for ways to represent both negative cups and negative cubes. Help them to understand the idea that as long as we apply the same operation to both sides, the equation will maintain its balance.

12-13 Note Taking, Identify a Subtask, Simplify the Problem, Group Presentation Students may or may not use properties to justify their answers. For middle school students, an explanation like "add 6 to both sides" is sufficient.

Some of the Try These problems will be challenging for students. You may want to choose one or more of them for students to record in their notebooks, paying particular attention to combining like terms, distributing fractions, and negative numbers.

TRY THESE A

Explanations may vary.

a. $x = -5$

b. $x = \dfrac{8}{9}$

c. $x = 15.5$

d. $x = 17$

e. $x = 2\dfrac{2}{3}$

f. $x = \dfrac{1}{6}$

14 Note Taking, Identify a Subtask, Create Representations, Simplify the Problem, Debriefing Monitor progress on recording the equation solving steps in a systematic and careful manner. Explanations can be brief as shown in the answers on the reduced student page.

Debrief Items 12 to 14 and emphasize that writing solution steps algebraically is more efficient than building a cup and cube model every time we want to solve an equation.

Suggested Assignment

CHECK YOUR UNDERSTANDING
p. 98, #6–13

UNIT 2 PRACTICE
p. 111, #27–30

CHECK YOUR UNDERSTANDING

1. There are 4 cubes in each cup.

2. There are 4 cubes in each cup.

3. $x = 2$

4. $x = 2$

5. $x = 3$

6. $x = -10.5$

7. $x = 6$

8. $x = -15$

9. $x = -\frac{28}{3}$

10. $x = -\frac{21}{5}$

11. no solution

12. all numbers

13. Answers may vary. Sample answer: Use the distributive property to remove grouping symbols. Use inverse operations to isolate the variable.

My Notes

15. a. Students should wind up with a true statement such as 2 = 2.
   b. Conjectures may vary. Sample conjecture: No matter what value the variable has, the result is a true statement, so the equation has all numbers as its solution.
16. a. Students should wind up with a false statement such as −5 = −15
   b. Conjectures may vary. Sample conjecture: No matter what value the variable has, the result is a false statement so the equation has no solution.
17. Answers may vary. Check students' equations.
18. Answers may vary. Check students' equations.

SUGGESTED LEARNING STRATEGIES: Note Taking, Identify a Subtask, Create Representations, Simplify the Problem

14. Solve the equation $2 - 3x = 17 + 2x$. Give an explanation for each step.

$2 - 3x = 17 + 2x$	original equation
$\underline{-2x \qquad -2x}$	subtract $2x$ from both sides
$2 - 5x = 17$	
$\underline{-2 \quad -2}$	subtract 2 from both sides
$-5x = 15$	
$\dfrac{-5x}{-5} = \dfrac{15}{-5}$	divide by -5
$x = -3$	solution

Work with a partner or group on Items 15 and 16.

15. Consider this equation.
$2(x + 1) = 3x - x + 2$
a. Solve the equation. Show each step.
b. Make a conjecture on what the solution of the equation is.

16. Consider this equation.
$6x - 5 = 5(x - 3) + x$
a. Solve the equation. Show each step.
b. Make a conjecture on what the solution of the equation is.

17. Create an equation whose solution is all numbers.

18. Create an equation that has no solution.

CHECK YOUR UNDERSTANDING

Write your answers on notebook paper. Show your work.

Use cups and cubes to model and solve each problem.

1. If there are 4 cups and 5 cubes on one side and 21 cubes on the other, how many cubes are in each cup?

2. If there are 5 cups and 8 cubes on one side and 2 cups and 20 cubes on the other side, how many cubes are in each cup?

Solve each equation. Use the cups and cubes model to help you if needed.

3. $4x + 10 = 18$

4. $15 = 3x + 9$

5. $6x + 4 = 2x + 16$

Solve each equation. Write an explanation for each step.

6. $5x + 10 - 7x = 31$

7. $7x - 10 = 3x + 14$

8. $3(x - 6) = 5x + 12$

9. $3 - 3(x + 5) = 16$

10. $\frac{1}{3}(6x - 9) = 5x + 2(x + 9)$

11. $7x + 5 + 2x = 4(x + 2) + 5x$

12. $4x - 12 - x = 3(x + 1) - 15$

13. **MATHEMATICAL REFLECTION** Describe the steps for solving an equation like those given in questions 6–10.

Solving and Graphing Inequalities
It Plays to Save

SUGGESTED LEARNING STRATEGIES: Create Representations, Simplify the Problem, Quickwrite

My Notes

Kevin needs money to pay for soccer camp next summer. The camp will cost $600. He is able to save $40 per month from his allowance and mowing lawns in his neighborhood, and Kevin's grandmother has offered to pay for the other half of the camp, once he has saved his half.

1. Record Kevin's total savings in the table below.

Month	Savings
1	$40
2	$80
3	$120
4	$160
5	$200

2. Use the table to write an expression for the amount of money Kevin has saved. Let x equal the number of months since he started saving for soccer camp. *$40x$*

Kevin starts saving in August, has $40 on September 1st, and needs to pay at least $250 by March 1st. Stated another way,

$$\text{Kevin's savings} \geq \$250$$
$$\$250 \leq \text{Kevin's savings}$$

The statement above is called an **inequality**. The process of solving an inequality is very similar to that of solving an equation.

3. Substitute the expression you wrote in Question 2 for Kevin's savings.

$$\underline{40x} \geq \$250$$
$$\$250 \leq \underline{40x}$$

4. Solve the inequality like you would solve an equation to determine if Kevin can save enough money by March 1st to pay the deposit.
$x \geq 6.25$. Kevin will have $260 in the account on March 1st, so he can pay the deposit for soccer camp.

ACADEMIC VOCABULARY

An **inequality** is a mathematical statement showing that one quantity is greater than or less than another.
Inequalities use these symbols:
>: is greater than
<: is less than
≥: is greater than or equal to
≤: is less than or equal to

TEACHER TO TEACHER — The activity uses a familiar context, saving for extracurricular activities and lessons that will be familiar to many students. The second half of this activity helps students to understand what happens when you divide or multiply both sides of an inequality by a negative number.

ACTIVITY 2.5 Guided

Solving and Graphing Inequalities

Activity Focus
- Multiple representations of inequalities
- Solving and graphing 1-variable inequalities
- Multiplication and division property of inequality
- Compound inequalities $a < x < b$

Materials
- No additional materials are needed.

Chunking the Activity

#1–2	#10	#21–24
#3	#11	#25
#4–5	#12–13	#26
#6	#14	#27–28
#7	#15–17	
#8–9	#18–20	

1-2 Create Representations, Debriefing Students will use the table to help them write an expression for the amount of money Kevin has saved after x months.

3-4 Simplify the Problem, Quickwrite, Debriefing After recording the term inequality on the word wall and in their vocabulary organizers, students write and solve an inequality. Later questions will help them understand the meaning of the solution set to an inequality. This inequality has a non-integer solution. However, the relationship between months and money saved is discrete in this instance. Students will need to round their answers. Regardless, Kevin has enough money in his account by March 1.

ACTIVITY 2.5 *continued* Solving and Graphing Inequalities
It Plays to Save

5 Think/Pair/Share, Create Representations, Simplify the Problem, Debriefing This item gives students practice solving inequalities by applying the same techniques they used when solving equations.

TEACHER TO TEACHER This portion of the activity will help you to hone student understanding of the differences between equations and inequalities. Students also learn to represent the solution set to an inequality as a graph on the number line.

6–10 Guess and Check, Quickwrite, Create Representations, Debriefing Help students to understand that the solution set to an inequality is an interval containing infinitely many values of the variable that make the inequality a true statement. Students should be encouraged to use a guess and check strategy as they answer these questions. By Item 10, students should realize there are many solutions to an inequality.

My Notes

SUGGESTED LEARNING STRATEGIES: Think/Pair/Share, Create Representations, Simplify the Problem, Guess and Check, Quickwrite

5. Solve each inequality like you would solve an equation.

a. $2x - 10 < 80$

$x < 45$

b. $5x - 8 + 7x > 40$

$x > 4$

c. $7(x - 11) \leq 100$

$x \leq \frac{177}{7}$

d. $5x + 8.5 \geq 3x - 10.3$

$x \geq -9.4$

Although you can solve an inequality like you do an equation, there are many values of the variable that make an inequality true instead of just one.

6. Find the value of x that will make both sides equal.

$$2x + 5 = 15$$

$x = 5$

7. Find at least 4 values of x that will make the inequality true.

$$2x + 5 < 15$$

Answers may vary. Sample answers: $x = 0, 1, 2,$ and 3.

8. Will $x = 4.9$ be a solution to the inequality? Find at least 4 fractions or decimals that are solutions to the inequality.

Yes, $2(4.9) + 5 < 15$. Answers may vary. Sample answers: $x = \frac{1}{2}$, 2.5, 4.5, and 4.99.

9. Plot the solutions from Questions 7 and 8 on a number line.

Answers may vary.

10. Compare the points on your number line to those of a classmate. How many values of x do you think are in the solution of the inequality?

Answers may vary. Sample answer: There are infinitely many solutions. All numbers less than 5 will satisfy the inequality.

SUGGESTED LEARNING STRATEGIES: Create Representations,
Predict and Confirm, Quickwrite

A convenient way to represent the many solutions to an inequality is a number line graph. On the number line, use an open circle for a **strict inequality**. Fill in the circle for an inequality that includes the number.

EXAMPLE 1

Graph the inequality $x > 3$.

Step 1: *Plot the number and draw the endpoint.*

The end point will be an open circle because the inequality is strictly greater than 3. Put an open circle on 3.

Step 2: *Determine the direction the solution will point.*

The arrow will point to the right because the solution includes all values greater than 3. Shade the number line to the right of 3.

Solution: (number line from 2 to 9 with open circle at 3, shaded right)

Graph the inequality $x \leq -2$.

Step 1: *Plot the number and draw the endpoint.*

The end point will be a closed circle because the inequality indicates that the solution may include -2. Fill in a circle on -2.

Step 2: *Determine the direction the solution will point.*

The arrow will point to the left because the solution includes all values less than or equal to -2. Shade the number line to the left of -2.

Solution: (number line from -8 to 0 with closed circle at -2, shaded left)

TRY THESE A

Graph each inequality on a number line.

a. $x < -1$　　**b.** $x \geq 5$　　**c.** $x > 4.5$　　**d.** $x \leq \frac{3}{4}$

11. Is the graph you made in question 9 a complete solution to the inequality $2x + 5 < 15$? Explain why or why not.

No. Answers may vary. Sample answer: Because all of the numbers less than 5 are solutions to the inequality and that graph only included a few of them.

12. Could the graph shown below be a solution to the inequality $2x + 5 < 15$? Explain why or provide a **counterexample** to justify your response.　　No. Explanations may vary. Sample answer: It leaves out the solutions between -2 and 5.

(number line from -8 to 0 with closed circle at -2)

My Notes

> **MATH TIP**
>
> A **strict inequality** is the inequality that is greater than ($>$) or less than ($<$) and does not include the endpoint. The symbols greater than or equal to ($\geq$) and less than or equal to ($\leq$) include the endpoints.

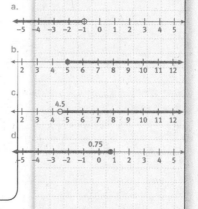

a. (number line -5 to 5)
b. (number line 2 to 12)
c. (number line 2 to 12, 4.5)
d. (number line -5 to 5, 0.75)

> **MATH TERMS**
>
> A **counterexample** is an example that shows that a statement is not true.

ACTIVITY 2.5 *Continued*

TEACHER TO TEACHER Students may be unfamiliar with the term "strict inequality." If so, make sure you post it on the word wall and record this in your vocabulary organizer. Students can also record the steps to graph an inequality along with some examples in their notebooks.

TRY THESE A Create Representations Debrief after students spend 5–10 minutes on the Try These A problems to see how well they did graphing parts c and d. Do not spend an excessive amount of time having them accurately plot $\frac{3}{4}$ on a number line. They should know it is midway between $\frac{1}{2}$ and 1.

11 Predict and Confirm, Quickwrite Further reinforce the notion that the complete solution to an inequality is all numbers in the solution interval.

12 Predict and Confirm, Quickwrite, Debriefing

MINI-LESSON: Graphing Inequalities

Some students might find a graphic organizer helpful as they learn to graph inequalities. A sample is shown below.

Words	less than	less than or equal to	greater than	greater than or equal to
Symbol				
Graph				

Students may wonder why an open circle is used. It means that all numbers up to (or above depending on the whether its less than or greater than), but not including, the number are in the solution interval.

13 Create Representations
This item provides additional practice with graphing solutions to inequalities on a number line.

14 Create Representations, Quickwrite, Debriefing Some students may just write the inequality $40x \geq 300$. You can show them that this inequality is equivalent to $40x + 300 \geq 600$ when you subtract 300 from each side. Students will need to round their solution to a whole number.

Suggested Assignment

CHECK YOUR UNDERSTANDING
p. 106, #1–4

UNIT 2 PRACTICE
p. 111, #29–31

TEACHER TO TEACHER This portion of the activity leads students to understand that multiplication or division by a negative number reverses the inequality.

15-16 Create Representations
Students complete a table where the values decrease as the months increase. If they are stuck when it comes to writing the expression, you may need to focus them on how many times $40 has been taken away from the starting balance.

17 Create Representations, Simplify the Problem, Debriefing

18 Create Representations
Students write the inequality that can be solved to determine during which months the account will stay above the $50 mark.

My Notes

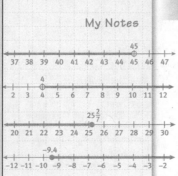

13. Go back to question 5 and graph the solutions to each inequality on a number line. Use the My Notes space.

14. Kevin has to pay for camp by June 1st. Will he have enough money saved? Write an inequality to help you answer this question.

   $40x + 300 \geq 600$ when $x \geq 7.5$. Eight months after August 1st is April 1st. So Kevin will have the money he needs by April 1st, in time for the June 1st deadline.

Kevin's grandmother, Mrs. Reynoso, is also helping Kerry, Kevin's sister, pay for guitar lessons. She has set up a special savings account to pay for the lessons. On the first of each month, the $40 monthly fee for guitar lessons is withdrawn from the account.

15. Grandmother Reynoso started the account with $300. Record the monthly balance in the account in the table below.

Month	Balance
0	$300
1	$260
2	$220
3	$180
4	$140

16. Use the table to write an expression for the amount of money in Kerry's guitar lesson account. Let x equal the number of months since Mrs. Reynoso deposited the $300. $300 - 40x$

17. Write and solve an equation to figure out when the account balance will equal $100. $300 - 40x = 100$ when $x = 5$

The bank will close the account if the balance falls below $50. To keep the account open, the balance must be greater than or equal to $50.

Balance ≥ 50

18. Substitute the expression you wrote in Question 16 for the balance.

   $300 - 40x \geq 50$

SUGGESTED LEARNING STRATEGIES: Create Representations, Simplify the Problem, Quickwrite, Mark the Text, Question the Text

My Notes

19. Based on the table in Question 15, write an inequality that represents the months when the account balance is greater than or equal to $50.

$$x \le \underline{\quad 6 \quad}$$

20. Solve the inequality in Question 18. Is the solution you found possible? Explain.

Answers may vary. Sample answer: $x \ge 6.25$. This solution is not possible because the money in the account is decreasing every month.

You learned before that solving an inequality is similar to solving an equation. However, there is one major difference when negative numbers are involved.

21. This investigation will help you understand what happens to an inequality when you multiply or divide both sides by a negative number.

   a. Start with this inequality: $4 < 7$

   b. Graph the points 4 and 7 on a number line.

   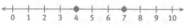

   c. From the graph, how do you know that 4 is less than 7?

   Four is located to the left of 7.

   d. Multiply 4 and 7 by -1.

   $(-1)(4) = -4;\ (-1)(7) = -7$

   e. Graph both of the resulting numbers on a number line.

   f. Write an inequality that represents this relationship between the two negative numbers.

   $-4 > -7$

   g. How does the direction of the inequality symbol in part f compare to the original $4 < 7$?

   The inequality symbol is reversed.

TEACHER TO TEACHER Students may find conflicting answers to Items 19 and 20. Which one is correct? When students examine the table, they should realize that the months, x, must be less than or equal to 6. However, when they attempt to solve the inequality like they would an equation, they may make the following error:

$$300 - 40x \ge 50$$
$$-40x \ge -250$$
$$x \ge 6\frac{1}{4}$$

The failure to reverse the inequality sign in the final step makes it appear that x must be greater than or equal to $6\frac{1}{4}$. Item 21 will help to resolve this error.

Other students may correctly find that $250 \ge 40x$ and $6\frac{1}{4} \ge x$, but may misinterpret the inequality as meaning that the answer must be greater than or equal to $6\frac{1}{4}$.

19-20 Discussion Group, Quickwrite, Debriefing Students should work in groups on these questions. You want them to notice that the inequalities might indicate very different solution sets. Visual learners may benefit from you showing the class the different solutions graphically on a number line.

21 Marking the Text, Questioning the Text, Create Representations, Quickwrite, Debriefing This item will help students to understand why the inequality reverses when you consider the opposites of a pair of numbers.

22 **Create Representations, Quickwrite** You may wish to select pairs of numbers for different groups to work with. Make sure some students are using two negative numbers and some are using a positive and a negative number.

23 **Quickwrite, Debriefing** Make sure students clearly describe what happened as a result of their experiments on the previous page. The words they write here and in Item 24, the parallel item about division by −1, will be valuable to their understanding of the lesson.

24 **Create Representations, Quickwrite, Debriefing** This item extends the exploration to division by −1.

My Notes

SUGGESTED LEARNING STRATEGIES: Create Representations, Quickwrite

22. Repeat this investigation with any two numbers. Do you notice the same results?

Students should notice that the inequality symbol is reversed when any two numbers are selected.

23. Summarize in words what you discovered about multiplying both sides of an inequality by a negative number.

Students should notice that the inequality symbol is reversed when they multiply by −1.

24. Repeat this investigation using division.

a. Complete the steps of the investigation in Question 21 by dividing 4 and 7 by −1.

$4 < 7$

```
<--+---+---+---+-●-+---+---+-●-+---+---+---+-->
   0   1   2   3   4   5   6   7   8   9   10
```

$$\frac{4}{(-1)} = -4; \frac{7}{(-1)} = -7$$

```
<--+---+---+-●-+---+---+-●-+---+---+---+---+-->
 -10  -9  -8  -7  -6  -5  -4  -3  -2  -1   0
```

$-4 > -7$

b. Summarize in words what you discovered about dividing both sides of an inequality by a negative number.

Answers will vary. Sample answer: When you multiply or divide two numbers by a negative number the direction of the inequality symbol that relates them is reversed.

Solving and Graphing Inequalities
It Plays to Save

My Notes

EXAMPLE 2

Solve the inequality.

a. $30 - 4x \geq 5$.

Step 1:	Original inequality.	$30 - 4x \geq 5$
Step 2:	Subtract 30 from both sides.	$30 - 30 - 4x \geq 5 - 30$
		$-4x \geq -25$
Step 3:	Divide by -4 and reverse the inequality.	$\dfrac{-4x}{-4} \leq \dfrac{-25}{-4}$

Solution: $x \leq 6.25$

b. $4x - 50 - 8x < -70$

Step 1:	Original inequality.	$4x - 50 - 8x < -70$
Step 2:	Combine like terms.	$-4x - 50 < -70$
Step 3:	Add 50 to both sides.	$-4x - 50 + 50 < -70 + 50$
		$-4x < -20$
Step 4:	Divide by -4 and reverse the inequality.	$\dfrac{-4x}{-4} > \dfrac{-20}{-4}$

Solution: $x > 5$

TRY THESE B

Solve each inequality.

a. $-5x + 7 > 22$ $x < -3$ **b.** $2x - 8x + 5 \geq 16$ $x \leq \dfrac{-11}{6}$

c. $-3(x + 5) < -21$ $x > 2$ **d.** $11x - 12 \leq 3x + 76$ $x \leq 11$

25. Re-solve the guitar lesson account inequality $300 - 40x \geq 50$. Be sure to reverse the inequality when you divide by a negative number. How does your answer compare to your response to Question 19? $x \leq 6.25$ Comparisions may vary.

A more precise solution to the guitar lesson account problem would involve using a **compound inequality**, which expresses two or more inequalities. A compound inequality is expressed either as a *greater than* relationship or a *less than* relationship. A compound inequality cannot have a greater than and a less than relationship in it.

26. In Kerry's guitar lesson account, it would not make sense for the number of months to be a negative number. Write a compound inequality that would represent the months x when the account balance would be above $50. $0 < x < 7$; or $0 \leq x \leq 6.25$

> **CONNECT TO AP**
>
> In advanced math courses, you will use inequalities to describe a range of values over which certain conditions are true or false.

> **MATH TERMS**
>
> A **compound inequality** combines two inequalities. For example, $2 < x < 8$ is a compound inequality for the inequalities $x > 2$ and $x < 8$.

> **CONNECT TO LANGUAGE ARTS**
>
> A compound inequality is like a compound sentence. In mathematics, using "and" in a compound inequality means both inequalities are true.

TRY THESE B

Have students record the examples in their notebooks and work in their groups on the Try These B problems. Debrief these problems as a class before starting on the Check Your Understanding problems. Part d in Try These B does not require students to reverse the inequality. Make sure they are not automatically doing it all the time now.

Suggested Assignment

CHECK YOUR UNDERSTANDING
p. 106, #5–8

UNIT 2 PRACTICE
p. 111, #32–33

TEACHER TO TEACHER   Students are introduced to compound inequalities of the form $a < x < b$. A more in-depth treatment is saved for Algebra 1. Add compound inequality to your interactive word wall and record this vocabulary word in students' vocabulary organizer. For more advanced classes you could introduce compound inequalities like $x < 1$ or $x > 4$ as two non-overlapping intervals on the number line.

26 Create Representations This item provides a more specific solution to the guitar lesson problem. It would not make sense for x to be a negative number in this context.

Connect to AP

Students will use inequalities to name intervals in both AP Statistics and AP Calculus. Inequalities are useful when describing a range of values over which certain conditions are true or false. In calculus, when students are asked to identify where a function is increasing, they can use an inequality to name set of x-values where this behavior occurs. In statistics, confidence intervals are often expressed using compound inequalities.

TRY THESE C

Debrief after students graph the Try These C problems so they can see the different possibilities when graphing these types of inequalities.

Suggested Assignment

CHECK YOUR UNDERSTANDING
p. 106, # 9–12

UNIT 2 PRACTICE
p. 111, #34–35

27-28 Create Representations, Debrief.

CHECK YOUR UNDERSTANDING

1. $x < -23$

2. $x \geq 75$

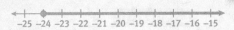

3. $x > 62.5$

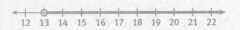

4. $x > 2$

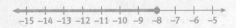

5. $x > -4$

6. $x \geq -24$

7. $x > 13$

8. $x \leq -8$

9. $x > 24$ days

SUGGESTED LEARNING STRATEGIES: Mark the Text, Create Representations, Create Representations

My Notes

Compound inequalities can also be graphed on a number line.

EXAMPLE 3

Graph $-4 < x < 2$

Steps: Place an open circle on -4 and 2. Shade the portion of the number line between the left and right endpoints.

Solution: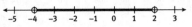

TRY THESE C

Graph each compound inequality on a number line.

a. $0 < x < 4$ **b.** $-1 \leq x \leq 5$ **c.** $-3 < x \leq 0.5$

27. Write a compound inequality for the graph shown below.

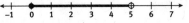 $0 \leq x < 5$

28. Write an inequality for each of the sentences below.

a. All the numbers between -4 and 5 including 5. $-4 < x \leq 5$

b. All numbers less than 3 but greater than -5. $-5 < x < 3$

CHECK YOUR UNDERSTANDING

Write your answers on notebook paper. Show your work.

Solve each inequality. Graph the solution on a number line.

1. $x + 15 < -8$

2. $\frac{2}{5}x \geq 30$

3. $2x - 50 > 75$

4. $15x + 20 > 50$

5. $-4x + 10 < 26$

6. $5 - \frac{2}{3}x \leq 21$

7. $3x + 70 - 7x < 18$

8. $18 \leq -6x - 30$

9. Arianna's mom deposits \$80 in her lunch money account. Lunch costs \$2.50 per day. When will there be less than \$20 left in Arianna's lunch account?

Write and graph a compound inequality that represents each situation described below.

10. The high temperatures last July varied from a low of 82° to a high of 112°.

11. The scores on Mrs. Jimenez' last test went from a low of 62% to a high of 98%.

12. MATHEMATICAL REFLECTION How do solutions of inequalities and equations compare? How does solving an inequality compare to solving an equation?

10. $82 \leq x \leq 112$

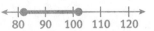

11. $62 \leq x \leq 98$

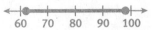

12. Answers may vary. Sample answer: The solutions to an equation are finite. The solutions to an inequality are infinite. Solving for the two is similar, until you multiply or divide by a negative number, or start graphing your solution.

Equations and Inequalities

A GOLD MEDAL APPETITE

Some male athletes, while in training for the Olympics, reportedly eat anywhere from 8000 to 10,000 calories per day.

1. Graph and write a compound inequality that represents the calories such an athlete eats in one day. Let c stand for the daily intake of calories.

Suppose the athlete eats three meals a day and consumes the same number of calories at each meal.

2. Write and solve an inequality that will tell you the calories he eats per meal if he consumes at least 8000 calories per day. Let m equal his calories in one meal.

To maintain his weight, the athlete needs to take in as many calories as he burns each day. On one day, he burns 1000 calories per hour while swimming and 3000 calories when he is not swimming.

3. Write and solve an equation to estimate the number of hours he swims per day. Use 9000 calories for his daily calorie intake.

$$\boxed{\begin{array}{c}\text{Calories Burned}\\\text{When Swimming}\end{array}} + \boxed{\begin{array}{c}\text{Calories Burned}\\\text{Not Swimming}\end{array}} = 9000$$

4. One way to judge a person's fitness level is to compute their body mass index (BMI). Body mass index is given by the formula $B = \dfrac{703w}{h^2}$, where B is the BMI, h is height in inches and w is weight in pounds.

  a. Use the formula to calculate the athlete's BMI if he is 76 inches tall and weighs 195 lbs.

  b. Solve the BMI formula for the variable w.

  c. Suppose a person that is 60 inches tall has a BMI of 20. How much does the person weigh in pounds?

Embedded Assessment 2

Assessment Focus

- Writing and solving equations
- Writing, graphing, and solving inequalities
- Using formulas
- Solving literal equations

Materials

- Scientific calculator needed for Item 4

TEACHER TO TEACHER Students are given information regarding the daily calorie intake of an Olympic athlete. They write and solve two different types of inequalities similar to the work they did in Activity 2.5. They also use a verbal model to write and solve an equation. Finally, students use the Body Mass Index formula to answer questions that involve evaluating expressions and solving a literal equation for a specified variable.

1 Students just learned about compound inequalities in the last part of Activity 2.5.

2 Students will have to make the connection that eating 3 meals per day translates to the expression $3m$ in their inequality.

3 A verbal model is provided to help students build the equation. The steps to solve this equation are not difficult. The emphasis in this assessment is modeling.

4 Without the aid of a calculator this problem is unmanageable. If students do not have access to a scientific calculator, you can skip Item 4 or only have them do part b. The skills in this item were assessed to some extent in the first embedded assessment in this unit.

Embedded Assessment 2

TEACHER TO TEACHER You may wish to read through the rubric with students and discuss the differences in the expectation levels. Make sure students understand the meanings of any terms used.

Answer Key

1. $8000 \leq c \leq 10{,}000$

2. $3m \geq 8000$; $m \geq \frac{8000}{3}$

3. $1000x + 3000 = 9000$, $x = 6$. The athlete swims 6 hours per day.

4a. The athlete's BMI is about 24.

  b. $w = \frac{(Bh^2)}{703}$

  c. about 102 lbs

Equations and Inequalities
A GOLD MEDAL APPETITE

	Exemplary	Proficient	Emerging
Math Knowledge #1, 2, 3, 4a	The student: • Writes a compound inequality to represent calories eaten. (1) • Writes an inequality to show calories in one meal. (2) • Writes an equation to estimate hours he swims per day. (3). • Calculates his BMI using the formula and given information. (4a)	The student attempts all four of the items but is able to answer only three of them correctly and completely.	The student attempts at least three of the items but is able to answer only one of them correctly and completely.
Problem Solving #2, 3, 4c	The student: • Solves the inequality for calories in one meal. (2) • Solves the equation to estimate hours he swims per day. (3) • Solves the BMI equation for *w*. (4c)	The student attempts all three of the items but is able to answer only two of them correctly and completely.	The student attempts at least two of the items but is able to answer only one of them correctly and completely.
Representation #1, 4b	The student: • Graphs the compound inequality that represents the calories he eats in one day. (1) • Rewrites the BMI equation solving for *w*. (4b)	The student responds to both items answering only one item correctly and completely.	The student responds to at least one item, but the answer is incorrect or incomplete.

ACTIVITY 2.1

Pattern blocks can be used to make tile patterns.

1. What is the perimeter of each figure shown? Assume each side is 1 unit. Draw the next 3 figures. What would be the perimeter of the tenth figure? Explain how you know.

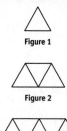

Figure 1

Figure 2

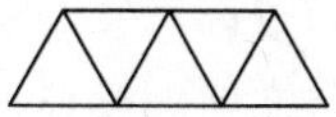

Figure 3

2. What is the perimeter of each figure shown? Assume each side is 1 unit. Draw the next three figures. What would be the perimeter of the tenth figure? Explain how you know.

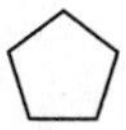

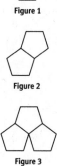

Figure 1

Figure 2

Figure 3

3. Write expressions using the variable n which can be used to find the perimeters of the nth figures in Questions 1 and 2. Use the expressions to determine the perimeter of the 50th figure.

4. Given the pattern of unit squares shown below. What is the area of each figure if each small square has an area of 1? Draw the next three figures in the pattern and find their area. What is the area of the tenth figure? Write an expression which can be used to find the area of the nth figure.

Figure 1

Figure 2

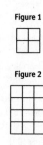

Figure 3

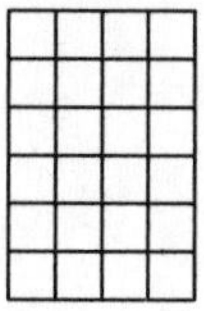

Activity 2.1

1. Perimeter of the first three figures is 3, 5, and 7 units. The perimeter of the 10th figure is 21 units. You begin with a perimeter of 3 in the first figure, and add 2 units 9 times.

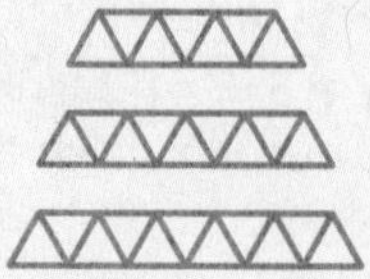

2. The perimeter of the first three figures is 5, 8, and 11 units. The perimeter of the 10th figure would be 32. You begin with a perimeter of 5 in figure 1, and add three units 9 times.

  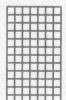

3. Question 1: $2n + 1$. The perimeter of the 50th figure is 101 units. Question 2: $3n + 2$. The perimeter of the 50th figure is 152 units.

4. Fig 1: 4 square units, Fig 2: 12 square units, Fig 3: 24 square units. Fig 4: 40 square units, Fig 5: 60 square units, Fig 6: 84 square units. The area of the 10th figure is 220 square units. The area of the nth figure is $(n + 1)(2n)$.

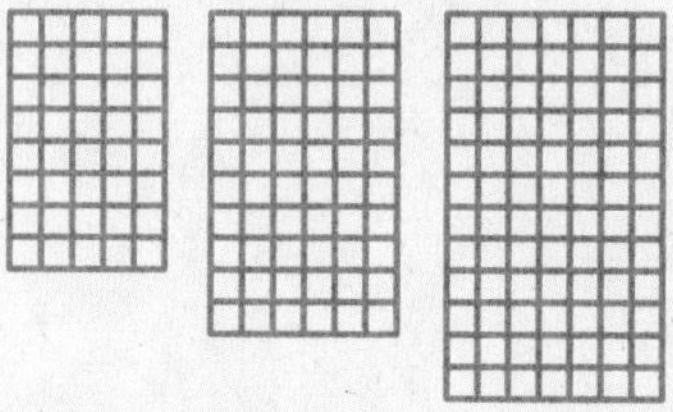

Activity 2.2

5. $x = 36$

6. $x = 60$

7. $x = 10$

8. $x = 3$

9. $x = 8$

10. $x = 24$

Activity 2.2 *(continued)*

11. $x = 11$

12. $x = 9$

13. $x = -1.1$

14. $x = 5$

15. $x + x + 9 = 25$; 17 inches fell in January and 8 inches fell in February.

16. $3x + 5 = 41$. Maria sold 12 discount cards the first week.

Activity 2.3

17a. False. Subtraction is not commutative.

b. False. The distributive property requires both numbers to be multiplied by 5.

c. False. There is an addition sign between the 5 and the 7x so it is not an example of distributive property.

18a. 20.5

b. −5

c. −3

19a. $y = 5 - 2x$

b. $c = d - ab$

c. $m = \frac{E}{c^2}$

ACTIVITY 2.2

Solve each equation.

5. $x - 11 = 25$

6. $\frac{x}{6} = 10$

7. $2x + 3 = 23$

8. $30 = 3x + 21$

9. $5x + 8 = 48$

10. $6 + \frac{x}{2} = 18$

11. $12 + 3x = 45$

12. $5x + 6 = 51$

13. $2.3 - 5x = 7.8$

14. $8x - 4 - 3x = 21$

15. Twenty-five inches of snow fell in January and February. Nine more inches fell in January than in February. How many inches of snow fell each month?

16. Maria sold a total of 41 discount cards for a choir fundraiser. She sold the same amount the first 3 weeks but only 5 the last week. How many did she sell the first week?

ACTIVITY 2.3

17. Classify each statement as true or false. Explain why.

a. $2 - x = x - 2$

b. $5(x + 3) = (5x) + 3$

c. $5 + (7x + 8) = 5(7x) + 5(8)$

18. Evaluate each expression for $a = -3$, $b = 5$, and $c = \frac{1}{2}$.

a. $2a^2 + bc$

b. $a - b + 6c$

c. $\frac{ab}{3 + 4c}$

19. Solve each equation for the indicated variable.

a. $2x + y = 5$, for y

b. $ab + c = d$, for c

c. $E = mc^2$, for m

20. Solve the equation $5(x - 3) = 50$ and justify each step using a property of numbers or a property of equality.

---

20. $5(x - 3) = 50$	Original equation
$5x - 15 = 50$	Distributive Property
$5x - 15 + 15 = 50 + 15$	Addition Property of Equuality
$5x + 0 = 65$	Additive Inverse Property
$5x = 65$	Additive Identity Property
$5x/5 = \frac{65}{5}$	Division Property of Equality
$1x = 13$	Multiplicative Inverse Property
$x = 13$	Multiplicative Identity Property.

ACTIVITY 2.4

Solve each equation.

21. $2x + 8 = 16$

22. $35 = 3x + 14$

23. $2x + 7 + 2x = 19$

24. $7x + 8 = 3x + 24$

25. $8x - 11 = 5x + 41$

26. $2(x - 11) = 6(x + 3)$

27. $5 - 2(x + 5) = 30$

28. $3.5x - 20 = 2.4x + 13$

ACTIVITY 2.5

Solve each inequality and graph the solution on a number line.

29. $15x > -60$

30. $7x + 18 \geq 25$

31. $-2x + 28 + 6x > 42$

32. $\frac{-x}{5} + 12 > 14$

33. $16 - 5x \geq 41$

34. Write a compound inequality that represents all the numbers between -2 and 5. Graph the inequality on a number line.

35. Maurice will earn a bonus if his weekly sales are greater than \$1000. If he works 5 days a week, how much will he need to sell per day to meet this goal? Write an inequality to help you solve this problem.

Activity 2.4

21. $x = 4$

22. $x = 7$

23. $x = 3$

24. $x = 4$

25. $x = \frac{52}{3}$

26. $x = -10$

27. $x = -17.5$

28. $x = 30$

Activity 2.5

29. $x > -4$

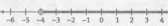

30. $x \geq 1$

31. $x > \frac{7}{2}$

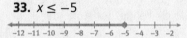

32. $x < -10$

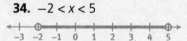

33. $x \leq -5$

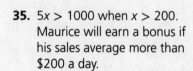

34. $-2 < x < 5$

35. $5x > 1000$ when $x > 200$. Maurice will earn a bonus if his sales average more than \$200 a day.

Reflection

Student Reflection

Discuss the essential questions with students. Have them share how their understanding of the questions has changed through studying the concepts in the unit.

Review the academic vocabulary. You may want students to revisit the graphic organizers they have completed for academic vocabulary terms and add other notes about their understanding of terms.

Encourage students to evaluate their own learning and to recognize the strategies that work best for them. Help them identify key concepts in the unit and to set goals for addressing their weaknesses and acquiring effective learning strategies.

Teacher Reflection

1. Of the key concepts in the unit, did any present special challenges for students?

2. How will you adjust your future instruction for students/ activities?

3. Which strategies were most effective for facilitating student learning?

4. When you teach this unit again, what will you do differently?

Reflection

An important aspect of growing as a learner is to take the time to reflect on your learning. It is important to think about where you started, what you have accomplished, what helped you learn, and how you will apply your new knowledge in the future. Use notebook paper to record your thinking on the following topics and to identify evidence of your learning.

Essential Questions

1. Review the mathematical concepts and your work in this unit before you write thoughtful responses to the questions below. Support your responses with specific examples from concepts and activities in the unit.
   - How are the properties of real numbers useful when solving equations and simplifying expressions?
   - What are the similarities and differences in the procedures for solving and expressing the solutions of equations and inequalities?

Academic Vocabulary

2. Look at the following academic vocabulary words:

   - equation
   - inverse operation
   - property
   - expression
   - literal equation
   - sequence
   - inequality
   - n^{th}
   - solution

   Choose three words and explain your understanding of each word and why each is important in your study of math.

Self-Evaluation

3. Look through the activities and Embedded Assessments in this unit. Use a table similar to the one below to list three major concepts in this unit and to rate your understanding of each.

Unit Concepts	Is Your Understanding Strong (S) or Weak (W)?
Concept 1	
Concept 2	
Concept 3	

   a. What will you do to address each weakness?

   b. What strategies or class activities were particularly helpful in learning the concepts you identified as strengths? Give examples to explain.

4. How do the concepts you learned in this unit relate to other math concepts and to the use of mathematics in the real world?

Additional Notes

1. Which graph represents the solution to $2x \geq -16$?

   F. ↔———————————————→
   −17 −16 −15 −14 −13 −12 −11 −10 −9 −8 −7

   G. ↔———————————————→
   −17 −16 −15 −14 −13 −12 −11 −10 −9 −8 −7

   H. ↔———————————————→
   −17 −16 −15 −14 −13 −12 −11 −10 −9 −8 −7

   J. ↔———————————————→
   −17 −16 −15 −14 −13 −12 −11 −10 −9 −8 −7

   1. Ⓕ **Ⓖ** Ⓗ Ⓘ

2. What is greatest integer value that will make
   $-5x + 9 \geq 44$ true?

   2.

Read
Solve
Explain

3. Nini wrote the formula $s = 8.50h - 25$ to help her determine how much money she will have to spend for the week. The variable h represents the number of hours she baby-sits, and s represents what she may spend. She will save the remaining amount.

   Part A: Rewrite the equation in terms of hours, h. What is the meaning of 25?

   Solve and Explain

   $s = 8.50h - 25; \; s + 25 = 8.50h; \; \dfrac{s + 25}{8.50} = h$

   The 25 represents money that Nini will not spend. Her

   spending money is the total amount earned 8.5h minus

   the 25 dollars she will not spend.

   Part B: Nini baby sits every saturday for 4.5 hours. She wants to spend $50 for a new outfit. How many saturdays must she work to have $50 to spend?

   Solve and Explain

   $50 = 8.50h - 25$

   $50 + \dfrac{25}{8.5} = 8.8$ hours.

   She must work two Saturdays.

These two pages provide practice with four standardized test question formats that are used in many national and state high-stakes tests:

- Multiple choice
- Gridded response
- Short response
- Extended response

These items also provide practice with the mathematics content of this unit.

1 Multiple choice
- Graph single variable inequalities

2 Gridded Response
- Solve inequalities

3 Short Response
- Solve linear equations
- Interpret the meaning of variables

4 Extended response
- Write expressions and equations from verbal problems

TEACHER TO TEACHER: You might read through the extended-response item with students and discuss your expectation levels. Make sure students understand the meanings of any terms used.

Read
Solve
Explain

4. Juli and Javier started saving money for their 8th grade trip at the same time. Juli started with $50 and saved $5 a week. Javier did not have any money saved but began saving $10 a week.

Part A: Create a table to display the amount each person will have saved weekly for 5 weeks.

Week	1	2	3	4	5
Juli	55	60	65	70	75
Javier	10	20	30	40	50

Part B: Write an expression for each person that shows what he or she will have saved in *w* weeks.

Solve and Explain

Juli: $5w + 50$

Javier: $10w$

Part C: If the trip costs $85, determine how many weeks each student must save to pay for their trip. Show your work or explain in words how you got your answer.

Answer and Explain

Juli: $85 = 5w + 50$

$35 = 5w$

$w = 7;$ 7 weeks

Javier: $85 = 10w$

$w = 8.5;$ 9 weeks

In prior units, students have explored patterns, deepened their understanding of fundamental number and operations concepts, and have learned to solve multi-step equations and inequalities. This unit continues the exploration of linear relationships through the introduction of functions, slope-intercept form of linear equations, horizontal and vertical slopes, linear inequalities, and systems of linear equations.

Academic Vocabulary

Blackline masters for use in developing students' vocabulary skills are located at the back of this Teacher's Edition. Encourage students to explore the meanings of the academic vocabulary words in this unit, using graphic organizers and class discussions to help students understand the key concepts related to the terms. Encourage students to place their vocabulary organizers in their math notebooks and to revisit these pages to make notes as their understanding of concepts increases.

Embedded Assessments

The three Embedded Assessments for this unit follow Activities 3.2, 3.5, and 3.7.

Algebra/AP/College Readiness

Unit 3 continues to develop algebraic and graphical representations of linear and nonlinear relationships and provides deeper understanding of linear functions and inequalities by:

- Providing contextual situations for students to investigate functions and relations and apply the concepts to an appropriate domain and range.

- Giving students opportunities to represent linear functions in a variety of forms; graphical, algebraic, analytic, and verbal.

- Allowing students to differentiate between discrete and continuous data.

- Modeling applications of bivariate data, trend lines, and correlations through physical experimentation.

- Offering students opportunities to communicate about mathematics verbally, visually, and in writing.

Embedded Assessment 1	Education Pays

- Linear relationships
- Function vs. relation
- Discrete vs. continuous

Embedded Assessment 2	Linear Kindness

- x- and y-intercepts
- Graphing an equation of a line in slope-intercept form
- Finding the equation of a line given a table
- Finding the equation of a line given a graph

Embedded Assessment 3	Is It Hot in Here or Is It Me?

- Bivariate data association
- Systems of equations

Suggested Pacing

The following table provides suggestions for pacing either a 45-minute period or a block schedule class of 90 minutes. Space is left for you to write your own pacing guidelines based on your experiences in using the materials.

	45-Minute Period	90-Minute Period	Comments on Pacing
Unit Overview	$\frac{1}{2}$	$\frac{1}{4}$	
Activity 3.1	4	2	
Activity 3.2	3	$1\frac{1}{2}$	
Embedded Assessment 1	1	$\frac{1}{2}$	
Activity 3.3	5	$2\frac{1}{2}$	
Activity 3.4	4	2	
Activity 3.5	3	$1\frac{1}{2}$	
Embedded Assessment 2	1	$\frac{1}{2}$	
Activity 3.6	5	$2\frac{1}{2}$	
Activity 3.7	3	$1\frac{1}{2}$	
Embedded Assessment 3	1	$\frac{1}{2}$	
Total	$30\frac{1}{2}$	$15\frac{1}{4}$	

Unit Practice

Practice Problems for each activity in the unit appear at the end of the unit.

Math Standards Review

To help accustom students to the formats and types of questions they may encounter on high stakes tests, additional problems are provided at the end of the unit. These problems are constructed for multiple choice, short response, extended response, and gridded responses.

Equations and the Coordinate Plane

Unit 3

Unit Overview

In this unit you will compare and contrast linear and non-linear patterns and write expressions to represent these patterns. You will study functions, domain, range, slope, and forms of linear equations. You will model and solve problems involving systems of equations and you will collect and analyze bivariate data.

Academic Vocabulary

Add these words to your vocabulary notebook.

- bivariate data
- continuous data
- discrete data
- domain
- function
- linear data
- range
- rate of change
- relation
- slope
- solution to a system of linear equations
- system of linear equations
- trend line
- *x*-intercept
- *y*-intercept

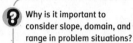

Essential Questions

? Why is it important to consider slope, domain, and range in problem situations?

? How can graphs be used to interpret solutions of real world problems?

EMBEDDED ASSESSMENTS

This unit has three Embedded Assessments—after Activities 3.2, 3. 5, and 3.7. These embedded assessments allow you to demonstrate your understanding of linear relations and linear equations, systems of equations, and applications of bivariate data.

Embedded Assessment 1

Linear Relationships and Functions   p. 135

Embedded Assessment 2

Slopes and Intercepts   p. 161

Embedded Assessment 3

Bivariate Data and Systems   p. 175

115

Unit Overview

Ask students to read the unit overview and mark the text to identify key phrases that indicate what they will learn in this unit. Ask them to relate the concepts to topics they have studied in previous courses.

Essential Questions

Read the essential questions with students. Remind students to think about these questions as they work through the unit.

Materials

- Beans
- Cube template
- Cone template
- Ruler or measuring tape
- 16 oz water bottle per group
- Large cup or bucket
- Marker
- A tool to poke a hole in the bottle
- Stop watch
- A doll for each group
- A small rock or weight for each group
- Rubber bands (new)
- Meter Stick or tape measure
- Graph Paper
- Calculator

Academic Vocabulary

Read through the vocabulary list with students. Assess prior knowledge by asking students if they can define any of the terms. Monitor student vocabulary entries for completeness and understanding of words from this and previous units.

You may wish to assign some or all of these exercises to gauge students' readiness for Unit 3 topics.

Prerequisite Skills
- Meaning of linear (Items 1, 3)
- Ordered pairs (Items 2, 4)
- x-, y-intercepts (Item 5)
- Plotting points (Item 6)
- Horizontal and vertical lines (Item 7)
- Ratio (Item 8)

Answer Key

1. Students should draw a line, or points through which a line can be drawn

2. Answers will vary. (0, 0), (20, 4), (25, 5), (30, 6), (35, 7)

3. The output for 1 is 2. The output for 4 is 14.

4. Sample answers: (0, 1), (1, 3), (2, 5)

5a. It crosses the x-axis at (−8, 0).

 b. It crosses the y-axis at (0, 4).

6a. See graph.

 b. T (4, 1)

7. Check that students have drawn one vertical and one horizontal line. See graph.

8. $\frac{5}{9}$, 5:9, or 5 to 9

Write your answers on notebook paper. Show your work.

1. On the grid below, draw a figure that illustrates the meaning of linear.

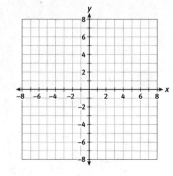

2. Name five ordered pairs that would be on a graph made from the following table.

input	output
5	1
10	2
15	3

3. Complete the table below so that the data is linear.

input	output
1	
2	6
3	10
4	

4. Name 3 ordered pairs that satisfy the equation $y = 2x + 1$.

5. A line contains the points (2, 5) and (4, 6):
 a. Where does it cross the x-axis?
 b. Where does it cross the y-axis?

6. Use the graph below to:
 a. Plot and label the points $R(3, 5)$ and $S(6, 0)$.
 b. Give the coordinates of point T.

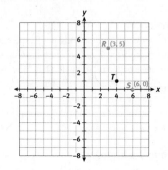

7. Draw a horizontal line that contains the point (2, 3) and a vertical line that contains (1, 4).

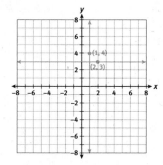

8. Write a ratio that compares the shaded region in the figure below to all the regions.

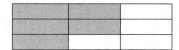

Linear and Non-Linear Patterns
Fill It Up

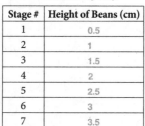

SUGGESTED LEARNING STRATEGIES: Predict and Confirm, Use Manipulatives, Create Representations, Look for a Pattern, Quickwrite

My Notes

Using the template that your teacher gave you, create the cube and cone, which you will use in an experiment. You will be filling the cube and the cone by adding 20 beans at a time. Before you begin the experiment, make the following predictions.

1. Predict how many groups of 20 beans you can add to the cube until it is full. Answers may vary.

2. Predict how many groups of 20 beans you can add to the cone until it is full. Answers may vary.

3. Are your predictions different? Explain how the shape of the figure affected your predictions. Answers may vary.

Do the following experiment for the cube. Each stage of the experiment consists of 3 steps. Each time you complete the three steps you complete a stage.

Step 1:   Add 20 beans to the cube.

Step 2:   Shake the figure gently to allow the beans to settle.

Step 3:   Measure the height of the beans in centimeters.

4. Complete the experiment for the cube. Answers may vary.

a. Enter the data in the table.
   Sample data:

Stage #	Height of Beans (cm)
1	0.5
2	1
3	1.5
4	2
5	2.5
6	3
7	3.5

b. Do you see a pattern in the data in the table?
   Sample answer: The height is increasing at a constant rate.

c. Plot the values from the table on the grid.

d. Looking at the graph, what do you notice about the relationship between the stage number and the height of the beans?
   Sample answer: They are both increasing.

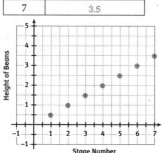

Unit 3 • Equations and the Coordinate Plane   117

TEACHER TO TEACHER The experiments were done using black beans. If you choose to use another type of bean, you may want to change the number of beans used per stage. For example, using lentils will work well, but to match the tables and graphs in this book, students would need to use about 40 lentils per stage.

Suggested Assignment

CHECK YOUR UNDERSTANDING
p. 124, #1

UNIT 3 PRACTICE
p. 177, #1

Linear and Non-Linear Patterns

Activity Focus
- Number patterns
- Linear vs. Non-linear patterns
- Multiple representations of data

Materials
- Beans
- Cube template, BLM 21
- Cone template, BLM 22
- Ruler or measuring tape

Chunking the Activity

#1–3	#8–9	#16–17
#4	#10	#18–19
#5	#11	#20
#6	#12	
#7	#13–15	

1-2 Predict and Confirm Have students create the cube and cone using the templates given. These templates can be used with normal paper, but card stock is more effective for supporting the beans. To save time, you may want to assign creating the cube and cone as homework before class.

3 Quickwrite This is meant to get students to think about how the shape of the object will affect how quickly it will fill. This can help students identify linear vs. non-linear patterns as the lesson continues.

4 Use Manipulatives, Create Representations, Look for a Pattern, Quickwrite, Debrief Students will do the "fill it up" experiment and measure the height of the beans at the completion of each stage. For Part c, some students may need to be reminded that each row of the table translates into an ordered pair for the graph. Students should be able to recognize that the change in data is constant.

TEACHER TO TEACHER A common misconception for students is that all patterns are linear. This misconception manifests in different ways throughout their mathematical education. Having them explore the concept of non-linearity physically will help some students grasp the concept better. This will make the concept more accessible later on.

5 Use Manipulatives, Create Representations, Look for a Pattern, Quickwrite, Debrief Students will follow the same experiment they performed in Item 4 with the cone. They should see that the rate at which the height increases is not constant as the stage number increases. This will allow students to have a model of something that is non-linear as they progress through the course and into higher levels.

My Notes

SUGGESTED LEARNING STRATEGIES: Use Manipulatives, Create Representations, Look for a Pattern, Quickwrite

5. Complete the experiment for the cone.
   Answers may vary.

   a. Fill in the table for each stage and plot the points on the grid.

Sample data:

Stage #	Height of Beans (cm)
1	1
2	1.9
3	2.5
4	3
5	3.2
6	3.4
7	3.5

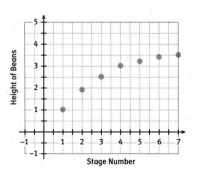

b. Look at the data in the table. What, if any, patterns do you notice?
   Sample answer: As the stage number increases the height increases, but at smaller values.

c. Look at the graph. What patterns do you notice about the relationship between the stage number and the height of the beans?
   Sample answer: As the stage number increases, the graph flattens out.

Linear and Non-Linear Patterns
Fill It Up

SUGGESTED LEARNING STRATEGIES: Create Representations, Look for a Pattern, Quickwrite

My Notes

The following data was collected as beans were added to a cylinder.

Stage #	Height of Beans (cm)
1	3
2	6
3	9
4	12
5	15
6	18
7	21

6. Plot the points on the grid for the cylinder.

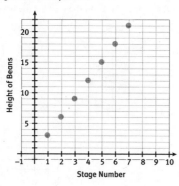

a. What patterns do you notice for the data in the table?

For each additional stage there is an increase in the height of 3 cm.

b. Looking at the graph, what patterns do you notice about the relationship between the stage number and the height of the beans?

Sample answer: The points look like a line can connect them.

c. What conjecture can you make about the **rate of change** of the height of the beans as the stages increase?

For each additional stage there in an increase in the height of 3 cm; the rate of change is constant.

ACADEMIC VOCABULARY

The **rate of change** in a relationship represents the ratio of vertical change in the output to the horizontal change in the input. The output is often represented by the variable y. The input is often represented by the variable x.

TEACHER TO TEACHER Discussions of what "rate of change" means should take place after students have completed their graphs for Item 6. While you should not extend the idea to slope yet, you do want students to look at how the dependent variable data changes with respect to the independent variable data. It is important that students think of the "rate of change" as a *rate* and not just a number. Referring to other real world examples of rates of change (speed limits, download/upload speeds for songs, or beats per minute in music) can be helpful.

6 Create Representations, Look for a Pattern, Quickwrite, Debrief This Item allows students to continue to investigate patterns that could be linear or non-linear, but transitions them out of the experiment. Students go through the same progression as that for Items 4 and 5.

Suggested Assignment

CHECK YOUR UNDERSTANDING
p. 124, #2

UNIT 3 PRACTICE
p. 177, #2

---

7 Create Representations, Look for a Pattern, Quickwrite, Debrief This data allows students to analyze a non-linear pattern. It may be helpful to discuss the concept of rate of change here, too. Refer to both the table and the graph and give representations of how the dependent variable data is changing with respect to the independent variable data.

My Notes

The following data was collected as beans were added to an irregular polyhedron.

Stage #	Height of Beans (cm)
1	1
2	2
3	5
4	10
5	15
6	18
7	19

7. Plot the points on the grid for the irregular polyhedron.

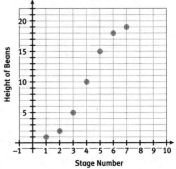

Answers may vary.

a. What patterns do you notice for the data in the table?

Sample answer: The height increases slowly, then more quickly, and finally more slowly.

b. Looking at the graph, what patterns do you notice about the relationship between the stage number and the height of the beans?

Sample answer: It is increasing but not at a constant rate.

c. What conjecture can you make about the *rate of change* of the height of the beans as the stage numbers increase?

Sample answer: The rate of change increases initially and then decreases.

SUGGESTED LEARNING STRATEGIES: Look for a Pattern, Quickwrite, Group Discussion, Group Presentation, Create Representations, Simplify a Problem

Answers may vary.

8. How does the rate of change from the cylinder experiment differ from the rate of change for the irregular polyhedron experiment?

Sample answer: The rate is constant for the cylinder, and the rate is changing for the irregular polyhedron.

9. Explain how the shape of the object affects the rate of change.

Sample answer: The wider the shape, the slower the rate of change. If the sides of the object are straight then the rate of change is constant.

10. If the height of the cylinder and the irregular polyhedron were extended indefinitely, explain how the height of the beans would change as the stage number increased.

Sample answer: For the cylinder, the height would increase by 3 cm every time. For the irregular polyhedron, the rate would continue to decrease so that the graph would flatten out.

11. The graphs and tables below show what happened when the bean experiment was performed with each of the vases shown. Match each vase to a graph and a table. Explain the reasoning behind your choices.

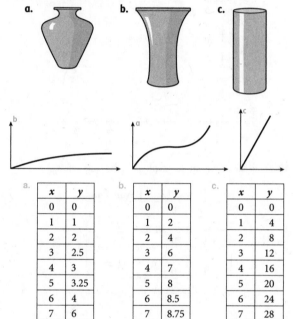

a.	x	y
	0	0
	1	1
	2	2
	3	2.5
	4	3
	5	3.25
	6	4
	7	6

b.	x	y
	0	0
	1	2
	2	4
	3	6
	4	7
	5	8
	6	8.5
	7	8.75

c.	x	y
	0	0
	1	4
	2	8
	3	12
	4	16
	5	20
	6	24
	7	28

My Notes

ACTIVITY **3.1** *Continued*

TEACHER TO TEACHER If you have students do group presentations, have them show differences in the rates of change using multiple representations. This will set them up for understanding the concept of a rate of change from multiple viewpoints. Have them try to attach the concept of rate of change to the shape of the solid. Having a physical connection to the concept will allow you to reference back to it as you progress through the rest of the course.

8-9 Look for a Pattern, Quickwrite, Group Discussion, Group Presentation Group presentations or discussions will allow students to see how others viewed the situation. If the discussion does not head in this direction on its own, lead students to talk about the ideas of constant rate of change versus rates that are increasing or decreasing.

10 Create Representations, Quickwrite This question is designed to get students to think about what happens to the graphs from Items 5 and 6 as the stage number approaches infinity. Students should see that the rate will always be constant for the cylinder, and the height will continue to increase without bound. For the irregular polyhedron, the wider the top gets, the less effect any additional beans will have on the height. So, graphically, the graph would flatten out.

11 Simplify a Problem, Look for a Pattern Students have the opportunity to practice within the same context and make connections to multiple representations.

Suggested Assignment

CHECK YOUR UNDERSTANDING
p. 124, #3–4

UNIT 3 PRACTICE
p. 177, #3–5

12 Think/Pair/Share, Quickwrite, Debrief This question can be used as a formative assessment to see if students understand the concept of constant rate of change versus non-constant rate of change.

13 Create Representations This is the first set of data with a negative rate of change.

My Notes

ACADEMIC VOCABULARY

linear data

Data is linear if it has a constant rate of change. When you plot the points of **linear data** on a coordinate plane, they lie on a straight line.

12. Compare and contrast the graphs and tables of the three figures in Item 10. Which of the figures appeared to encourage a *linear* relationship? Explain your reasoning. Answers may vary. Sample answer: The cylinder created a linear increase in height as beans were added. The graph formed a line, and the values in the table increased by the same amount every time. The other two vases have changing rates of change. Their graphs do not form a line.

A person is drinking water from a cylindrical cup using a straw. The following graph gives the height of the water at different time intervals.

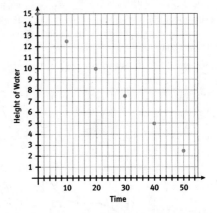

13. Using the data from the graph fill in the table below.

Time (sec)	Height (cm)
0	15
10	12.5
20	10
30	7.5
40	5
50	2.5

Linear and Non-Linear Patterns
Fill It Up

SUGGESTED LEARNING STRATEGIES: Quickwrite, Create Representations, Group Presentation, Identify a Subtask, Discussion Group

My Notes

14. Using the table, describe any patterns you see in the height of the water over time.

The height decreases by 2.5 cm every 10 seconds.

15. Is the relationship between time and the height of the water linear?

 a. Explain using the graph.

 Yes. Explanations may vary. Sample explanation: it is linear because you can draw a straight line through them; all the points lie on the same line.

 b. Explain using the table.

 Yes. Explanations may vary. Sample explanation: it is linear because the increase is constant.

16. What is the rate of change in the water level from 20 seconds to 30 seconds?

 $\dfrac{-2.5\ \text{cm}}{10\ \text{sec}}$

17. Connect the data points, and determine what the rate of change in the water level is from 20 seconds to 21 seconds.

 $\dfrac{-.25\ \text{cm}}{\text{sec}}$

18. Predict the height of the water at 25 seconds. How did you make your prediction? If you wanted to look at many different times, would your method still be effective?

 8.75 cm; Answers may vary. Sample answer: By using the rate of change per second and adding it 5 times to the values at $t = 20$ seconds.

19. Create an expression that gives the height of the water in terms of the time (t).

 $15 - 0.25t$

20. How long will it take for the water to completely empty out of the cup? Explain using multiple representations.

 60 seconds. Answer may vary.

14 Quickwrite As you circulate in the room, make sure students are seeing that the time interval is 10 seconds, and not just one second.

15 Create Representations, Quickwrite, Group Presentation The decimals and the fact that the independent variable increases by 10 makes this question more complicated for students to evaluate. If students struggle with this question, hold a group discussion. Lead the students to realize that the data is linear, referencing both the graph and the table.

16-17 Identify a Subtask, Discussion Group If students are forgetting to add the negative sign, remind them that the data is decreasing, and ask how they are accounting for that in their expressions. Remind struggling students that a rate of change is just a ratio. Lead them to understand that the ratio they are looking for is the change in height over the change in time.

TEACHER TO TEACHER If students struggle too much with Item 18, replace it with the mini-lesson. It scaffolds the process so that students can better see the expression being developed. It also encourages them to use multiple representations to help them as they progress in mathematics.

18 Quickwrite This question could be hard for students. Use the mini-lesson to help students who aren't able to make progress on their own.

19-20 Create Representations, Quickwrite, Debrief

Suggested Assignment

CHECK YOUR UNDERSTANDING
p. 124, #5–7

UNIT 3 PRACTICE
p. 177, #6–7

MINI-LESSON: Finding an Expression From Data

1. Have students fill in a table using their rate of change from Item 16.

2. Ask students what they do to the 15 to get 14.75. You want the answer, "Subtract 0.25." Ask what they would do to 15 to get 14.5. Guide them to say "subtract 0.25 twice" using the table as a reference. Continue this line of questioning until they answer readily. Ask students how many times they subtract 0.25 when t equals 10. Finally, how many times would they subtract 0.25 from 15 for t seconds? Point out that they have now derived an expression from the data, and that it can be used for any value of t.

t	h
0	15
1	14.75
2	14.5
3	14.25
10	12.5
t	15−0.25t

CHECK YOUR UNDERSTANDING

1. 4

2. −2

3. a is not linear; b is not linear

  a. The data constantly decreases at first, and then constantly increases.

  b. The data show two separate linear parts. But, together, that is not considered linear data since the same rule does not apply to all the data.

4. d

5.

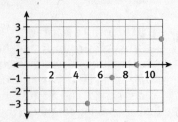

not linear

6. a, b, and d are linear. Explanations will vary, but should include multiple representations.

7. Answers will vary.

CHECK YOUR UNDERSTANDING

Write your answers on notebook paper. Show your work.

1. Find the rate of change for the table.

x	y
0	5
1	9
2	13
3	17
4	21
5	25
6	29
7	33

2. Find the rate of change for the table.

x	y
−2	6
−1	4
0	2
1	0
2	−2
3	−4
4	−6
5	−8

3. Determine which of the following tables displays linear data. Explain your reasoning.

a.

x	y
0	45
10	40
20	35
30	30
40	35
50	40
60	45
70	50

b.

x	y
−5	−2.5
−3	−5.5
−1	−8.5
1	−11.5
3	14.5
5	17.5
7	20.5
9	23.5

4. Which equation matches the data in the table?

  a. $y = x + 5$

  b. $x = y − 5$

  c. $y = 7x − 1$

  d. $y = 2x + 4$

x	y
1	6
2	8
3	10
4	12

5. Graph the following points and determine if the data is linear.

$$\{(5, −3), (7, −1), (9, 0), (11, 2)\}$$

6. Determine which of the following expressions displays a linear relationship. Use multiple representations to explain your reasoning.

  a. $2x$

  b. $−2x + 2$

  c. $x(4x)$

  d. $4 − 3x$

7. **MATHEMATICAL REFLECTION** In this activity, you explored three ways to represent linear data: in a table, graphically, and with an expression. Which representation of linear data do you understand most easily and why?

Functions
Who Am I?

SUGGESTED LEARNING STRATEGIES: Create Representations,
Quickwrite

Relationships can exist between different sets of information.
For example, the pairing of the names of students in your class
and their heights is one such relationship.

1. Collect the following information for 15 members of your class.
   Answers will vary.

Student Number	First Name	Height (cm)	Length of Index Finger (cm)
1			
2			
3			
4			
5			
6			
7			
8			
9			
10			
11			
12			
13			
14			
15			

2. Write the student numbers of 5 students in the class and their
   height in the following form: (Number, Height).
   Answers will vary.

My Notes

ACTIVITY 3.2 Guided

Functions

Activity Focus
- Relation
- Function
- Discrete and continuous data
- Domain and Range

Materials
- Ruler or measuring tape

Chunking the Activity

#1	#7	#11–12
#2	#8	#13
#3–4	#9	
#5–6	#10	

1-2 Create Representations,
Quickwrite Students collect
data for at least 15 students in
the class. They will use this data
to look at relations and functions.
One method to help collect the
data is to have student groups
collect their data and have one
member of the group bring all
their data to the board. Groups
can then add data from other
groups to their table.

TEACHER TO
TEACHER It is helpful for the rest of
the activity if there are at
least two heights that are the
same. If there are not, you may
want to invent one piece of data
to achieve this result. This will
affect the answer to Item 9 later
in the Activity.

3 Create Representations
Students review plotting points on a grid by plotting their data.

4 Think/Pair/Share, Debrief
Students will come up with many possibilities. Have them share their answers. They should be encouraged to look at relationships both forward and backward, for example, Length of Index Finger to Student Number, and Student Number to Length of Index Finger. There are 12 possible relationships in all.

> **Differentiating Instruction**
> Ask advanced students if any of the relationships they found resemble a linear pattern. Depending on data collection, height to finger length can be close to linear.

5 Create Representations This question is designed to get students to go beyond just identification of a relationship, and to identifying members of the set that represents the relationship.

SUGGESTED LEARNING STRATEGIES: Create Representations, Think/Pair/Share

My Notes

> **MATH TERMS**
> An **ordered pair** is two numbers written in a certain order. Most often, the term "ordered pair" will refer to the *x* and *y* coordinates of a point on the coordinate plane, which are always written (*x*, *y*). The term can also refer to any values paired together according to a specific order.

The number and height that you wrote for the five students in your class is called an **ordered pair**. Given the *input* (*x*) of a student's number, you can get an *output* (*y*) of that student's height. In a cartesian coordinate plane, ordered pairs are represented by (*x*,*y*).

3. Graph and label the coordinates of a point for each of the five ordered pairs you wrote in Question 2.

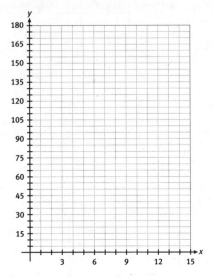

4. Using the information from the table, what other relationships can you create?
   Answers may vary. Possible answers: (First Name, Height), (Height, Length of Index Finger), (Student Number, First Name)

5. Using one of the relationships you described in Question 4 that contains numeric values only, create five ordered pairs of students in your class.
   Answers will vary but students should have 5 points.

SUGGESTED LEARNING STRATEGIES: Question the Text, Marking the Text, Vocabulary Organizer, Note Taking, Think/Pair/Share, Summarize/Paraphrase/Retell, Quickwrite

A **relation** is a **set** of ordered pairs. For example, the pairing of students' index finger length with their height is a relation. The set of all the starting values or inputs is called the **domain**. In a relation, all domain values must be matched with an output value. The set of all output values is called the **range**.

EXAMPLE 1

Find the domain and range of the following set:

$$\{(1,2), (2,4), (4,5), (8,3)\}$$

Step 1:   *Look at the first number in each pair to identify the domain.*

Step 2:   *Look at the second number in each pair to identify the range.*

Solution: The domain is $\{1, 2, 4, 8\}$, and the range is $\{2, 3, 4, 5\}$

TRY THESE A

Determine the domain and range of the following sets.

a. $\{(2,4), (2,5), (2,6), (2,7), (2,8)\}$

b. $\{(3,12), (4,12), (12,12), (1,8)\}$

6. From Question 1, what would be the domain of the relation that associates Length of Index Finger to Height?
   The set of values found in the Length of Index Finger column of their tables.

7. What would be the range of the relation that associates Length of Index Finger to Height?
   The set of values found in the Height column of their tables.

A function is a special kind of relation. Like a relation, a function must match an input to an output, but functions have the additional restriction that each element in the input can match only one element in the output.

8. Is the relation that associated student numbers and their height a function? Explain your reasoning.
   Yes, it is a function since for each input there is exactly one output.

My Notes

MATH TERMS
A **set** is a collection of objects, like points, or a type of number. The symbols { } indicate a set.

ACADEMIC VOCABULARY
domain
range
relation

ACTIVITY 3.2 Continued

TEACHER TO TEACHER Understanding a relation is an important step towards understanding functions. Impress upon students that all input values must be matched with an output in order for a set of associated values to be a relation. To help reinforce the definition of a relation, have several students share the relationships they created in Item 4. For each example shared, discuss why it fits the definition of a relation.

TRY THESE A These problems provide practice in identifying the domain and range of a set.

6-7 Think/Pair/Share, Debrief These questions act as a formative assessment for the concept of domain and range. Students may struggle if they fail to recognize that the expression, "the relation that associates Length of Index Finger to Height," is meant to imply that Length of Index Finger is the input.

Suggested Assignment

CHECK YOUR UNDERSTANDING
p. 134, #1–2

UNIT 3 PRACTICE
p. 177, #8–9

8 Quickwrite, Debrief This question should spur discussion regarding the concept that even though there are outputs that are the same value, for each input there is one and only one output.

TRY THESE A
a. Domain: {2};
    Range: {4, 5, 6, 7, 8}.
b. Domain: {1, 3, 4, 12};
    Range: {8, 12}

The Try These B problems are designed as a formative assessment. For those students that need more assistance with the function concept, this time will allow you to float and give support where necessary.

Part c can be difficult for some students to classify. A common misconception is that every *output* value can have only one *input* value.

TRY THESE B

a. Not a function

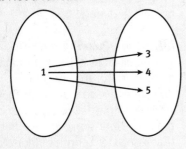

b. It is a function.

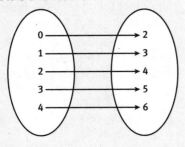

c. It is a function.

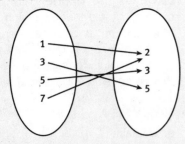

9 Create Representations, Quickwrite If you followed the *Teacher to Teacher* note from p. 125, the relation will not be a function.

My Notes

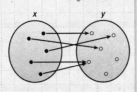

ACADEMIC VOCABULARY

A **function** is a special kind of relation in which each element of the domain is paired with exactly one element of the range.

CONNECT TO AP

Functions and relations, which describe how two varying quantities are related, form the basis of much of the work you will do in calculus.

SUGGESTED LEARNING STRATEGIES: Marking the Text, Vocabulary Organizer, Note Taking, Create Representations, Quickwrite

One type of representation that helps to determine if a relation is a function is a *mapping*. The illustration to the left is a mapping. The particular relation that was mapped is a **function**. Every input (*x*-value) is mapped to exactly one output (*y*-value). Note that a *y*-value can be associated with more than one *x*-value. Each input (*x*) has exactly one output (*y*).

EXAMPLE 2

Consider the relation {(1,2), (2,4), (4,5), (8,3)}.

Use mapping to determine if the relation is a function. Explain.

Step 1: Write all domain values in an oval.

Step 2: Write all range values in another oval.

Step 3: Connect the input values with their output values using arrows.

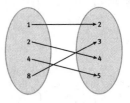

Solution: From the mapping, we can see that every element in the input set is mapped to exactly one element in the output set. Therefore, the relation is a function.

TRY THESE B

Use mapping to determine if the following are functions. Explain.

a. {(1,3), (1,4), (1,5)}

b. $x + 2$ for $x = \{0, 1, 2, 3, 4\}$

c.

x	1	3	5	7
y	2	5	3	2

9. Use mapping to determine if the relation that associates height to student number is a function. Explain your reasoning. If any two students are the same height, the relation is not a function.

Connect to AP

Functions and relations which describe how two varying quantities are related form the basis of virtually all the work students do in calculus. Students express these relationships algebraically and then use the techniques of differentiation and integration to solve problems related to how functions change and change accumulates.

My Notes

Another representation that helps to determine if a relation is a function is a *table*.

EXAMPLE 3

Determine if the following relations are functions.

a. {(1,2), (2,4), (4,2), (8,4)}.　　**b.** {(6,2), (6,3), (8,3)}

x	y
1	2
2	4
4	2
8	4

x	y
6	2
6	3
8	3

Step 1: *Look at the number of output values for each input.*

Solution: The relation A is a function since each input has only one output. The relation B is not a function because one input, 6, has two different outputs.

TRY THESE C

Determine if the following relations are functions. Explain why they are or are not.

a.

x	y
−3	2
5	5
2	8
3	−3
−5	−5
6	2
−2	5
8	8

b.

x	y
2	3
4	5
6	7
8	9
3	11
4	13
5	15
6	17

c.

x	y
−5	5
−4	4
−3	3
−2	2
−1	1
0	0
1	1
2	2

d.

x	y
−8	9
4	−5
−8	8
4	−4
−8	7
4	−3
−8	6
4	−2

10. Create a table of values that represents a function and a second table that does not represent a function. How would you identify any table that does not represent a function?

The table does not represent a function when there is an input value that appears more than once and has different output values.

Another representation that helps to determine if a relation is a function is *graphing*. An example on how to use graphing this way is on the next page.

TEACHER TO TEACHER Show students Example 3. Afterwards, have the class go back to the original data collection and look at which of the relations they created earlier are functions and which are not, based on their table.

TRY THESE C

a. It is a function since each input has only one output.

b. It is not a function since 4 and 6 have two outputs.

c. It is a function since each input has only one output.

d. It is not a functions since both 4 and −8 have multiple outputs.

10 Create Representations, Look for a Pattern, Group Presentation, Debrief Having students generate the table allows them to extend their understanding. Have them present their table and a generalized method for determining if the relation is a function.

ACTIVITY 3.2
continued   **Functions**
Who Am I?

TEACHER TO TEACHER Example 4 is a good time to discuss the *vertical line test* for determining if a graph is a function. This test can be especially helpful for students who have been struggling with other representations of functions. Remind them to use the test as they work through the Try These problems.

As extra practice, you may want to have students plot 5 data points for the relationship between Student Number and Height from their tables. Have a few groups share their graphs, and discuss whether or not they are functions.

TRY THESE D

a. It is not a function because at least one input has more than one output.

b. It is a function because each input has only one output.

c. It is not a function because one input has more than one output.

d. It is a function because each input has only one output.

My Notes

EXAMPLE 4

Determine which of the following graphs represents a function.

Step 1: *Plot the ordered pairs.*

Relation A
$\{(-2,-1), (-1,2), (0,0),$
$(1,-2), (2,2)\}$

Relation B
$\{(-1,-1), (-1,2), (0,0),$
$(1,2), (1,-2)\}$

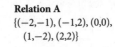

Step 2: *Look at the graph to determine if any of the x-values have more than one y-value.*

Solution: Relation A is a function since each input has only one output. Relation B is not a function because at least one input has two different outputs.

Relation C
$y = |x|$

Relation D
$x = y^2$

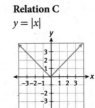 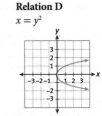

Solution: Relation C is a function since each input has only one output. Relation D is not a function because at least one input has two different outputs.

TRY THESE D

Which of the following graphs represent functions? Explain your reasoning.

a.

not a function

b.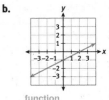

function

MATH TERMS

A function *increases* if its graph rises from left to right. A function *decreases* if its graph falls from left to right.

ACTIVITY 3.2 *Continued*

My Notes

11 Look for a Pattern, Debrief
This question gives students
the opportunity to verbalize the
concept of the vertical line test.

TEACHER TO
TEACHER
After students have
answered Item 11,
discuss the concept of the vertical
line test one last time to help
make sure students understand
and will remember this useful
tool.

Suggested Assignment

CHECK YOUR UNDERSTANDING
p. 134, #3–5

UNIT 3 PRACTICE
p. 177, #10–12

TRY THESE D (continued)

c.

not a function

d.

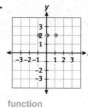

function

11. When looking at a graph of a relation, how can you determine
if it is a function?

Answers may vary. Sample answer: If you draw a vertical line
and it hits the graph in more than one place then the graph is
not a function.

Discrete data are data that can only have certain values such as the
number of people in your class. On a graph there will be a space
between every two possible values. **Continuous data** can take on
any value within a certain range; for example, height. On a graph
continuous data and continuous functions have no breaks, holes,
or gaps. In the following example, Function A is discrete and
Function B is continuous.

ACADEMIC VOCABULARY

Data are **discrete** if there
are only a finite number of
values possible or if there
is a space on the number
line or on a graph between
each 2 possible values.

Data are **continuous** if there
are no breaks in their domain
or range or if the graph has
no breaks, holes or gaps.

Function A

Function B

12 Shared Reading, Think/Pair/Share You may want to give a few examples of how the graphic organizer works to help students that are still struggling with the concept of a variable.

My Notes

Functions can be represented by expressions.

12. If a function that is represented by the expression $x + 5$ has inputs labeled x and outputs labeled y, then the diagram below represents the mapping from the input x to the output y.

a. If $x = 5$ is used as an input in the diagram, what it the output? 10

b. If $x = -3$ is used as an input in the diagram, what it the output? 2

c. If $x = 0.03$ is used as an input in the diagram, what it the output? 5.03

d. If $x = -\frac{1}{2}$ is used as an input in the diagram, what it the output? $4\frac{1}{2}$

e. Is there any limit to the number of input values that can be used with this expression? Explain your reasoning.
There is no limit; Answers may vary. Sample answer: There are no restrictions on the input.

f. Is the function discrete or continuous? Explain.
Continuous; Answers may vary. Sample answer: The function is continuous since there are no restrictions on the input and output of the function.

SUGGESTED LEARNING STRATEGIES: Activate Prior
Knowledge, Debrief

My Notes

Mr. Walker collected the following data about shoe size and height
from five members in his class.

Shoe Size	Approximate Height (in centimeters)
6	140
6.5	144
7	148
8	156
9.5	168

13. Consider the relation that associates the shoe size of one
of Mr. Walker's student to his or her approximate height.

a. Use a mapping to determine if the relation is a function.
Explain how you arrived at your answer.

Mapping with 6 going to 140
6.5 to 144
7 to 148
8 to 156
9.5 to 168

It is a function because each input has one output.

b. Draw a graph and explain how it confirms your answer
to part a.

Student graphs should have five points plotted (6, 140),
(6.5,144), (7,148), (8,156), (9.5,168). Explanations may vary.
Sample explanation: it is a function because each x has
one y.

c. An expression that can be used to represent the relation
is $8x + 92$, where x represents the students' shoe size. Is
there any limit to the input values that can be used with
this expression? Explain your reasoning.

Yes. Explanations may vary. Shoe sizes are in halves and
range from 1 to about 16. Possible input values: 1, 1.5, 2,
2.5, …, 16.

d. Is the relation discrete or continuous? Explain your
reasoning.

This is a discrete relation because only certain values can
be used for the input.

ACTIVITY 3.2 Continued

13 Activate Prior Knowledge,
Debrief This question returns
students to a context and allows
them to pull the various ideas of
the activity together.

Suggested Assignment

CHECK YOUR UNDERSTANDING
p. 134, #6–9

UNIT 3 PRACTICE
pp. 177–178, #13–15

CHECK YOUR UNDERSTANDING

1. Domain: {−1, −2, 6}; Range: {−3, 4, 7}

2. Domain: {−2, 1, 5, 9}; Range: {0, 2, 3, 9}

3. Not a function

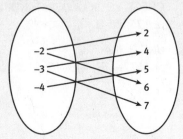

4. It is a function.

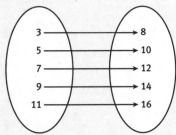

5. It is a function.

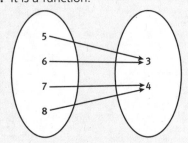

6. It is a function because each input has only one output.

7. It is not a function because the inputs 1 and −1 have more than one output.

8. It is a function because each input has only one output.

9. Sample answer: If any member of the domain has more than one corresponding value in the range, the relation is not a function.

CHECK YOUR UNDERSTANDING

Use notebook paper to write your answers. Show your work.

Find the domain and range for the data in questions 1 and 2.

1. {(−1,7), (−2,4), (−2,−3), (6,−3)}

2.

x	y
5	2
9	3
1	0
−2	9

Use mapping to determine if the information in Questions 3–5 represent functions.

3. {(−2,2), (−3,4), (−4,5), (−2,6), (−3,7)}

4. $x + 5$ for $x = 3, 5, 7, 9, 11$

5.

x	y
5	3
6	3
7	4
8	4

For Questions 6–8 determine if the relations represent a function. Explain your reasoning.

6.

x	y
−2	5
−5	7
8	8
22	17
−1	32
0	76
−12	0
17	22

7.

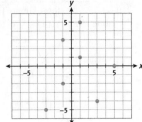

8.

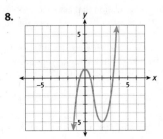

9. **MATHEMATICAL REFLECTION** How do the domain and range of a relation help to determine if a relation is a function?

Linear Relationships and Functions

EDUCATION PAYS

The following data was taken from an article, "Education Pays," by Sandy Baum and Jennifer Ma.

Age	Median Annual Income with a High School Diploma	Median Annual Income with a Bachelor's Degree
22	$19,882	$26,547
23	19,882	26,547
24	19,882	26,547
25	27,713	41,593
26	27,713	41,593
27	27,713	41,593
28	27,713	41,593
29	27,713	41,593
30	27,713	41,593

1. Does the data relating age with income for those with a high school diploma represent a linear relationship? Explain your reasoning.

2. Is the median annual income for either the High School Diploma or the Bachelor's Degree a function of age? Explain your reasoning.

3. Explain why the data in the table is considered discrete.

4. Three relations follow. For each relation, explain whether:

   • The information represents a linear relationship.
   • The information is discrete or continuous.
   • The information represents a function.

a.

x	y
1	−3
2	−7
3	−11
4	−15

b. $y = -2x + 3$

Embedded Assessment 1

Assessment Focus
• Linear relationships
• Function vs. relation
• Discrete vs. continuous

Materials
• No special materials needed

Differentiating Instruction

The data in the table could be considered piecewise defined linear, so adjustments to student answers should be taken into account for students that may be thinking about the concept beyond the average student.

Answer Key

1. No; sample answer: The data is not linear since there is not a constant rate of change from age to age.

2. The income is a function of age for both since for any age there is one and only one income.

3. Sample answer: The data is discrete because the domain and range have gaps between values. The data are all whole numbers.

4a. It is linear, discrete, and a function.

b. It is linear, continuous, and a function.

Embedded Assessment 1

4c. It is not linear, it is continuous, and it is a function.

> **TEACHER TO TEACHER** You may wish to read through the rubric with students and discuss the differences in the expectation levels. Make sure students understand the meanings of any terms used.

Linear Relationships and Functions
EDUCATION PAYS

c.

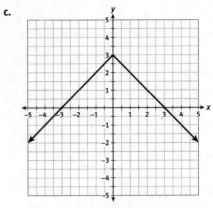

	Exemplary	Proficient	Emerging
Math Knowledge #1, 2, 4	The student: • Correctly identifies the data as linear or nonlinear. (1) • Correctly identifies whether or not income is a function of age for both relations. (2) • Correctly identifies data as linear or nonlinear, discrete or continuous, and determines if the data represents a function. (4)	The student provides complete and correct identification for two of the items.	The student provides at least two identifications, but only one is complete and correct.
Communication #1, 2, 3	The student: • Correctly explains why the data is nonlinear or nonlinear. (1) • Correctly explains why income is or is not a function of age for both relations. (2) • Correctly describes why the data is discrete. (3)	The student gives explanations for the three items, but only two are complete and correct.	The student gives at least two of the required explanations for questions 1, 2, and 3, but they are incomplete and incorrect.

Exploring Slope
High Ratio Mountain

SUGGESTED LEARNING STRATEGIES: Create Representations,
Look for a Pattern, Activate Prior Knowledge, Discussion Group

My Notes

Misty Flipp worked odd jobs all summer long and saved her money
to buy passes to the ski lift at the High Ratio Mountain Ski Resort.
In August, Misty researched the lift ticket prices and found several
options. Since she worked so hard to earn this money, Misty
carefully investigated each of her options.

**High Ratio Mountain
Ski Resort**

Student Lift Ticket prices

Daily Lift Ticket	$30
10-Day Package	$80 upon purchase and $20 per day (up to 10 days)
Unlimited Season Pass	$390

1. Suppose Misty purchased a daily lift ticket each time she goes
skiing. Complete the table below for the total cost of the lift
tickets.

Number of Days	0	1	2	3	4	5	6
Total Cost of Lift Tickets	0	30	60	90	120	150	180

2. Use the table to complete the statement: When the number
of days in the row increases by ___1___, Misty's cost increases
by __$30__.

3. Does the data in the table represent a linear relationship?
Explain your reasoning.
Answers may vary. Sample answer: Yes, there is a constant
increase in the cost for each additional day.

4. Determine the following:
   a. Does the data represent a function?
   Yes.

   b. Is the data discrete or continuous in this context?
   It is discrete.

ACTIVITY 3.3 Guided

Exploring Slope

Activity Focus
• Slope of a line

Materials
• No special materials needed

Chunking the Activity

#1–2	#11–14	#21–23
#3–5	#15–16	#24
#6–8	#17	#25
#9	#18	#26–27
#10	#19–20	

1 Create Representations
Students will represent the
relationship between the number
of days that Misty skis and the
total cost of her ski season.

2 Look for a Pattern This Item
is designed to get students to
start looking for a way to express
rate of change verbally. As students progress, the scaffolding
will be removed and they will be
expected to create these verbal
descriptions on their own.

3 Activate Prior Knowledge,
Discussion Group

4 Activating Prior Knowledge,
Debrief These questions are
designed to activate the students'
prior knowledge and see if they
can make connections to the new
material. This allows for a logical entry into the lesson and will
allow more students to access the
material.

5-7 Activating Prior Knowledge, Create Representations

8 **Look for a Pattern** This
item is designed to build student
capacity for verbalizing the rate of
change appropriately. It is worded
in such a way as to encourage
students to verbalize the rate as a
change in the dependent variable
with respect to the independent
variable.

9 **Look for a Pattern** This
question has students think
about the rate of change through
horizontal and vertical movements
on the graph. It leads directly into
the concept of finding a slope
graphically.

My Notes

SUGGESTED LEARNING STRATEGIES: Activating Prior
Knowledge, Create Representations, Look for
a Pattern

5. State the domain and the range of the data in the table.

Domain: {0, 1, 2, 3, 4, 5, 6}; Range: {0, 30, 60, 90, 120, 150, 180}

6. Plot the data from the table on the grid below.

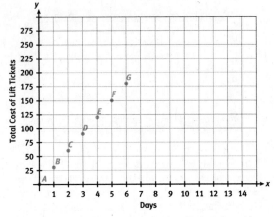

7. Label the left most point on the graph point *A*. Label the next
6 points, from left to right, points *B*, *C*, *D*, *E*, *F*, and *G*.

8. Use the graph to complete the statement: When the number of
days increases by ___1___, Misty's cost increases by ___$30___.

9. Describe how you move along the grid to get from one point to
another.

From *A* to *B*: Go Up $ _30_ and Go Right _1_ Day(s)

From *B* to *C*: Go Up $ _30_ and Go Right _1_ Day(s)

From *C* to *D*: Go Up $ _30_ and Go Right _1_ Day(s)

From *D* to *E*: Go Up $ _30_ and Go Right _1_ Day(s)

From *E* to *F*: Go Up $ _30_ and Go Right _1_ Day(s)

From *F* to *G*: Go Up $ _30_ and Go Right _1_ Day(s)

SUGGESTED LEARNING STRATEGIES: Marking the Text, Vocabulary Organizer, Think/Pair/Share, Look for a Pattern, Activating Prior Knowledge

10. The movements you traced in Question 9 can be written as a ratio, $\frac{up}{right}$. Write ratios in the form $\frac{up}{right}$ that describe how to move from:

A to B: $\frac{30}{1}$ B to C: $\frac{30}{1}$

C to D: $\frac{30}{1}$ D to E: $\frac{30}{1}$

Another way to think of the movement "Go Up" is as the *change in y*. Similarly, the movement "Go Right" is the *change in x*. With this in mind, the ratio, $\frac{up}{right}$, can be rewritten as $\frac{change\ in\ y}{change\ in\ x}$. The illustration to the right shows the change in *y* and the change in *x* between two points on a line.

11. Find the change in *y*, the change in *x*, and write the ratio:

From A to C: $\frac{60}{2}\left(or\ \frac{30}{1}\right)$

From B to E: $\frac{90}{3}\left(or\ \frac{30}{1}\right)$

From A to E: $\frac{120}{4}\left(or\ \frac{30}{1}\right)$

12. What do you notice about these ratios?   They are equivalent.

13. What are the units of the ratios you created?   dollars per day

14. Explain how the ratios relate to Misty's situation.

Answers may vary. Sample answer: The ratios describe Misty's cost per day for buying a daily lift ticket.

15. Find the change in *x*, the change in *y*, and write a ratio:

From B to A: $\frac{-30}{-1}\left(or\ \frac{30}{1}\right)$

From E to B: $\frac{-90}{-3}\left(\frac{30}{1}\right)$

16. How do these ratios compare to those you found in Question 10?

They are the same.

My Notes

MATH TERMS

A **ratio** is an expression that compares two values or quantities.

The *rate of change* of a relation is a ratio.

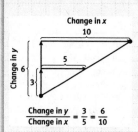

$$\frac{Change\ in\ y}{Change\ in\ x} = \frac{3}{5} = \frac{6}{10}$$

WRITING MATH

When writing a ratio, you can also represent the relationship by separating each quantity with a colon. For example, the ratio 1:4 is read "one to four."

10 Mark the Text, Vocabulary Organizer, Debrief This question has students write the rate of change as a ratio. Take the time to hold a class discussion on ratios. Place a particular emphasis on units. A Mini-Lesson is given if students need extra practice with ratios.

Suggested Assignment

CHECK YOUR UNDERSTANDING
p. 144, #1–3

UNIT 3 PRACTICE
p. 178, #16–18

11 Think/Pair/Share This item is designed to get students to see that the ratio that represents the rate of change is constant.

12-13 Look for a Pattern

14 Activating Prior Knowledge, Debrief This question mirrors Item 8. Students are given the opportunity to write the rate of change without the scaffolding. Students should share their answers and discuss the most appropriate wording.

15 Think/Pair/Share Have students look at the negative horizontal and vertical movements on the graph and see that the sign of the ratio is not dependent on direction. Some students may need to be reminded that division of two negative numbers yields a positive quotient.

16 Quickwrite, Debrief

MINI-LESSON: Ratios

There are three ways to represent a ratio: with a semicolon, a : b; fractional notation, $\frac{a}{b}$; and verbally, "a to b."

To give students extra practice with ratios, work through the following examples in class:

In a group of 35 people, 15 are wearing white shoes and the rest are wearing black shoes. What is the ratio of white to black shoes? Black to white shoes?

Answer: 15 : 20; 20 : 15

The local humane society picked up 25 stray animals one day. Ten were dogs and fifteen were cats. Express the ratio of cats to dogs three different ways. Answer: 15 to 10, 15:10, $\frac{15}{10}$

TEACHER TO TEACHER — This activity discusses slope as a constant rate of change. Students can use this concept to find slope given a graph, a table, or two points. The slope formula itself can confuse some students.

Having a strong grounding in the concept of slope as a rate of change will make the transition to the formulaic understanding in Algebra I easier for students.

17 Create Representations, Discussion Group This question ties the concept back to the original context by having students create an equation that will give the cost of Misty's ski trip. It may be helpful to have students go back to the table or the graph and question them about the cost for 1 day, then 2 days, then 3 days, then 10 days, then *d* days. This helps students see that they are multiplying the number of days by the rate of change.

TRY THESE A These problems provide practice for students as a check on their understanding of finding slope and *y*-intercept.

18 Debrief

Suggested Assignment

CHECK YOUR UNDERSTANDING
p. 144, #4–5

UNIT 3 PRACTICE
p. 178, #19

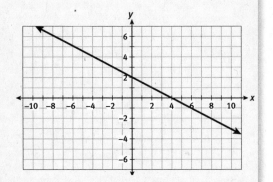

My Notes

ACADEMIC VOCABULARY

Slope is the ratio of vertical change to horizontal change or

$$\frac{\text{change in } y}{\text{change in } x}$$

***y*-intercept**

READING MATH

The slope of a line, $\frac{\text{change in } y}{\text{change in } x}$, is also expressed symbolically as $\frac{\Delta y}{\Delta x}$.

Δ is the Greek letter, delta.

CONNECT TO SPORTS

Longboards are larger than the more trick-oriented skateboards. Longboards are heavier and sturdier than skateboards. Some people even use them instead of bicycles.

The **slope** of a line is determined by the ratio $\frac{\text{change in } y}{\text{change in } x}$ between any two points that lie on the line. The slope is the *constant rate of change* of a line. All linear relationships have a constant rate of change. The slope of a line is what determines how steep or flat it looks on a graph.

The ***y*-intercept** of a line is the *y*-coordinate when the *x*-coordinate is 0. It is the point at which the line crosses the *y*-axis, (0, *y*).

17. Let *d* represent the number of days Misty plans to ski and let *C* represent Misty's total cost. Write an equation for *C* in terms of *d*.

$C = 30d$

TRY THESE A

Find the slope and *y*-intercept for the following.

a. $\frac{3}{2}$; 0 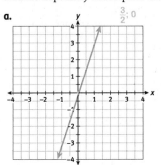   b. -2; -1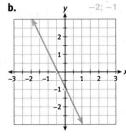

c.

x	y
0	0
1	2.5
2	5
4	10

2.5; 0

d.

x	y
−1	4
0	2
1	0
3	−4

−2; 2

e. John is longboarding at a constant rate down the road. If 2 min after he leaves his house he is 1000 ft away and at 5 minutes he is 2500 ft from his house what would his average rate of change be?

500 feet per min

18. Draw a line that contains the points you plotted in Question 6. Using the graph, find the slope and *y*-intercept of the line.

slope = 30; *y*-int = 0

MINI-LESSON: Finding Slope Given a Table or a Graph

- Show students the graph. Find a lattice point, and show the vertical change and the horizontal change to another lattice point. Then find the ratio and reduce the ratio if necessary. It may be helpful to show the process between multiple lattice points to reinforce the idea that no matter the size of the step, the slope is constant.

- Show students the table. Show the changes in the *y*-values and the *x*-values in the table, and write them as a ratio. Once again, it may be helpful to show the steps larger than one unit in order to demonstrate that the slope is constant.

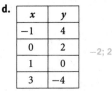

x	y
−1	−3
2	2
3	7
4	17

SUGGESTED LEARNING STRATEGIES: Create Representations, Look for a Pattern, Shared Reading, Interactive Word Wall

19. Suppose Misty purchased the 10-Day Ticket Package that costs $80 plus $20 per day.

a. Complete the table below for the total cost of the lift tickets in the 10-day package for 0 through 6 days. Be sure to include the initial cost of $80.

Number of Days	0	1	2	3	4	5	6
Total Cost of Lift Tickets	80	100	120	140	160	180	200

b. Explain how you know the data in the table above is linear.

Answers may vary. Sample answer: For every extra day her cost increases by $20.

20. Plot the data from the table on the given axes.

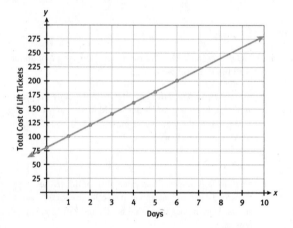

21. Draw a line that contains the points you plotted in Item 20.

My Notes

CONNECT TO **AP**

The concepts of slope and y-intercept will continue to be developed in later math courses.

ACTIVITY 3.3 *Continued*

TEACHER TO TEACHER   The next set of questions gets students to start looking at linear equations with an offset, and what that means for the y-intercept of a line.

19-21 Create Representations, Look for a Pattern Students will create a table, and look at the rate of change. Students should notice that even though the "start" of the data is not 0, the rate of change is still constant.

Connect to AP

Items 19 and 20 provide students with the opportunity to make connections between numerical representations and graphical representations of important concepts like slope and y-intercept. Both of these concepts will continue to develop as students take additional mathematics courses. For example, all polynomial functions, regardless of their degree, have a y-intercept which can be found by substituting 0 for the independent variable, and all of them have a slope at any point which can be calculated by finding value of the derivative of the function. Finding a y-intercept of a function for a higher degree polynomial is relatively easy because it is always the constant term. For example the y-intercept of $f(x) = 2x^3 - 3x^2 + 4x - 1$ is -1. Finding the slope of this polynomial is a topic students will address in calculus.

22-23 Quickwrite, Group Presentation

24 **Create Representations**
Students may need more support in creating the equation. One way to help them is to build a table showing what is done each time to the starting value.

d	*K*
0	80
1	80 + 20
2	80 + 20 + 20
3	80 + 20 + 20 + 20

Ask students if there is an easier way to represent the multiple additions of 20.

TEACHER TO TEACHER Items 25–27 allow students to analyze the situation and write a paper to recommend what Misty should do. While there are distinct values that show one method of purchase to be better than others, the actual decision is open-ended. Students may address all the possible situations, but since there is truly no way to know how many days Misty will be able or willing to ski, the recommendation itself is just an opinion.

25 Summarize/Paraphrase/ Retell

My Notes

22. Find the slope and the *y*-intercept of the line that contains the points in the graph for Question 20, and explain how they relate to Misty's situation.

y-intercept: 80, slope = 20; Answers may vary. Sample answer: The *y*-intercept is the initial price of the ticket package. The slope is the additional daily cost.

23. Compare and contrast the lines associated with the data for the Daily Lift Tickets in Question 6, and the data for the 10-Day Package.

Answers may vary. Sample answer: Both graphs are linear relationships. The first has a larger slope than the second, and the second has a larger *y*-intercept than the first.

24. Let *d* represent the number of days Misty plans to ski and let *K* represent Misty's cost. Write an equation for *K* in terms *d* for Misty's cost.

$K = 80 + 20d$

25. Although it seemed like a lot of money, Misty thought about the unlimited season pass for $390.

a. First, she compared the season pass to the daily lift tickets at $30 each. How many times would Misty have to go skiing before she would save money with the $390 season pass? Show your work.

390 ÷ 30 = 13; 13 days

b. Next, Misty compared the price of an unlimited season pass to two 10-Day packages that she would use for 20 days of skiing. Which package would be the best buy? Explain your reasoning.

Answers may vary. Sample answer: The total cost of two 10-day packages would be $560. It would make sense to purchase the season pass if she planned to ski 20 days.

SUGGESTED LEARNING STRATEGIES: Create Representations,
Identify a Subtask, Discussion Group, RAFT

26. If Misty skis the following number of days, which of the three
packages should she purchase? Explain why.

Explanations will vary. The table below compares the prices of
the different passes for each number of days.

a. 6 days

Daily

b. 8 days

Daily or 10-day

Days Skiing	Daily	10-day Package(s)	Season Pass
6	$180	$200	$390
8	$240	$240	$390
13	$390	$420	$390
16	$480	$480	$390

c. 13 days

Daily or Season Pass

d. 16 days

Season Pass

27. Write a persuasive letter to Misty based on your analysis
that makes a recommendation of which package she should
purchase. Include multiple representations (graphs, tables,
and/or equations) to support your reasoning.

Student answers may vary based on their analysis of the
circumstances. Any of the three options is a possibility,
depending on the number of days that Misty will ski. The daily
pass is the least expensive from 1–8 days. From 8 to 10 days,
a 10-day pass is the least expensive. From 11–13 days a daily
pass is the least expensive again, then from 13 days and beyond
the season pass is the least expensive. Students should
include multiple representations in their answers to help Misty
understand which package will be best for her.

My Notes

ACTIVITY 3.3 *Continued*

26 Create Representations,
Identify a Subtask, Discussion
Group, Debrief Students may
wish to create a table to help
organize the information. It will
help to have multiple groups
share what they found so that any
errors in computation are found
before students begin working on
the RAFT.

27 RAFT This letter is designed as
a RAFT. Students should be given
the opportunity to work on this
as homework so they can turn in
a more polished letter. Remind
them to include their analysis
and multiple representations
of how they decided on their
recommendation.

R: Persuasive expert

A: Misty

F: Persuasive letter

T: Analysis of the 3 possible lift
ticket options

Suggested Assignment

CHECK YOUR UNDERSTANDING
p. 144, #6–7

UNIT 3 PRACTICE
p. 178, #20

CHECK YOUR UNDERSTANDING

1. $\dfrac{64 \text{ miles}}{2 \text{ gallons}}$

2. 32 miles

3. 384 miles

4. b

5a. 2; 1

   b. −2; 4

   c. −2; 4

   d. $\dfrac{1}{2}$; −2

6. b

7. Sample answer: As the line becomes steeper, the absolute value of the slope becomes larger.

CHECK YOUR UNDERSTANDING

Write your answers on notebook paper. Show your work.

Misty determined that she gets 64 miles on 2 gallons of gas from her car as she drives from her house to go skiing.

1. Create a ratio of Misty's miles per gallon.

2. Using the ratio you found in Question 1, determine how far Misty can go on 1 gallon of gas.

3. How many miles could Misty travel on a full tank of 12 gallons of gas?

4. What is the slope of the line shown?

   a. −4
   b. $-\dfrac{3}{2}$
   c. $-\dfrac{2}{3}$
   d. $\dfrac{3}{2}$
   e. 4

5. Find the slope and y-intercept of the following:

   a.

x	y
0	1
3	7
6	13

   b.

x	y
−3	10
0	4
4	−4

c.

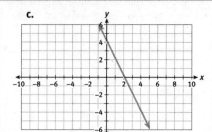

d.

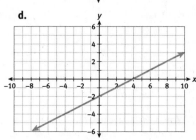

6. If a line has a slope of $\dfrac{3}{4}$, and contains the point (3, 1), then it must also contain which of the following points?

   a. (−2, −2)
   b. (−1, −2)
   c. (0, −3)
   d. (2, 2)
   e. (7, 3)

7. **MATHEMATICAL REFLECTION** How does the steepness of a line affect the slope of the line?

Slope Intercept Form
The Leaky Bottle

SUGGESTED LEARNING STRATEGIES: Use Manipulatives, Create Representations, Discussion Group, Think/Pair/Share, Activating Prior Knowledge

Owen's water bottle leaked in his bookbag. He did the following experiment to find how quickly water drains from a small hole placed in a water bottle.

1. Follow the steps below and fill in the table.
   - Get a water bottle and a container to catch the water.
   - Poke a small hole in the bottom of the water bottle
   - Ensure the hole is facing down, and open the bottle cap.
   - Draw a line on the bottle every 5 seconds to mark the water level.
   - After the water is drained from the bottle, measure the heights at each of the times that you marked.

   Sample data given:

Time in Seconds	0	5	10	15	20	25	30	35	40
Height of Water (cm)	15	13.5	12	10.5	9	7.5	6	4.5	3

2. Make a scatter plot of the data on the grid below.

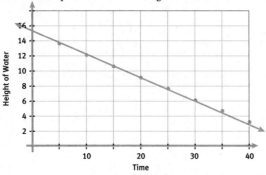

3. Does the relationship between time and the height of the water appear to be linear? Explain your reasoning.
   Yes. Answers may vary. Sample answer: While there may be a small amount of variation the relationship is basically linear.

4. Is the data you collected continuous or discrete? Explain your reasoning. Discrete. Answers may vary. Sample answer: Even though the information from the experiment could be continuous, we only collected data at discrete time intervals.

5. Draw a line through the points on the scatterplot you created.
   Answers based on the sample data:
   a. Find the slope of the line you drew. $-\frac{3}{10}$
   b. Find the y-intercept of the line you drew.
      15 cm (depends on water bottle size)

MATH TERMS
The **y-intercept** of a line is the y-value when $x = 0$. It is the place where the line crosses the y-axis.

1-5 Use Manipulatives, Create Representations, Discussion Group, Debrief, Think/Pair/Share, Activate Prior Knowledge

Suggested Assignment

CHECK YOUR UNDERSTANDING
p. 152, #1

UNIT 3 PRACTICE
p. 179, #21

ACTIVITY 3.4 Investigative

Slope Intercept Form

Activity Focus
- Slope intercept form of equation of the line

Materials
- 16 oz water bottle per group
- Large cup or bucket
- Ruler or tape measure
- Marker
- A tool to poke a hole in the bottle
- Stop watch

Chunking the Activity

#1	#10	#18
#2–3	#11	#19
#4–5	#12–13	#20
#6	#14	#21–22
#7–8	#15–16	#23
#9	#17	#24
		#25
		#26

TEACHER TO TEACHER This investigation starts with students collecting data. Each group should have one inexpensive cylindrical water bottle. Each group will poke a small hole in their water bottles. The water will not leak out until the cap is opened, and air can flow into the bottle. Have students mark a line on the bottle where the water starts, and then every 5 seconds afterwards. When the bottle is empty, have students measure the heights in cm, and record them in the table. The data students collect may vary from the Sample Data, but should be fairly linear, and have a negative rate of change. This activity is not designed for students to create trend lines. The data should be clean if students are careful when collecting it. If any group has data that is not close to linear, then they should use another group's data, or the sample data given in the answers.

6 Group presentation
Writing this equation may be hard for students. In the previous activities the rates of change were very clear. Have students present their equations and how they came up with them.

Differentiating Instruction

Students that are having a hard time seeing the equation should be walked through the table strategy that was used in the previous activity. Have them create a table and show the rate of change being added to or subtracted from the starting value multiple times. For students that easily found the equation, have them look at the other groups' tables and create equations of those lines. They can verify their answers with the groups when they share their equations.

7-8 Think/Pair/Share, Debrief

9 Create Representations, Debrief This question is quite involved. Students must find the slope, and create tables and graphs for the equations. This is the first in a series of questions that will walk students through the transformations of linear equations. They will first look at direct variation equations and see how larger and larger coefficients affect the table and graph of the line. Discuss the connection between the rate of change in the table and the steepness of the line.

TEACHER TO TEACHER Technology such as graphing calculators or computer graphing programs can allow students to look at many equations very quickly, and can be used to enhance or extend this lesson.

My Notes

6. Write an equation that gives the height of the water H given the time t. $H = 15 - \dfrac{3}{10}t$

7. How does the coefficient of t in your equation relate to the experiment? Be certain to include appropriate units in your answer.
It is the rate at which the water is leaking from the bottle in cm per sec.

8. How does the constant term in the equation relate to the experiment? Be certain to include appropriate units in your answer.
It is the initial height of the water in cm.

9. For each linear equation below:
- Make a table of values.
- Graph using a different color for each line.
- Determine the slope.

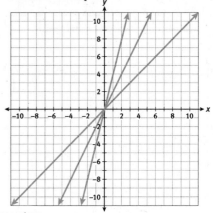

$m = $ slope:

a. $y = x$ $m = 1$

x	$y = x$
-3	-3
-2	-2
-1	-1
0	0
1	1
2	2
3	3

b. $y = 2x$ $m = 2$

x	$y = 2x$
-3	-6
-2	-4
-1	-2
0	0
1	2
2	4
3	6

c. $y = 4x$ $m = 4$

x	$y = 4x$
-2	-8
-1.5	-6
-1	-4
0	0
1	4
2	8
2.5	10

Slope Intercept Form
The Leaky Bottle

SUGGESTED LEARNING STRATEGIES: Think/Pair/Share,
Create Representations, Look for a Pattern

My Notes

10. How does the slope you found for each linear equation relate
to the coefficients of x in the equations for Question 9?
    The coefficient is the same as the slope.

11. For each linear equation below:
    • Make a table of values.
    • Graph using a different color for each line.
    • Determine the slope.

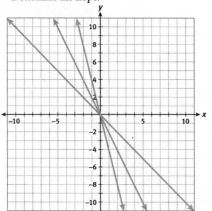

a. $y = -x$ $m = -1$ **b.** $y = -2x$ $m = -2$ **c.** $y = -4x$ $m = -4$

x	$y = -x$
−3	3
−2	2
−1	1
0	0
1	−1
2	−2
3	−3

x	$y = -2x$
−3	6
−2	4
−1	2
0	0
1	−2
2	−4
3	−6

x	$y = -4x$
−2	8
−1.5	6
−1	4
0	0
1	−4
2	−8

12. How does the slope you found relate to the coefficients of x in
the equations for Question 11?
    The slope is the same as the coefficient of x.

13. Write an equation of a line that is: Answers may vary.

    a. Steeper (increasing) than the ones you graphed in Question 9.
    $y = 6x$

    b. Steeper (decreasing) than the ones you graphed in Question 11.
    $y = -6x$

---

10 **Think/Pair/Share** Have multiple groups share their results. While discussing these results, help students make the connection that the coefficient of x is the same as the slope of the line.

Suggested Assignment

CHECK YOUR UNDERSTANDING
p. 152, #2–3

UNIT 3 PRACTICE
p. 179, #22

11 **Create Representations, Debrief** This question continues to look at the transformations of linear functions. Students follow the same process they used in Item 9, but should be more proficient with the process. They will look at how a negative rate of change affects the tables and graphs of linear equations. Students should recognize that as the absolute value of the rate of change gets larger, the line becomes steeper.

TEACHER TO TEACHER Students will often overlook the fact that a slope of −4 is actually smaller than a slope of −2. Because the graph looks more steep, they will tend to think of this change as an increase in slope. You may wish to incorporate this concept into the lesson for more advanced students.

12 **Look for a Pattern**

13 **Look for a Pattern, Think/Pair/Share** Having students share their equations will help them see that there are many (actually infinite) equations that meet the conditions of the question.

14 Create Representations, Debrief
Students will again go through the process of looking at how different slopes affect the graph of a linear equation. This time, students will look at fractional rates of change between 0 and 1. Students should again make connections between the slope of the line and how the graph looks.

15 Look for a Pattern, Group Presentation, Debrief
Have group presentations to share ideas. Questioning should be used to help extend student understanding in areas that the students have not addressed.

16 Think/Pair/Share, Look for a Pattern, Guess and Check, Create Representations
This question is a good formative assessment to see if students can create an equation given the constraints.

Suggested Assignment

CHECK YOUR UNDERSTANDING
p. 152, #4–6

UNIT 3 PRACTICE
p. 179, #24–26

My Notes

SUGGESTED LEARNING STRATEGIES: Create Representations, Look for a Pattern, Group Presentation, Think/Pair/Share, Guess and Check

14. For each linear equation below:
- Make a table of values.
- Graph using a different color for each line.
- Determine the slope.

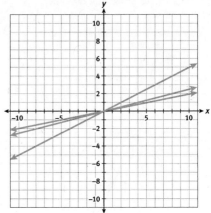

Sample tables are shown.

a. $y = \frac{1}{2}x$ $m = 0.5$

x	$y = 0.5x$
-4	-2
-2	-1
-1	$-\frac{1}{2}$
0	0
1	$\frac{1}{2}$
2	1
4	2

b. $y = \frac{1}{4}x$ $m = 0.25$

x	$y = 0.25x$
-4	-1
-2	$-\frac{1}{2}$
-1	$-\frac{1}{4}$
0	0
1	$\frac{1}{4}$
2	$\frac{1}{2}$
4	1

c. $y = \frac{1}{5}x$ $m = 0.2$

x	$y = 0.2x$
-5	-1
-2	$-\frac{2}{5}$
-1	$-\frac{1}{5}$
0	0
1	$\frac{1}{5}$
2	$\frac{2}{5}$
5	1

15. Compare and contrast the slopes you found in Questions 9, 11, and 14. Refer to the representations you've created in your comparisons. What conclusions can you draw about the slope of lines? Answers will vary.

16. Write the equation of a line that is steeper than $\frac{1}{2}$ but less than one. Sample answer: $y = \left(\frac{3}{4}\right)x$

SUGGESTED LEARNING STRATEGIES: Create Representations,
Look for a Pattern, Think/Pair/Share

17. For each linear equation below:
- Make a table of values.
- Graph using a different color for each line.
- Determine the y-intercept.
- Determine the slope.

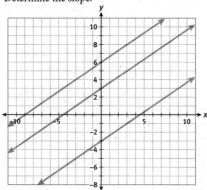

Sample tables are shown.

a. $y = \frac{2}{3}x + 3$ **b.** $y = \frac{2}{3}x + 6$ **c.** $y = \frac{2}{3}x - 3$

18. How is the y-intercept related to the constant term in the equations? They are the same.

19. Look at the lines you graphed in item 17.

a. How do the three lines appear to be related? They are parallel.

b. Look at the three equations and make a conjecture based on your answer to part a. Lines with the same slope are parallel.

c. What would happen to the graph of $y = \frac{2}{3}x - 3$ if it were shifted 6 units up?
It would become the same as the graph of $y = \frac{2}{3}x + 3$.

d. What would happen to the graph of $y = \frac{2}{3}x + 6$ if it were shifted 9 units down?
It would become the same as the graph of $y = \frac{2}{3}x - 3$.

20. Identify the slope and y-intercept in each of the following equations.

a. $y = \frac{3}{2}x + 5$ **b.** $y = -x + 1$ **c.** $y = 4x - 3$

$\frac{3}{2}$; 5   −1; 1   4; −3

My Notes

17 a. $m = \left(\frac{2}{3}\right)$

x	$y = \left(\frac{2}{3}\right)x + 3$
−9	−3
−6	−1
−3	1
0	3
3	5
6	7
9	9

y-intercept = 3

b. $m = \left(\frac{2}{3}\right)$

x	$y = \left(\frac{2}{3}\right)x + 6$
−9	0
−6	2
−3	4
0	6
3	8
6	10
9	12

y-intercept = 6

c. $m = \left(\frac{2}{3}\right)$

x	$y = \left(\frac{2}{3}\right)x - 3$
−9	−9
−6	−7
−3	−5
0	−3
3	−1
6	1
9	3

y-intercept = −3

ACTIVITY 3.4 *Continued*

17 **Create Representations, Debrief** Students will now transition into looking at how the constant term in the equation of a line affects the graph. The graphs of the equations are parallel so that students can focus on the y-intercept.

18 **Look for a Pattern, Debrief**

20 **Create Representations, Think/Pair/Share** This question allows for formative assessment on student understanding of how to find the slope and y-intercept of a line given an equation. Walk around the class and assist students that have not yet made the connection.

21 Create Representations This question walks students through the process of graphing an equation of a line in slope-intercept form, using the y-intercept and the slope. You may want to give a few more examples for students who are having a hard time seeing the process.

22 Discussion Group, Debrief

| TEACHER TO TEACHER | Discuss the meaning of m and b, and have students find the slopes and y-intercepts from a few previous questions. This should not be hard for students to see after the progression they have gone through, but the new parameters may be confusing to some students.

23 Create Representations This question will allow you to help those students who are still not making the connections between the equation of a line in slope-intercept form, and the parameters m and b. Walk around the room, and use questioning strategies to guide students.

Some students will quickly realize that they only need to plot two points to graph a line. Urge them to graph three or even four points. By doing this, they can minimize the chance of mis-drawing a line because of an arithmetic error. When three or more points are plotted, an arithmetic error can reveal itself through the non-collinearity of those points.

My Notes

SUGGESTED LEARNING STRATEGIES: Shared Reading, Interactive Word Wall, Discussion Group, Create Representations

21. Identify and plot the y-intercept of the equation $y = \frac{1}{2}x + 3$ on the coordinate grid and use the slope to find two more points on the line. *y-intercept: (0,3)*

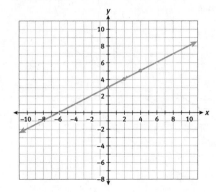

22. Sketch a line through the three points.

Equations of the form $y = mx + b$ are written in **slope-intercept form**, where m is the slope of the line, and b is the y-intercept of the line.

> **MATH TERMS**
> The **slope-intercept form** of a linear equation is $y = mx + b$, where m is the slope and b is the y-intercept.

23. Use the y-intercept and the slope to graph the following equations of lines.

a. $y = \frac{1}{3}x - 2$ **b.** $y = -2x + 1$ **c.** $y = -3x + 4$

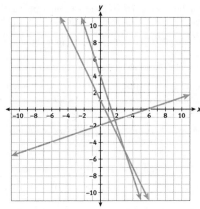

SUGGESTED LEARNING STRATEGIES: Work Backwards, Quickwrite, Group Presentation

24. Owen found that the equation $y = -3x + 24$ represented the water leaking from his bottle.

   a. What is the y-intercept, and what would it represent in this context?
   24; the amount of water in the bottle (height) before it started leaking.

   b. What is the slope, and what would it represent in this context?
   −3; the rate at which water is leaking from the bottle

   c. Explain to Owen what would have to happen to the bottle for the slope to change to −4.
   Answers may vary. Sample answer: A larger hole could cause this change.

25. Explain how to graph the equation $y = 2x - 3$ without using a table of values.
   Answers may vary. Sample answer: Plot the y-intercept, (0,−3). Since the slope is 2, move 1 unit right and 2 units up, and plot the second point there. Draw a line through the two points.

26. The table and the equation below represent different functions.

x	−2	−1	0	1	2
y	1	5	9	13	17

   $y = 3x - 4$

   Which function has the greater rate of change? How do you know?
   The table. The slope gives the rate of change. The slope of the function given in the equation is 3. The slope in the table using (−2, 1) and (−1, 5) is $\frac{5-1}{-1-(-2)} = \frac{4}{1} = 4$.

My Notes

ACTIVITY 3.4 *Continued*

24 Work Backwards, Quickwrite This question returns to the original context of the activity. Students should be able to associate the linear equation given with the ones they created from their experiments.

25 Quickwrite, Group Presentation A verbal description can be a good indication as to whether or not a student understands how to graph an equation of a line. Use this question to help focus any extra help that students need.

Suggested Assignment

CHECK YOUR UNDERSTANDING
p. 152, #7–12

UNIT 3 PRACTICE
p. 179, #27–30

CHECK YOUR UNDERSTANDING

(*Continued*)

   10. $y = \frac{1}{2}x - 4$

   11. Answers may vary. Any equation with a slope greater than ½

   12. Answers may vary. Sample answer: place a point at the y-intercept. Then use the slope to find another point and draw a line through the points; or substitute a value for x in the equation, find the corresponding y-value, and use that as the second point.

ACTIVITY 3.4 Continued

CHECK YOUR UNDERSTANDING

1. $m = -0.5$

2.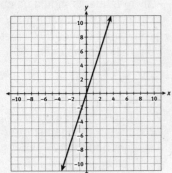

3.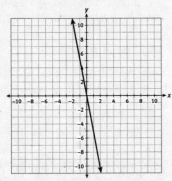

4.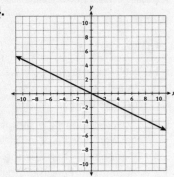

5. Possible answer: $y = \frac{3}{2}x$

6. $y = -\frac{2}{3}x$

7.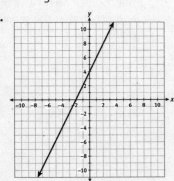

10–12. See page 151.

CHECK YOUR UNDERSTANDING

Write your answers on notebook paper. Show your work.

1. Find the slope.

x	y
0	10
3	8.5
6	7

Graph the linear equations.

2. $y = 3x$

3. $y = -5x$

4. $y = -\frac{1}{2}x$

5. Write an equation of a line that has a slope that is greater than 1 but less than 2.

6. Write the equation of the line graphed below.

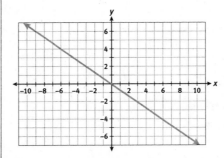

Graph the linear equations.

7. $y = 2x + 4$

8. $y = -3x + 2$

9. $y = \frac{2}{3}x - 5$

10. Write an equation for the line graphed below.

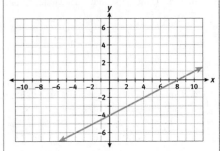

11. Write the equation of a function with a greater rate of change than the function graphed in item 10.

12. **MATHEMATICAL REFLECTION** Explain two ways to graph a linear equation of the form $y = mx + b$, where m and b represent any real number.

8.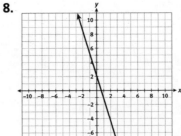

9.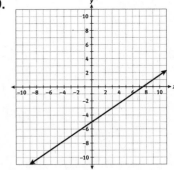

Intercepts, Horizontal and Vertical Lines
Drive Time

SUGGESTED LEARNING STRATEGIES: Shared Reading, Marking the Text, Create Representations, Interactiving Word Wall, Vocabulary Organizer, Activating Prior Knowledge

My Notes

Matt is driving from Tucson to Flagstaff, Arizona. After driving 20 miles on two-lane roads, he gets on the interstate highway where he will drive 65 mph.

1. Write a linear equation that gives Matt's distance from Tucson given the number of hours since Matt has been driving on the interstate.

$y = 20 + 65x$

2. What are the slope and y-intercept of the line in Question 1?

$m = 65$, $b = 20$

The **x-intercept** of a line is the point where the line crosses the x-axis. Its coordinates will be in the form $(c, 0)$ where c is a real number.

ACADEMIC VOCABULARY

x-intercept

EXAMPLE 1

Find the x-intercept on a graph.

Step 1:   *Find the intersection of the line with the x-axis.*

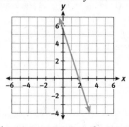

Solution: The x-intercept is 2, or the point $(2, 0)$.

TRY THESE A

Find the x- and y-intercepts of the graphs below.

a. x-int $= -2$, y-int $= 3$

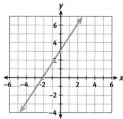

b. x-int $= 4$, y-int $= 2$

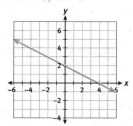

ACTIVITY 3.5 Guided

Intercepts, Horizontal and Vertical Lines

Activity Focus
• Horizontal and vertical lines
• *x*-intercepts

Materials
• No special materials needed

Chunking the Activity

#1–2	#7–9
#3	#10–11
#4–6	#12–16

1-2 Create Representations, Activate Prior Knowledge
These questions are designed as ease of entry questions. Students use what they have learned in previous activities to find an equation of a line, and identify the slope and *y*-intercept in context.

TEACHER TO TEACHER Explain the example to students. If they need more than one example, draw a few more lines and show them how to identify the *x*-intercept.

The Try These will allow you time to walk around and verify that students are able to find the *x*-intercepts. For students that finish quickly, you can ask them to find the slopes and *y*-intercepts of the lines as well.

TEACHER TO TEACHER — Show students the examples on how to find the *x*- and *y*-intercepts algebraically.

TRY THESE B Use the Try These to verify that students are able to find the *x*- and *y*-intercepts algebraically. To extend students, you can have them identify the slope, too.

3 Think/Pair/Share, Quick-write This question allows students to make a connection back to the initial context and see if they can use their skills with a more complex equation.

Suggested Assignment

CHECK YOUR UNDERSTANDING
p. 160, #1–8

UNIT 3 PRACTICE
p. 179, #31–38

My Notes

To find the *x*-intercept of a line algebraically, use the fact that the intercept lies at the point $(c, 0)$.

EXAMPLE 2

A. Find the *x*-intercept of the line $y = 4x - 24$ algebraically.

Step 1: Substitute 0 for y.

$$0 = 4x - 24$$

Step 2: Solve for x.

$$0 = 4x - 24$$
$$+24 \quad +24$$
$$\frac{24}{6} = \frac{4x}{4}$$
$$6 = x$$

Solution: The *x*-intercept is 6. The coordinates are $(6, 0)$.

To find the *y*-intercept of a line algebraically, use the fact that the intercept lies at the point $(0, d)$.

B. Find the *y*-intercept of the line $y = 4x - 24$ algebraically.

Step 1: Substitute 0 for x.

$$y = 4(0) - 24$$

Step 1: Solve for y.

$$y = -24$$

Solution: The *y*-intercept is -24. The coordinates are $(0, -24)$.

TRY THESE B

Find the *x*- and *y*-intercepts of the following equations.

a. $y = -5x - 10$
    x-int = −2, *y*-int = −10

b. $y = \frac{1}{4}x + 5$
    x-int = −20, *y*-int = 5

c. $y = 0.5x + 2$
    x-int = −4, *y*-int = 2

d. $y = 7 + 2x$
    x-int = $-\frac{7}{2}$, *y*-int = 7

e. $2x + 3y = 9$
    x-int = $\frac{9}{2}$, *y*-int = 3

3. Find the *x*- and *y*-intercepts of the equation you found in Question 1 algebraically.

   x-int = $-\frac{20}{65}$, *y*-int = 20

SUGGESTED LEARNING STRATEGIES: Create Representations, Look for a Pattern

My Notes

4. Graph each of the following equations.

a. $y = \frac{1}{2}x$ **b.** $y = \frac{1}{5}x$ **c.** $y = \frac{1}{10}x$

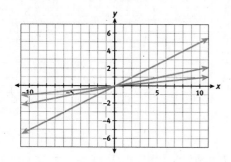

5. What happens to the graph of the equation of a line as the slope gets closer to zero?

Answers may vary. Sample answer: The line flattens out.

6. Predict what a line with a slope that is equal to zero would look like.

It will be horizontal.

---

4 **Create Representations, Debrief** This question follows a similar process to that of the previous activity. In this case, students will look at graphs of multiple lines and see what patterns they notice. The students will be making a conjecture about what will happen as the slope approaches zero. This concept of looking at a limiting factor is a an important milestone towards AP Calculus.

5-6 **Create Representations**

TEACHER TO TEACHER Some students might have trouble seeing how the slope is approaching zero. Have them rewrite the slopes as decimals and then label the decimals 0.5, 0.2, and 0.1 on their respective lines.

7 **Create Representations** This question looks at equations of horizontal lines.

8 **Create Representations** Students can use their knowledge about slope and *y*-intercepts to graph the equations.

9 **Create Representations, Debriefing**

My Notes

SUGGESTED LEARNING STRATEGIES: Create Representations

7. Fill in the table values for the following equations.

a. $y = 0x + 3$

x	y
−3	3
−2	3
−1	3
0	3
1	3
2	3
3	3

b. $y = 0x + 6$

x	y
−3	6
−2	6
−1	6
0	6
1	6
2	6
3	6

c. $y = 0x - 3$

x	y
−3	−3
−2	−3
−1	−3
0	−3
1	−3
2	−3
3	−3

8. Graph the equations from Question 7.

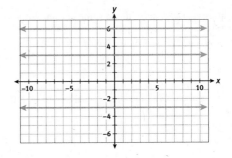

9. Simplify and rewrite the equations in Question 7. What patterns do you notice about equations of lines that have a slope of zero?

Answers may vary. $y = 3$, $y = 6$, $y = -3$

Intercepts, Horizontal and Vertical Lines
Drive Time

SUGGESTED LEARNING STRATEGIES: Create Representations, Look for a Pattern, Interactive Word Wall, Vocabulary Organizer

10. Graph each of the following equations.

   a. $y = 5x$ **b.** $y = 7x$ **c.** $y = 10x$

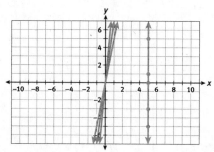

11. What happens to the graph of the line as the slope gets larger?
Answers may vary. Sample answer: It becomes more vertical.

12. On the coordinate grid above, draw a vertical line through the point $(5, 0)$.

13. Using the line you drew in Question 12:

   a. Plot and label the coordinates of 4 additional points on the line.
     Sample points are given.

   b. Express the slope of the line in the form $\dfrac{\Delta y}{\Delta x}$. $\dfrac{\infty}{0}$

As the slope of a line increases, the line becomes closer to a vertical line. When the denominator of a slope ratio is zero, the slope is said to be undefined. The slope of a vertical line is **undefined**.

14. Look at the line you drew in drew in Question 12.

   a. What do you notice about the y values?
     Answers may vary. Sample answer: There are infinitely many.

   b. What do you notice about the x values?
     Answers may vary. Sample answer: There is only one.

   c. Why do you think the equation of the line is $x = 5$?
     Answers may vary. Sample answer: It is much simpler to describe this line in terms of x than in terms of y.

My Notes

ACTIVITY 3.5 Continued

10 Create Representations
Students will look at what happens to a line as the slope gets very large. This concept, too, is significant as students continue on in mathematics.

11 Look for a Pattern, Debrief

Suggested Assignment
CHECK YOUR UNDERSTANDING
p. 160, #9–10

UNIT 3 PRACTICE
p. 179, #39–40

12-14 Create Representations, Debrief

TEACHER TO TEACHER   Students often have trouble distinguishing between an undefined slope and a 0 slope. One way to help is to discuss a distance versus time graph. Have students explain how to make a horizontal line. Discuss the fact that, for a horizontal line, the distance does not change, but the time continues to change. Next ask them how they would walk a vertical line: They would have to be at an infinite number of distances at any one time.

15-16 Create Representations
These will help you determine which students still need help finding the equations of horizontal and vertical lines, and graphing these lines. As students progress through their mathematics courses, these two kinds of lines are often the ones they have trouble graphing.

SUGGESTED LEARNING STRATEGIES: Look for a Pattern, Create Representations

My Notes

15. Graph the following horizontal and vertical lines.

    a. $x = -3$

    b. $y = -2$

    c. $x = 6$

    d. $y = 4$

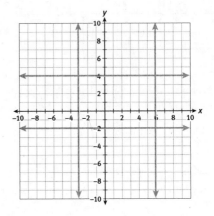

16. Write the equations of the following horizontal and vertical lines.

    a.

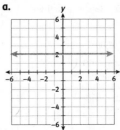

$y = 2$

    b.

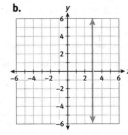

$x = 3$

Intercepts, Horizontal and Vertical Lines
Drive Time

SUGGESTED LEARNING STRATEGIES: Create Representations

My Notes

EXAMPLE 3

Graph $y = 2x + 6$ using x- and y-intercepts.

Step 1: *Find the x- and y-intercepts algebraically.*

Find the x-intercept   Find the y-intercept

$0 = 2x + 6$ $y = 2(0) + 6$

$-6 = 2x$ $y = 6$

$-3 = x$

Step 2: *Plot the coordinates of the x- and y-intercepts.*

Step 3: *Connect the intercepts with a line.*

Solution:

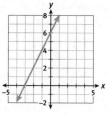

TRY THESE C

Graph the equations of the following lines using x and y-intercepts.

a. $y = x + 5$

b. $y = -x - 4$

c. $y = -3x + 6$

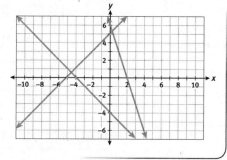

TEACHER TO TEACHER Show students the example on how to graph the equation of a line using the x- and y- intercepts, and have them work through the Try These.

Suggested Assignment

CHECK YOUR UNDERSTANDING
p. 160, #11–12

UNIT 3 PRACTICE
p. 180, #41–42

ACTIVITY 3.5 *Continued*

CHECK YOUR UNDERSTANDING

1. x-int = 6, y-int = -3
2. x-int = 6, y-int = 4
3. x-int = -3, y-int = 24
4. x-int = $-\frac{4}{3}$, y-int = 4
5. x-int = $\frac{5}{2}$, y-int = 5
6. x-int = $\frac{8}{5}$, y-int = 8

7.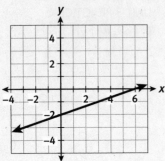

8.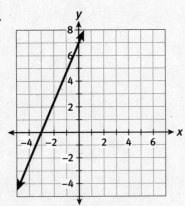

9.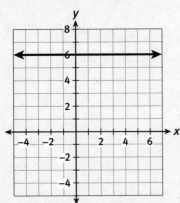

10.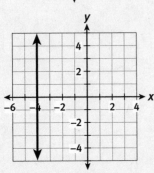

CHECK YOUR UNDERSTANDING

Write your answers on notebook paper. Show your work.

Find the x- and y-intercepts of the following graphs.

1.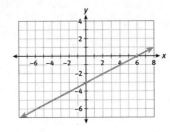

2.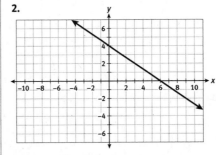

For 3–6, find the x- and y-intercepts of the equations.

3. $y = 8x + 24$
4. $y = 3x + 4$
5. $y = -2x + 5$
6. $5x + y = 8$

Graph the lines that have the following intercepts.

7. x-intercept: 6
   y-intercept: -2

8. x-intercept: -3
   y-intercept: 7

Graph the following lines

9. $y = 6$

10. $x = -4$

11. Write the equation of the lines graphed below.

a.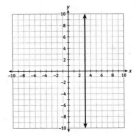

b.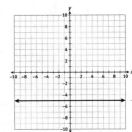

12. **MATHEMATICAL REFLECTION** When would it be easier to graph a line using its slope and y-intercept than to graph it using its x- and y-intercepts? Explain your reasoning.

11a. $x = 3$
  b. $y = -5$

12. Sample answer: When the x-intercept is a fraction, it will be harder to use the x- and y-intercepts than the y-intercept and the slope.

Slopes and Intercepts

LINEAR KINDNESS

Ben's Bells, a community service organization, started hanging ceramic wind chimes randomly in trees, on bike paths, and in parks around the country in 2003 with a written message to simply take one home and pass on the kindness. The linear equation $y = 2000x + 1000$ represents the total number of bells, y, that have been hung by the project given the years, x, since 2003.

1. What is the slope of the line and what does it represent?

2. What is the y-intercept of the line?

3. Graph the equation on the grid below.

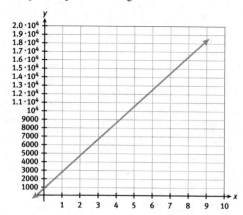

4. Write the equation of the line represented by:

a. the data in the table.

x	y
−2	5
−1	7
0	9
1	11
2	13

Embedded Assessment 2

Assessment Focus
- x-intercepts
- y-intercepts
- Graphing an equation of a line in slope-intercept form
- Finding the equation of a line given a table
- Finding the equation of a line given a graph

Materials
- No materials needed

TEACHER TO TEACHER This assessment looks at linear equations and intercepts from tables, graphs and equations. Students can use multiple representations to find the information. Use their methodology to determine how they are viewing and understanding equations of lines. This will allow you to help students transition into a more abstract understanding of lines.

Answer Key

1. 2000 bells per year

2. 1000

4a. $y = 2x + 9$

b. $y = 5x - 3$

TEACHER TO TEACHER You may wish to read through the rubric with students and discuss the differences in the expectation levels. Make sure students understand the meanings of any terms used.

Slopes and Intercepts
LINEAR KINDNESS

4. b. the data in the graph.

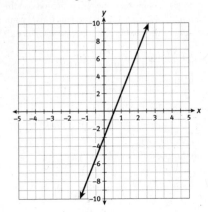

	Exemplary	**Proficient**	**Emerging**
Math Knowledge #1, 2, 3, 4	The student: • Correctly determines the slope of the line and what it represents in the problem situation. (1) • Correctly identifies the y-intercept of the line. (2) • Correctly graphs a line given its equation. (3) • Correctly determines the equation of a line from a table of values. (4a) • Correctly determines the equation of a line given its graph. (4b)	The student provides complete or correct answers for three or four of the items.	The student provides at least two answers for the five items, but they may be incorrect or incomplete
Representation #3	The student correctly represents the equation as a graph.		The student is unable to produce a graph of the equation.
Communication #1	The student correctly explains what the slope of the line represents in the context of this problem situation. (1)		The student is unable to explain what the slope represents in this context.

Analyzing Bivariate Data
Sue Swandive

SUGGESTED LEARNING STRATEGIES: Shared Reading, Role Play

The famous bungee jumper, Sue Swandive, is coming to visit your community to promote her new doll line. There will be a bungee competition with the new doll. The winning group will get a special prize. Rumor has it that they may get to go bungee jumping with Sue herself.

The competition rules are as follows:

a. Attach a rock to the back of a Sue Swandive doll.
b. Make a bungee cord by connecting rubber bands and attach it to the doll.
c. Drop the doll, with bungee cord attached, from a height specified by your teacher. Height:_____.
d. The winning group's Sue doll will come as close to the ground as possible without hitting her head.

To help your group predict how long to make the bungee cord for the competition, you will collect data in your classroom first. You will use this data to make a prediction for the number of rubber bands it will take to win the competition. When it is time for your doll to bungee from the height your teacher specified, you will use the prediction your group made.

Begin the classroom part of your experiments as follows:

• With one rubber band attached to the Sue doll, have a student hold the end of the rubber band *and* the doll's feet at the 0 position on the tape measure.
• Let go of the doll's feet but not the bungee cord.
• Have your group watch carefully to record the height of the doll's head at its lowest position. (It may be helpful to tie the doll's hair back.)
• Be prepared to repeat each jump a few times to get an accurate measurement.
• Record your findings in the table on the next page.
• Add rubber bands and continue to take readings until just before Sue's head touches the floor.

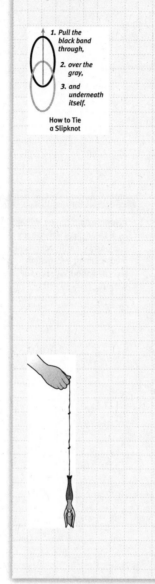

My Notes

1. Pull the black band through,
2. over the gray,
3. and underneath itself.

How to Tie a Slipknot

Some more notes on the experiment:

• The rocks are necessary so that the dolls will be heavy enough to bungee properly. Attach rocks with rubber bands or sturdy tape.
• Secure the doll's feet together using two rubber bands. This will be used to attach the first bungee band with a slipknot.
• Tape a measuring tape or meter stick to a classroom wall so that it is vertical and the low numbers are at the top. Student groups will use this to collect data.
• Attach the rubber bands as needed to extend the bungee using slipknots.

ACTIVITY 3.6 Investigative

Analyzing Bivariate Data

Activity Focus
• Trend Line
• Extrapolating data
• Positive Association
• Negative Association
• No Association

Materials
• A doll for each group (or any object of appropriate size/ weight)
• A rock/weight for each doll
• Rubber bands (new)
• Meter sticks or tape measures
• Graph paper
• Calculator

Chunking the Activity

#1	#6–7	#13–15
#2–3	#8–9	#16
#4	#10–11	#17
#5	#12	#18

TEACHER TO TEACHER The idea behind the experiment is for students to collect data in the classroom, create a trend line based on their data; and then use this line to predict the number of rubber bands a bungee jumping doll will need to jump from a height that you've specified.

Before class begins, find a place like a stairwell or bleachers where the dolls can bungee jump from, and measure the height. This will be the distance that students put in the blank for part c of the competition rules.

Please note: You must measure a height for the final bungee jump before class to give to students.

TEACHER TO TEACHER Take the time to walk students through the data collection process:

With one bungee band attached, one student should hold the end of the bungee band and the doll's feet at the 0 position on the tape measure. Another student should watch carefully and record the lowest position of the doll's head during the bungee. After this value has been recorded, another rubber band should be added to the bungee cord, and the process should be repeated.

Several readings should be taken for each number of rubber bands to ensure accuracy. Data should be collected until just before the doll's head hits the floor.

This will most likely take the entire period the first day. The next day students will create a trend line and extrapolate to see how many bungee bands it will take for the doll to bungee from the height you selected without hitting the floor.

1-2 Create Representations, Think/Pair/Share The data students collect will be the basis for their predictions on the number of rubber bands needed for the final bungee jump.

3 Create Representations
After doing the investigation with the leaking water, students may want to assume that the data is linear. Have them look at the slope of the data to see if it is constant, and have them look at the slope in the table of data to see if it is constant.

My Notes

SUGGESTED LEARNING STRATEGIES: Create Representations, Think/Pair/Share

ACADEMIC VOCABULARY

Bivariate data can be written as ordered pairs where each numerical quantity represents measurement information recorded about a particular subject.

1.

Number of Rubber Bands Attached to the Sue Doll	Length of Bungee Jump
1	
2	
3	
4	
5	
6	
7	
8	
9	
10	

Answers will vary depending on unit of measure used and rubber band size.

The data you have recorded is an example of **bivariate data**. Bivariate data is data with two variables.

2. Create a scatter plot of the data on the grid below.
Answers will vary depending on measurement and rubber band size.

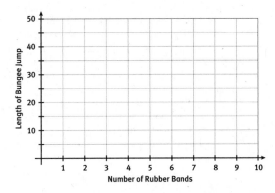

3. Does the data represent a linear relationship? Explain your answers using both the scatterplot and the table.
Answers may vary. Sample answer: No, it is not strictly linear in either since there is not a constant rate of change, but it is close.

SUGGESTED LEARNING STRATEGIES: Quickwrite, Interactive
Word Wall, Create Representations, Think/Pair/Share

4. Describe how the length of the bungee jump changes as the number of rubber bands increases.

Answer may vary. Sample answer: As the number of rubber bands increases the length of the bungee jump increases.

5. What type of association does the data represent?

Answer may vary. Sample answer: There is a positive association between the number of rubber bands and the length of the bungee jump.

A **trend line** is a line that indicates the general course or tendency of data.

6. Use a tool like spaghetti or a ruler, and place it on the scatter plot in a position that has about the same number of points above and below the line. On the coordinate grid, mark two points that the line passes through. They do not have to be data points.

Answers may vary.

7. Draw the line that passes through the two points.

Answers may vary.

8. Write an equation for your trend line in slope intercept form.

Answers may vary, but should have a positive slope.

9. Explain what the variables in the equation of your trend line represent.

The input is the number of rubber bands, and the output is the distance the doll travels on the bungee jump.

10. How does the slope relate to the Sue Doll situation?

Answers may vary. Sample answer: It is the change in the jump length per rubber band.

ACADEMIC VOCABULARY

trend line

MATH TERMS

A collection of data points has a **positive association** if it has the property that *y* tends to increase as *x* increases. It has a **negative association** if *y* tends to decrease as *x* increases. If the data have no clear relationship, they have **no association**.

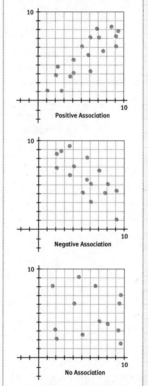

Positive Association

Negative Association

No Association

ACTIVITY 3.6 *Continued*

4 Quickwrite

5 Interactive Word Wall This question gets students to look at how the independent and dependent variables are related. Discuss the meaning of positive, negative, and no association of data.

6-7 Create Representations, Think/Pair/Share Walk around the room and help students to find a trend line that has about the same number of points above and below their lines. Students often pick the first and last data points to create trend lines. Help them to see that the line does not necessarily have to contain any of the data points. It just needs to be representative of most of the points.

8 Create Representations, Think/Pair/Share Students may have a hard time creating the equation of a line with an obscure slope and a possible non-integer *y*-intercept. Walk around the room and help groups make connections to the data and the slope-intercept form of a line. This is the line they will use to make a conjecture about how far the doll will bungee given *x* rubber bands.

9 Quickwrite, Debriefing

10 Quickwrite This question will help students connect the line they've created to the competition. After answering this question, students should understand how to make their prediction about the number of rubber bands it will take for the doll to travel the distance you established at the beginning of the activity.

ACTIVITY 3.6 Continued

11 Quickwrite, Think/Pair/Share

12 Work Backwards Students will use their equation to find the number of rubber bands needed to travel a specific bungee distance.

TEACHER TO TEACHER After students have made their predictions, take the groups out to the designated site and have them set up their dolls with the number of rubber bands they predicted. The group that wins the competition will get the doll's head as close to the ground as possible without hitting it.

TEACHER TO TEACHER For advanced students you may want to have them solve for the independent variable, finding the inverse function. They could then use the equation to solve for the number of rubber bands needed at many different heights.

Suggested Assignment

CHECK YOUR UNDERSTANDING
p. 168, #1–4

UNIT 3 PRACTICE
p. 180, #43–46

13-15 Group Presentation, Debriefing Students are expected to use whatever tools they have to come to their conclusions. You may suggest that they create scatter plots, or that they try to visualize the trends by studying the numbers in the table. Group presentations can help explore possible methods for answering these questions.

My Notes

SUGGESTED LEARNING STRATEGIES: Quickwrite, Think/Pair/Share, Work Backwards

11. Could you use the equations you wrote to predict the length of the bungee jump with 3.5 rubber bands?

Answers may vary. Sample answer: No, 3.5 rubber bands would not make sense in the context. The domain is discrete values of positive integers.

12. Use your equation to predict how many rubber bands it will take to give Sue a maximum bungee jump without touching the ground in the contest.

Answers may vary.

The following data was collected on a group of students. There are many possible ways to pair the data: TV to homework, homework to TV, TV to test scores, test scores to TV, homework to test scores, test scores to homework.

Hours of TV per Week	32	13	28	19	11	21	15	11	15	12	17	20
Percent of Homework Completed	58	82	65	87	98	78	75	92	75	91	90	81
Test Score	66	85	75	85	100	88	85	90	90	95	85	85

13. Which pairs of data seem to have a positive association? Explain your reasoning.

Homework to Test Scores, Test Scores to Homework; Explanations may vary. Sample answer: The dependent variable tends to increase with the independent variable.

14. Which pairs of data seem to have a negative association? Explain your reasoning.

TV to Homework, TV to Test Scores, Test Scores to TV, and Homework to TV; Explanations may vary. Sample answer: The dependent variable tends to decrease with the independent variable.

15. Which pairs of data seem to have no association? Explain your reasoning.

Answers may vary. Sample answer: None of the pairs of data have no association. All of these sets have either positive or negative associations.

Analyzing Bivariate Data
Sue Swandive

SUGGESTED LEARNING STRATEGIES: Create Representations, Activating Prior Knowledge, Discussion Group

My Notes

16. For each pair of variables listed below, create a scatter plot with the first variable shown on the *x*-axis and the second variable on the *y*-axis. Find a trend line that represents the data.

a. Hours of TV per week versus the percent of homework completed

b. Hours of TV per week versus Test Score

c. Percent of homework done versus Test Score

a.
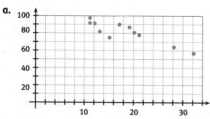

b.
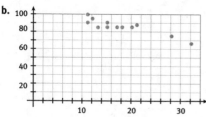

c.
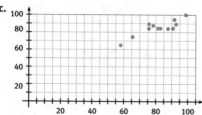

CONNECT TO AP

In AP Statistics, you will find trend lines for bivariate data using a line called the Least Squares Regression.

17. One student came in late to take the test. He had watched 30 hours of TV during the week, but he scored 100 on the test. How would adding this student's data change the trend line?

Answers may vary. Sample answer: If the point is used, it causes the line to flatten out a little more. Since the point is an outlier it would be more appropriate to not account for it with the trend line.

---

16 Create Representations, Activate Prior Knowledge

17 Discussion Group, Debriefing
Students may have a hard time with this question. Showing them an example of how an outlier affects the trend line and discussion of the use of the outlier will be important. You may also want to talk about the fact that a trend line is really an estimation of one kind of best-fit line called a regression equation.

TEACHER TO TEACHER There are other types of best-fit lines like the median-median line that would not be affected by an outlier like the one mentioned in the problem. Just as an average is a good measure of center, but can be affected by extreme values, and the median is also a measure of center that is not affected by extreme values, the regression lines and median-median lines have similar results.

Connect to AP
Students find a trend line by sketching a line that appears to model the data points. They will use the *y*-intercept of the line and two points on their line to determine the slope. In AP Statistics, students will also find trend lines for bivariate data using a line called the Least Squares Regression. The slope and *y*-intercept of this line are computed to minimize the sum of the squares of the distances between data points and the trend line. A computer program or graphing calculator is usually used to quickly find the equation of a Least Squares Regression line.

ACTIVITY 3.6 Continued

18 Discussion Group, Think/Pair/Share This question is designed to once again have students think about the idea of causality.

Suggested Assignment

CHECK YOUR UNDERSTANDING
p. 168, #5–6

UNIT 3 PRACTICE
p. 181, #47

CHECK YOUR UNDERSTANDING

1. Positive

2. No association

3. Positive

4. Negative

5. Answers will vary significantly, but sample equations are:
   1. $y = 2 + \frac{1}{2}x$
   3. $y = \frac{45}{8} + \frac{25}{8}x$
   4. $y = 50 - 2x$

6. Sample answer: The slope of a trend line is positive when there is a positive association. This is because the dependent variable is increasing when the independent variable is increasing. The slope of a trend line is negative when there is a negative association. This is because the dependent variable is decreasing when the independent variable is increasing.

ACTIVITY 3.6
continued

Analyzing Bivariate Data
Sue Swandive

My Notes

SUGGESTED LEARNING STRATEGIES: Discussion Group, Think/Pair/Share

18. Does the data tell you that watching TV causes you to score lower on tests? Explain your reasoning.

   Answers may vary. Sample answers: No. All the data says is that watching TV and test scores have a negative association. It is unknown whether watching TV causes low test scores since correlation does not equal causation.

CHECK YOUR UNDERSTANDING

Write your answers on notebook paper. Show your work.

Determine if the following graphs have a positive, negative, or no association.

1.

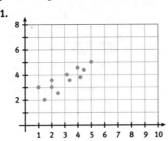

2.

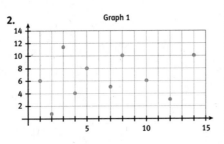

Graph 1

3.

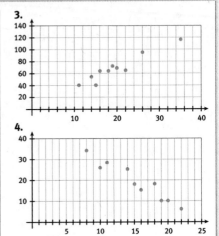

4.

5. Find the equations of the trend lines for any of the questions, 1–4, that had a positive or negative association.

6. **MATHEMATICAL REFLECTION** What does the association of a set of bivariate data indicate about the slope of the trend line?

Systems of Linear Equations
Systems of Trees

SUGGESTED LEARNING STRATEGIES: Marking the Text, Summarize/Paraphrase/Retell, Work Backwards, Create Representations, Group Presentation, Quickwrite, Activating Prior Knowledge

Bob decided to plant some trees in his yard. He bought a 10-gallon mesquite tree and a 50-gallon desert willow and planted them in his yard. After one year he was shocked at the growth of both trees, so he measured their heights. The mesquite was 5 ft tall, and the desert willow was 8 ft tall. The next year he measured again and found the mesquite was 6 ft 6 in. tall, and the desert willow was 8 ft 8 in. tall.

1. List all the numerical information associated with each tree.
Mesquite: 10 gallon; year 1, 5 ft tall; year 2, 6.5 ft tall
Willow: 50 gallon; year 1, 8 ft tall; year 2, 8 ft 8 in tall

2. What information in the paragraph is not needed to find an equation that will predict the height of the trees in a given year?
the container sizes

3. If the trees grew at a constant rate the first two years, how tall were they when Bob planted them?
Mesquite: 3.5 feet; Willow: 7 ft 4 inches

4. Let M be the height of the mesquite tree in inches. Find a linear equation that represents the height of the tree in a given year, t.
$M = 18t + 42$

5. Find a linear equation that represents the height, W, in inches of the desert willow in a given year.
$W = 8t + 88$

6. Could you use the equations you came up with in Questions 4 and 5 to predict the height at 1.5 years?
Yes, since the tree is growing at a constant rate, the equation would give the height at any point during a year.

7. Is the domain continuous or discrete? Explain your reasoning.
Explanations may vary. Sample explanation: The domain is continuous since time is continuous.

8. What is the domain of the functions M and W?
All real numbers such that $t \geq 0$

My Notes

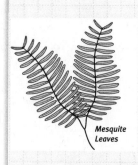

Mesquite
Leaves

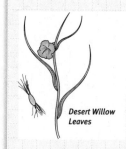

Desert Willow
Leaves

8 Activate Prior Knowledge You may want to discuss the difference it makes to take these equations in context as compared to just seeing them as equations. As linear equations, their domain is all real numbers. In the context of the problem, however, we do not consider the trees before they are planted.

ACTIVITY 3.7 Guided

Systems of Linear Equations

Activity Focus
- Systems of Linear equations

Materials
- No special materials needed

Chunking the Activity

#1–2	#6–8	#15
#3	#9–11	#16–17
#4–5	#12–14	#18–22

TEACHER TO TEACHER The first few questions are designed as ease of entry questions to make sure all students get into the activity.

1-2 Analyze the Text These questions are designed to help students organize the information in the paragraph and determine which information is relevant to the problem.

3 Work Backwards, Debrief Students find the y-intercept using the rate of change and working backwards. This will help them write the equation in Items 4 and 5. It may help to have the students write the information for each tree in a table and look at extending the table in both directions using the rate of change.

4-5 Create Representations, Group Presentation Students may struggle with these questions. If they are not making progress, suggest that they convert feet to inches. Afterwards, have students share their answers, and discuss the question as a class.

6-7 Quickwrite Have students look at the situation and determine if the contextual domain is continuous or discrete. Discussing measuring at different times during the year may help.

9 Create Representations, Quickwrite, Group Presentation

Suggested Assignment

CHECK YOUR UNDERSTANDING
p. 174, #1

UNIT 3 PRACTICE
p. 181, #48

10 Create Representations
Have students examine the graphs they drew carefully. To find when the trees reach the same height, focus students on the vertical axis. Ask them, "What will it mean on the graph for the two trees to have the same height?"

11 Think/Pair/Share Students may have a hard time seeing that they can set two equations equal to each other on their own. This question helps them to see that if *W* and *M* are equal, then their expressions are also equal.

My Notes

9. Use the table below to help explain how the height of the mesquite tree compares to the height of the willow over time.

Year	M (inches)	W (inches)
0	42	88
1	60	96
2	78	104
3	96	112
4	114	120
5	132	128
6	150	136
7	168	144

10. Graph each of the equations on the following grid and use the graph to determine in what year the mesquite reaches the same height as the desert willow.

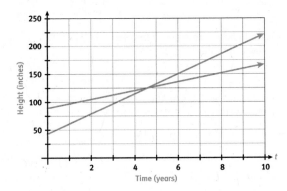

11. When the mesquite tree and the desert willow are the same height, what is true about the values of W and M?

They are equal.

SUGGESTED LEARNING STRATEGIES: Create Representations, Quickwrite, Shared Reading, Interactive Word Wall, Think/Pair/Share

12. Write and solve an equation to find the value of t when the mesquite tree and the desert willow are the same height.

$42 + 18t = 88 + 8t; t = 4.6$

13. What is the meaning of your solution in Question 12?

The two trees will be the same height when they are both 4.6 years after they are planted.

14. How does the solution you found in Question 12 relate to the table and the graph?

Answers will vary. Sample answer: Both the table and the graph indicated that the two trees would be the same height sometime between 4 and 5 years. The solution is between those values.

One way to categorize equations M and W is as a **system of linear equations**. The **solution to a system of linear equations** will always be the point where the two lines intersect. The value you determined in Question 12 was the solution to this particular system of linear equations.

Systems of linear equations can be solved in many different ways. One way is numerically.

15. Determine which ordered pair in the set $\{(2,2), (2,3), (2,4), (3,3)\}$ is the solution to the system of linear equations.

$$\begin{cases} y = -x + 5 \\ y = x + 1 \end{cases} \quad (2,3)$$

16. Create a table of values to find the solution to the following system of equations.

$$\begin{cases} y_1 = -x - 2 \\ y_2 = \frac{2}{3}x + 3 \end{cases}$$

$(-3,1)$

x	y_1	y_2
-6	4	-1
-5	3	$-\frac{1}{3}$
-4	2	$\frac{1}{3}$
-3	1	1
-2	0	$1\frac{2}{3}$
-1	-1	$2\frac{1}{3}$
0	-2	3
1	-3	$3\frac{2}{3}$

My Notes

ACADEMIC VOCABULARY

A **system of linear equations** is a collection of equations which are all considered simultaneously.

The word *linear* indicates that there will only be equations of lines in this collection.

A point, or set of points, is the **solution to a system of equations** in two variables, when it makes both equations true.

WRITING MATH

When working with two or more sets of data in a system of equations, the output variables can be differentiated by writing them with subscripts. For instance, y_1 and y_2 are used in problem 16.

12 **Create Representations** Use questioning techniques to get students to find the equation if they still don't see how to equate M and W from Items 4 and 5.

13 **Quickwrite**

14 **Debrief** Students should see that all three methods yield the same solution.

15 **Create Representations** Students should plug the values in for x and y to see which of the points is a solution to both equations. It is possible that you will need to show them how to do this with an example. Using the point $(4,1)$ will show students that a point can be a solution to one equation, but not both equations.

16 **Create Representations, Think/Pair/Share**

17 Create Representations If you direct students to look at values from −5 to 5, it will make the guess and check process easier.

Suggested Assignment

CHECK YOUR UNDERSTANDING
p. 174, #2–3

UNIT 3 PRACTICE
p. 181, #49–50

18 Quickwrite, Debrief

19 Create Representations

20 Think/Pair/Share Students should see that the lines are parallel. Discuss the fact that if lines have the same slope, they will have no solution because they will never intersect. Show them how this looks algebraically as well: $\dfrac{3x - 4 = 3x + 2}{-4 = 2}$.

Make a point of noting that if one of the slopes in this example were changed to be a negative 3, the lines *would* intersect.

My Notes

SUGGESTED LEARNING STRATEGIES: Create Representations, Think/Pair/Share

17. Create a table of values to find the solution to the following system of equations (use the My Notes space):
$$\begin{cases} y_1 = 5x + 4 \\ y_2 = 2x + 1 \end{cases} \quad (-1, -1)$$

18. What problems came up while solving the systems of equations numerically?
Answers may vary. Possible answer: It takes a large number of calculations.

Another way to solve systems of linear equations is by graphing.

19. Graph the following system of equations and write out the solution.
$$\begin{cases} y = 2x - 4 \\ y = -\frac{1}{2}x + 1 \end{cases}$$
(2, 0)

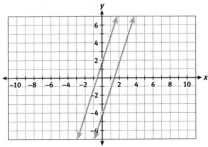

20. Graph the following system of equations and write out the solution.
$$\begin{cases} y = 3x - 4 \\ y = 3x + 2 \end{cases}$$
no solution

Systems of Linear Equations
Systems of Trees

SUGGESTED LEARNING STRATEGIES: Think/Pair/Share, Quickwrite, Interactive Word Wall, Note Taking

My Notes

21. Graph the following system of equations and write out the solution.

$$\begin{cases} y = \frac{1}{3}x + 2 \\ y = -x - 3 \end{cases}$$

$(-3.75, 0.75)$

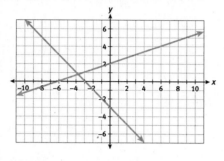

22. What problems came up while solving the systems of equations graphically?

Answers may vary. Sample answer: If the graph is not accurate, it is hard to find a solution. If the solution coordinates are not integer values, the answer is difficult to identify.

You can also solve a system of linear equations algebraically by using the **transitive property of equality**.

EXAMPLE 1

Solve the following system of equations algebraically. $\begin{cases} y = 4x - 1 \\ y = -x + 4 \end{cases}$

Step 1:	Set the equations equal to each other.	$4x - 1 = -x + 4$
		$\begin{array}{r} 4x - 1 = -x + 4 \\ +x \qquad +x \\ \hline \end{array}$
Step 2:	Solve for x.	$5x - 1 = 4$
		$\begin{array}{r} +1 \quad +1 \\ \hline 5x = 5 \end{array}$
		$x = 1$
Step 3:	Substitute x into one of the original equations, and solve for y.	$y = 4(1) - 1$ $y = 3$
Step 4:	Check your solution using the other equation.	$3 \overset{?}{=} -1 + 4$ $3 = 3$
Solution:	Write the solution as an ordered pair. The lines intersect at the point (1,3).	

MATH TERMS

The **transitive property of equality** states:

If $a = b$ and $b = c$, then $a = c$.

ACTIVITY 3.7 *Continued*

21-22 Think/Pair/Share, Debrief, Quickwrite The equations in Item 21 do not yield an easy solution when graphed. This should lead to a discussion about the effectiveness of using graphing to solve linear systems of equations.

Suggested Assignment

CHECK YOUR UNDERSTANDING
p. 174, #4–5

UNIT 3 PRACTICE
p. 181, #51–52

TRY THESE A

These problems provide practice in solving systems of equations algebraically.

Suggested Assignment

CHECK YOUR UNDERSTANDING
p. 174, #6–9

UNIT 3 PRACTICE
p. 181, #53–55

CHECK YOUR UNDERSTANDING

1. 20 minutes to travel 16 miles downstream; 30 minutes to travel the same 16 miles back upstream.

2. $(1, -2)$

3. $(-1, -8)$

4. $(-1, 1)$

5. $(3, 2)$

6. $(1, 4)$

7. No solution, parallel lines

8. $(3, 1)$

9. Answers will vary based on student confidence with each method.

My Notes

SUGGESTED LEARNING STRATEGIES: Create Representations

TRY THESE A

Solve the following systems of linear equations algebraically.

a. $\begin{cases} y = -x - 1 \\ y = -5x - 17 \end{cases}$ $(-4, 3)$

b. $\begin{cases} y = \frac{1}{2}x + 4 \\ y = -\frac{3}{2}x - 4 \end{cases}$ $(-4, 2)$

c. $\begin{cases} 2x - 3y = -1 \\ y = x - 1 \end{cases}$ $(4, 3)$

d. $\begin{cases} 4x + y = 6 \\ -5x - y = 21 \end{cases}$ $(-27, 114)$

CHECK YOUR UNDERSTANDING

Write your answers on notebook paper. Show your work.

Determine what information is needed to solve the following problem. Do not solve the problem.

1. A boat on a river traveled 16 miles in 20 minutes going downstream. The boat can hold 15 gallons of gas. It takes 30 minutes for the boat to travel back upstream to where it started. Find the speed of the current.

2. Determine which of the following points $\{(1, -2), (-1, 2), (1, 2), (-1, -2)\}$ are solutions to the system of equations.
$$\begin{cases} 3x - y = 5 \\ x + 4y = -7 \end{cases}$$

3. Create a table of values to find the solution to the system of equations.
$$\begin{cases} y = 5x - 3 \\ y = 2x - 6 \end{cases}$$

Solve the systems of equations graphically.

4. $\begin{cases} y = x + 2 \\ y = 2x + 3 \end{cases}$

5. $\begin{cases} 2x - 3y = 0 \\ x + 3y = 9 \end{cases}$

Solve the following systems algebraically.

6. $\begin{cases} y = -x + 5 \\ y = x + 3 \end{cases}$

7. $\begin{cases} x + y = 8 \\ y = -x + 4 \end{cases}$

8. $\begin{cases} x - 6y = -3 \\ 2x + 3y = 9 \end{cases}$

9. **MATHEMATICAL REFLECTION** Which method(s) you have learned for solving systems of equations do you prefer? Explain why.

Bivariate Data and Systems

IS IT HOT IN HERE OR IS IT ME?

The weather at places around the world changes daily, sometimes hourly. The average temperature over a period of several years is used to study weather trends. The average temperatures for two cities, one in the northern hemisphere and one in the southern, are shown below.

Guaymas, MX

Month	1	2	3	4	5	6
Temp °F	64	66	68	75	79	87

Johannesburg, SA

Month	1	2	3	4	5	6
Temp °F	69	68	66	61	57	51

1. Plot the data from both cities on the grid below. Use dots for Guaymas and triangles for Johannesburg.

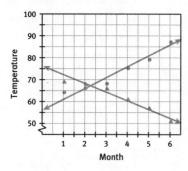

MATH TIP

The jagged part of the vertical axis means that the lower values are not included because there are no points with *y*-coordinates that are these lower values.

2. Describe the associations for each city.

3. Draw a trend line for each set of data.

4. Find the equations of the trend lines for both cities.

5. Explain what the *y*-intercept means for each line in this context.

6. Explain what the slope of each line represents in this context.

7. Determine the month in which the temperatures of both cities are the same.

8. Solve the following system of equations algebraically.

$$\begin{cases} y = 3x - 2 \\ y = 5x - 8 \end{cases}$$

Embedded Assessment 3

Assessment Focus
- Bivariate data association
- Systems of equations

Materials
- No materials needed

TEACHER TO TEACHER Students analyze data from two cities in different hemispheres and look at changing temperatures as months pass. Some students may wonder what happens to average temperatures as the entire year goes by. This would allow the opportunity to discuss periodic functions, but should be avoided during the assessment. Later on, such a discussion can form a very powerful connection to future learning for students.

Answers on this assessment are estimated values. Students may have similar answers, but depending on the lines they drew, they will have different values. You may want to create upper and lower bounds for the *y*-intercepts as well as the slopes that are acceptable as solutions.

Answer Key

1. See the graph on the reduced student page.

2. Guaymas has a positive association, and Johannesburg has a negative association.

3. See the graph for #1 on the preceding reduced student page.

4. Sample answers: $G = 56 + 5m$, $J = 76 - 4m$

5. The y-intercepts represent the average temperatures in those cities in "Month 0," or the month before Month 1.

6. The slope is the average change in temperature per month for each city.

7. Sample answer: The trend lines intersect some time in the second month.

8. $(3, 7)$

9.

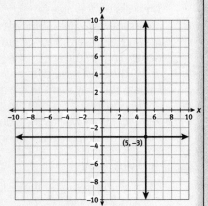

(5, −3)

TEACHER TO TEACHER You may wish to read through the rubric with students and discuss the differences in the expectation levels. Make sure students understand the meanings of any terms used.

Bivariate Data and Systems
IS IT HOT IN HERE OR IS IT ME?

9. Solve the following system of equations graphically.

$$y = -3$$
$$x = 5$$

	Exemplary	Proficient	Emerging
Math Knowledge #2, 4, 7, 8, 9	• Correctly identifies associations of data on the graph (2) • Correctly determines both equations of trend lines (4) • Correctly identifies the month when temperatures are the same (7) • Correctly solves the system of equations (8) • Correctly solves the system of equations graphically (9)	• Can only identify one of the two associations on the graph • Determines the correct equation for one of the trend lines • Identifies the common temperature but not the month • Identifies only one coordinate of the solution to the system • Graphs the equations but does not provide the correct solution	• Is unable to identify the associations present in the graph • Is unable to determine the equation of either line • Does not identify the common temperature or the month • Is unable to provide a solution to the system • Does not graph the equations
Problem Solving #2, 8	• Correctly interprets data on a graph to describe both associations (2) • Correctly uses an appropriate method to solve the system of equations (8)	Solves one of the two items correctly and completely	Is unable to solve either of the two problems correctly
Representation #1, 3, 9	• Creates representation of data (1) • Correctly represents associations with trend lines (3) • Correctly graphs the system of linear equations and determines the correct solution (9)	Provides appropriate representations for two of the three problems	Provides one of the required representations
Communication #2, 5, 6	• Correctly describes association of data plotted on the graph (2) • Correctly explains the meaning of the y-intercept for both trend lines (5) • Correctly explains the meaning of the slope for both of the trend lines (6)	Clearly communicates an explanation for two of the three items	Clearly communicates an explanation for only one of the items

ACTIVITY 3.1

1. Looking at the graph, what do you notice about the relationship between x and y?

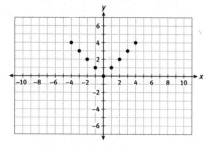

2. Looking at the graph, what do you notice about the relationship between x and y?

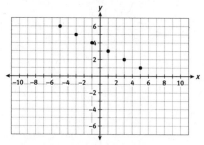

Graph the following data sets and identify each as linear or non-linear.

3. $\{(2,-3), (4,-2), (-2,-5), (0,4)\}$

4. $\{(3,0), (2,4), (-1,-4), (-2,1)\}$

5. $\{(0,5), (4,-3), (3,-1), (2,1)\}$

6. Determine which of the following expressions displays a linear relationship. Use multiple representations to explain your reasoning.

  a. $\sqrt{x}$

  b. $\frac{1}{2}x$

  c. $3 + 0.5x$

  d. $x + 7$

7. Explain how you can determine if an expression represents a linear pattern.

ACTIVITY 3.2

Find the domain and range for the data in Questions 8 and 9

8. $\{(11,2), (2,-14), (-5,13), (58,33)\}$

9.

x	y
1	-8
3	-6
5	-4
7	-3

Use mapping to determine if the information in Questions 10–12 represents a function.

10. $\{(-3,4), (-6,1), (6,0), (-1,5), (-6,4)\}$

11. $x - 9$ for $x = -1, -3, -5, -7, -9$

12.

x	y
-1	9
-5	0
9	0
-1	4

For Questions 13–15 determine if the relations represent functions. Explain your reasoning.

13.

x	y
0	7
2	5
-7	0
6	-5
0	12
5	2
-1	4
1	8

11. It is a function.

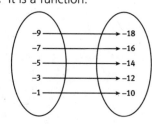

12. Not a function

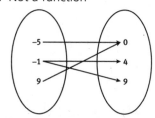

13. It is not a function because 0 has more than one output.

Activity 3.1

1. Sample answer: When x is negative the value of y decreases by one for each increase of 1 in x. When x is positive the value of y increases by one for each increase of 1 in x.

2. Sample answer: The data is decreasing at a constant rate.

3. Not linear

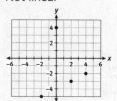

4. Not linear

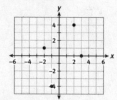

5. Linear

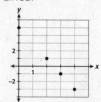

6. b, c, and d are linear. Answers may vary, but should include multiple representations.

7. Sample answer: An expression represents a linear pattern if a constant rate of change in x produces a constant rate of change in y.

Activity 3.2

8. Domain: $\{-5, 2, 11, 58\}$; Range $\{-14, 2, 13, 33\}$

9. Domain: $\{1, 3, 5, 7\}$; Range $\{-8, -6, -4, -3\}$

10. Not a function

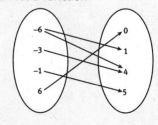

14. It is a function because each input has only one output.

15. It is not a function. There are multiple inputs the have more than one output.

Activity 3.3

16. 12 miles per hour

17. 60 miles

18. 3.5 hours

19a. 1; −3

b. 4; 9

c. 0.5; 3

d. −2; 5

20. d and e

14.

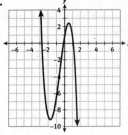

15.

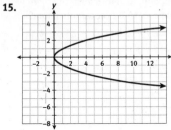

ACTIVITY 3.3

Veronika rides her bike 24 miles in 2 hours.

16. Create a ratio of Veronika's miles per hour.

17. Using the ratio you found in Question 16, determine how far Veronika can ride in 5 hours.

18. If Veronika rode her bike for 42 miles at the rate you found, how long was she riding?

19. Find the slope and y-intercept of the following:

a.

x	y
0	−3
2	−1
4	1

b.

x	y
−1	5
0	9
4	25

c.

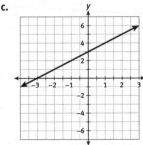

d.

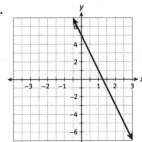

20. If a line with a slope of $-\frac{1}{2}$ contains the point (2, 3), then it must also contain which of the following points?

a. (−2, 6)

b. (0, 5)

c. (1, 2)

d. (4, 2)

e. (8, 0)

ACTIVITY 3.4

21. Find the slope.

x	y
0	11
2	7.5
4	4

Graph the following linear equations.

22. $y = 5x$

23. $y = -4x$

24. $y = \frac{1}{5}x$

25. A line with a slope of -2 goes through the point $(3, 5)$. It also goes through the point $(-2, p)$. What is the value of p?

26. Write the equation of the line graphed below.

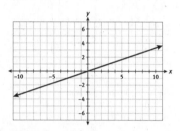

Graph the following linear equations.

27. $y = 5x - 2$

28. $y = 2x + 10$

29. $y = -25x + 100$

30. Write an equation for the line graphed below.

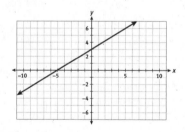

ACTIVITY 3.5

Find the x- and y-intercepts of the following graphs.

31.

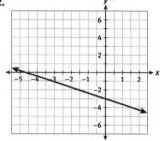

32.

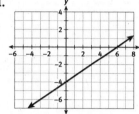

Find x- and y-intercepts of the following equations.

33. $y = 6x + 30$

34. $y = 3x + 12$

35. $y = -7x - 21$

36. $9x + y = 72$

For Questions 37 and 38, graph the line with the given intercepts.

37. x-intercept: 7
y-intercept: 4

38. x-intercept: -5
y-intercept: 3

Graph the following equations of lines.

39. $x = -7$

40. $y = 2$

Activity 3.4

21. $m = -1.75$

22.

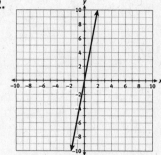

23.

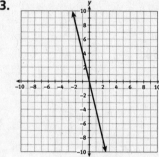

24.

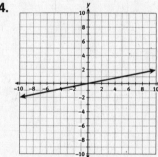

25. $p = 15$

26. $y = \frac{1}{3}x$

27.

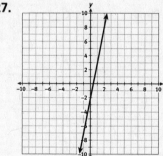

28.

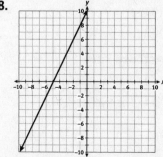

29.

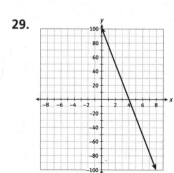

30. $y = 3 + \frac{3}{5}x$

Activity 3.5

31. x-int $= 6$, y-int $= -4$

32. x-int $= -4.5$, y-int $= -3$

33. x-int $= -5$, y-int $= 30$

34. x-int $= -4$, y-int $= 12$

35. x-int $= -3$, y-int $= -21$

36. x-int $= 8$, y-int $= 72$

37.

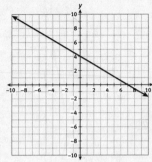

38.

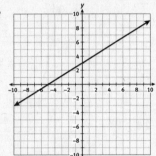

39.

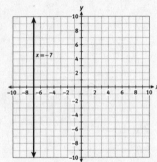

$x = -7$

40.

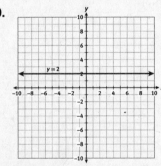

$y = 2$

41. $y = 8$

42. $x = -8$

Activity 3.6

43. No Association

44. Positive

For 41–42, write the equation of the line in the graph.

41.

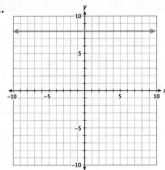

42.

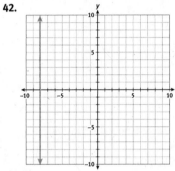

ACTIVITY 3.6

Determine if the graphs for Questions 43 through 46 have a positive, a negative, or no association.

43.

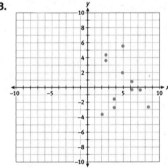

44.

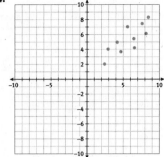

45.

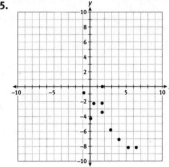

46.

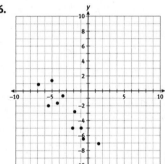

47. Find the equations of the trend lines for any of the graphs in 43–46 that had a positive or negative association.

ACTIVITY 3.7

Determine what information is relevant to solve the following problem. Do not solve the problem.

48. A monkey weighs 10 pounds. He eats 2 pounds of bananas in a day. How many pounds of bananas will he eat in 1 week?

49. Determine which of the following points $\{(0,3), (-1,4), (3,0), (4,-1)\}$ are solutions to the system of equations.
$$\begin{cases} 3x + 2y = 5 \\ x + 2y = 7 \end{cases}$$

50. Determine which of the following points $\{(-3,5), (3,-5), (3,5), (-3,-5)\}$ are solutions to the system of equations.
$$\begin{cases} 3x - y = -4 \\ 2x - 5y = 19 \end{cases}$$

Solve the following systems of equations by graphing.

51. $\begin{cases} y = 3x + 2 \\ y = -2x - 8 \end{cases}$

52. $\begin{cases} x + y = -1 \\ 2x + 2y = 4 \end{cases}$

Solve the following systems of equations algebraically.

53. $\begin{cases} y = 4 - x \\ y = x - 2 \end{cases}$

54. $\begin{cases} y = -3x + 6 \\ 3x + y = 5 \end{cases}$

55. $\begin{cases} 4x - y = 1 \\ 6x + y = -6 \end{cases}$

UNIT 3 PRACTICE *Continued*

45. Negative

46. Negative

47. Answers will vary
   44: $y = x$
   45: $y = -2 - x$
   46: $y = -6 - x$

Activity 3.7

48. 2 pounds in a day, and the 1 week time period.

49. $(-1, 4)$

50. $(-3, -5)$

51. $(-2, -4)$

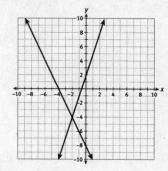

52. No solution

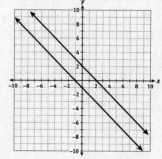

53. $(3, 1)$

54. No solution

55. $\left(-\frac{1}{2}, -3\right)$

Reflection

Student Reflection

Discuss the essential questions with students. Have them share how their understanding of the questions has changed through studying the concepts in the unit.

Review the academic vocabulary. You may want students to revisit the graphic organizers they have completed for academic vocabulary terms and add other notes about their understanding of terms.

Encourage students to evaluate their own learning and to recognize the strategies that work best for them. Help them identify key concepts in the unit and to set goals for addressing their weaknesses and acquiring effective learning strategies.

Teacher Reflection

1. Of the key concepts in the unit, did any present special challenges for students?

2. How will you adjust your future instruction for students/activities?

3. Which strategies were most effective for facilitating student learning?

4. When you teach this unit again, what will you do differently?

Reflection

An important aspect of growing as a learner is to take the time to reflect on your learning. It is important to think about where you started, what you have accomplished, what helped you learn, and how you will apply your new knowledge in the future. Use notebook paper to record your thinking on the following topics and to identify evidence of your learning.

Essential Questions

1. Review the mathematical concepts and your work in this unit before you write thoughtful responses to the questions below. Support your responses with specific examples from concepts and activities in the unit.
   - Why is it important to consider slope, domain, and range in problem situations?
   - How can graphs be used to interpret solutions of real-world problems?

Academic Vocabulary

2. Look at the following academic vocabulary words:
   - bivariate data
   - continuous data
   - discrete data
   - domain
   - function
   - linear data
   - range
   - rate of change
   - relation
   - slope
   - solution of a system of linear equations
   - system of linear equations
   - trend line
   - x-intercept
   - y-intercept

   Choose three words and explain your understanding of each word and why each is important in your study of math.

Self-Evaluation

3. Look through the activities and Embedded Assessments in this unit. Use a table similar to the one below to list three major concepts in this unit and to rate your understanding of each.

Unit Concepts	Is Your Understanding Strong (S) or Weak (W)?
Concept 1	
Concept 2	
Concept 3	

   a. What will you do to address each weakness?

   b. What strategies or class activities were particularly helpful in learning the concepts you identified as strengths? Give examples to explain.

4. How do the concepts you learned in this unit relate to other math concepts and to the use of mathematics in the real world?

Additional Notes

1. Which situation, when graphed, would be non-linear?

   A. the amount of water in a tub as it drains

   B. the height of a wedding cake as 5-inch layers are added

   C. the speed of each car passing through an intersection

   D. the weight of a sandbag as shovelfuls of dirt are added

2. What is the slope of the graph of $y = -2x + 6$?

1. Ⓐ Ⓑ Ⓒ Ⓓ

2. (gridded response grid)

Read Solve Explain

3. Jimmy joined Rhapsody internet music service at a cost of $12.99 per month. He received an MP3 player for a gift and wanted to start downloading songs. Rhapsody charges $0.99 per downloaded song.

   Part A: Complete the table for the cost of downloading 1, 2, 3, 4, or 5 songs in a month

# of songs	Cost
1	13.98
2	14.97
3	15.96
4	16.95
5	17.94

   Part B: List the domain and range of the function from the table. Write an equation that Jimmy can use to determine the cost C of any number of downloads d.

   Answer and Explain

   Domain: 1, 2, 3, 4, 5

   Range: 13.98, 14.97, 15.96, 16.95, 17.94

   Equation: $C = 0.99d + 12.99$

UNIT 3 Math Standards Review

These two pages provide practice with four standardized test question formats that are used in many national and state high-stakes tests:

- Multiple choice
- Gridded response
- Short response
- Extended response

These items also provide practice with the mathematics content of this unit.

1 Multiple choice
- Compare linear and non-linear functions

2 Gridded response
- Determine slope

3 Short Response
- Create representations from verbal situations
- Identify domain and range

4 Extended response
- Write from verbal problems
- Graph linear equations
- Interpret graphs

TEACHER TO TEACHER You might read through the extended-response item with students and discuss your expectation levels. Make sure students understand the meanings of any terms used.

Read Solve Explain

4. Itmar was 63 inches tall in August at the start of 8th grade. His best friend Megan was 65 inches tall at that time. Itmar grew an average of one-half of an inch each month through May. Megan grew one-fourth of an inch each month through May.

Part A: Write two equations, one to show Itmar's height at any time during the school year and one to show Megan's. Use h for height and m for number of months since August.

Answer and Explain

Itmar: $h = 0.5m + 63$

Megan: $h = 0.25m + 65$

Part B: Graph each student's height from August to May on this graph.

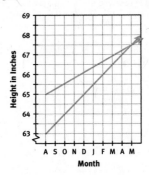

Part C: Will Itmar be taller than Megan by the end of 8th grade in May? If so, describe the point where their heights are the same.

Solve and Explain

Itmar will be taller than Megan by May. In April they will both be 67 inches tall.

This unit builds on students' knowledge of geometric concepts and understanding of formulas. Students classify and determine the measures of angles related to lines and polygons; they reason about structures and solve problems involving rates, ratios, and proportions; and they find solutions to application problems.

Academic Vocabulary

Blackline masters for use in developing students' vocabulary skills are located at the back of this Teacher's Edition. Encourage students to explore the meanings of the academic vocabulary words in this unit, using graphic organizers and class discussion to help students understand the key concepts related to the terms. Encourage students to place their vocabulary graphic organizers in their Math Notebooks and to revisit these pages to make notes as their understanding of concepts increases.

Embedded Assessments

The two Embedded Assessments for this unit follow Activities 4.3 and 4.7.

CollegeBoard
inspiring minds™

Algebra AP/College Readiness

Unit 4 continues to develop students' understanding of geometry by:

- Classify figures and determine measures.
- Allowing students to communicate mathematics and explain solutions verbally and in writing.
- Encouraging students to determine the reasonableness of solutions including size and relative accuracy.
- Providing contextual situations in which transformations of polygons can be applied.
- Using real world contexts to develop understanding of concepts.

Embedded Assessment 1 Sweet Hexagons

- Parallel lines and special pairs of angles
- Sum of angle measures in a triangle
- Angles in a polygon (hexagon)
- Rigid transformations

Embedded Assessment 2 Golden Rectangles

- Ratios and proportions
- Percents
- Similarity and scale factor
- Unit conversion

Suggested Pacing

The following table provides suggestions for pacing either a 45-minute period or a block schedule class of 90 minutes. Space is left for you to write your own pacing guidelines based on your experiences in using the materials.

	45-Minute Period	90-Minute Period	Comments on Pacing
Unit Overview	$\frac{1}{2}$	$\frac{1}{4}$	
Activity 4.1	4	2	
Activity 4.2	4	2	
Activity 4.3	4	2	
Embedded Assessment 1	1	$\frac{1}{2}$	
Activity 4.4	4	2	
Activity 4.5	4	2	
Activity 4.6	3	$1\frac{1}{2}$	
Activity 4.7	2	1	
Embedded Assessment 2	1	$\frac{1}{2}$	
Total	$27\frac{1}{2}$	$13\frac{3}{4}$	

Unit Practice

Practice Problems for each activity in the unit appear at the end of the unit.

Math Standards Review

To help accustom students to the formats and types of questions they may encounter on high stakes tests, additional problems are provided at the end of the unit. These problems are constructed for multiple choice, short response, extended response, and gridded responses.

Proportional Relationships

Unit Overview
In this unit you will study angle relationships in parallel lines and polygons. You will also study similar figures, proportions, and unit conversions.

Academic Vocabulary
Add these words to your vocabulary notebook.
- angle
- similar figures
- transformation (geometric)

Essential Questions

 How is proportional reasoning used to solve real-world problems?

 What are transformations and how are they useful in solving real-world problems?

EMBEDDED ASSESSMENTS

This unit has 2 Embedded Assessments. The first embedded assessment allows you to demonstrate your understanding of angle relationships in parallel lines and polygons and similar figures. In the second, you will demonstrate understanding of proportions and unit conversions.

Embedded Assessment 1
Lines, Angles, Transformations
p. 211

Embedded Assessment 2
Proportions, Similarity, and Conversions
p. 241

UNIT 4 OVERVIEW

Unit Overview
Ask students to read the unit overview and review what they know about lines, angles, and polygons.

Essential Questions
Read the essential questions with students and elicit any prior knowledge. Then ask students to think about these questions as they work through the unit.

Materials
- Whiteboard/chalkboard
- BLM1: Empty chute and pre-cut triangles
- Dry erase boards or chart paper and markers
- Protractors
- Centimeter rulers
- 4-function calculators (optional)
- US Flag (on display in classroom)
- Optional materials for demonstration in Activity 4.7: 4 matching glasses with at least 2 inches of water, a cookie sheet with an edge, 4 congruent cylinders, and 4 eggs.

Unit 4 Vocabulary
Discuss with students the importance of precise language in mathematics. Encourage students to use the mathematics vocabulary they been acquiring throughout the year whenever they are asked to discuss of write about a mathematical idea.

185

You may wish to assign some or all of these exercises to gauge students' readiness for Unit 4 topics.

Prerequisite Skills

- Measuring angles (Item 1)
- Points on the plane (Item 2)
- Writing equations from sentences and solving equations (Items 3, 4)
- Characteristics of figures (Item 6)
- Concept of ratio and percent (Items 5,7)
- Units of measure (Item 8)

Getting Ready

1. 45°, 75°

2. $A(3, 7)$; $B(-1, 5)$; $C(6, 0)$; $D(-5, -4)$

3a. $x = \frac{3}{4}$

b. $x = 0.8$

c. $x = \frac{1}{8}$

4. $3x + 4 = 22$; $x = 6$

5a. $\frac{2}{5}$ and $\frac{6}{15}$ because $\frac{6}{15}$ in simplified form is $\frac{2}{5}$

b. $\frac{1.2}{7}$ and $\frac{3.6}{21}$ because you can multiply $\frac{1.2}{7}$ by $\frac{3}{3}$ to get $\frac{3.6}{21}$

c. All are equivalent. Ratios can be written in each way shown and they all reduce to $\frac{2}{3}$

6. Answers may vary. Sample answers:

a. No two sides have the same length and no two angles have the same measure.

b. Two sides have the same length, and the two angles opposite those sides have the same measure.

c. All sides are the same length, and each angle measures 60°.

d. An angle that measures less than 90 degrees

e. An angle that measures more than 90 degrees

f. Two angles whose measures have a sum of 90 degrees

g. Two angles whose measures have a sum of 180 degrees

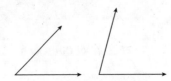

Write your answers on notebook paper. Show your work.

1. Use a compass to measure the following angles.

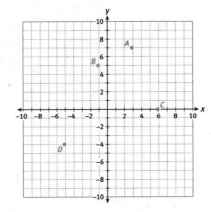

2. Give the coordinates of points A, B, C, and D on the graph below.

3. Solve the following equations.

a. $4x + 7 = 10$

b. $2x + 4.1 = 5.7$

c. $3x + \frac{1}{2} = 2x + \frac{5}{8}$

4. Write and solve an equation that represents the statement "four more than three times a number is twenty-two."

5. Name the equivalent ratios in each set of numbers. Justify your answer.

a. $\frac{2}{5}, \frac{3}{6}, \frac{4}{9}, \frac{6}{15}$

b. $\frac{1.2}{7}, \frac{2.4}{8.4}, \frac{3.6}{21}$

c. 2:3, $\frac{4}{6}$, 6 to 9

6. Give the characteristics of each of the following triangles and angles.

a. scalene triangle

b. isosceles triangle

c. equilateral triangle

d. acute angle

e. obtuse angle

f. complementary angles

g. supplementary angles

7. Tell which of the following graphs are about 33% shaded, which are about 50% shaded, and which are about 75% shaded. Explain how you made your decisions.

8. Explain how to convert $5\frac{1}{2}$ feet to inches.

---

7. 33%: c and f, about one third of these graphs are shaded.
50%: a and d, about one half of these graphs are shaded.
75%: b and e, about three fourths of these graphs are shaded.

8. Answers may vary. Sample answer: To convert $5\frac{1}{2}$ feet to inches multiply 5 by the number of inches in a foot, 12. Then add 6 to the product because $\frac{1}{2}$ of a foot is 6 inches. $5\frac{1}{2}$ ft = 66 in.

Angle Pair Relationships
The Winning Angle

SUGGESTED LEARNING STRATEGIES: Activating Prior
Knowledge, Think/Pair/Share, Interactive Word Wall

Bob Toose, football coach and geometry teacher at Johnny Unitas
High School, names his football plays after different geometric
terms. He knows that the players from other schools will not know
what is coming at them with these names.

He gives playbook quizzes to make sure his
players know their plays. A portion of one of his
quizzes follows. For this quiz, the scrimmage line is
shown at the 20 yard line.

1. Match the play with the mathematical term
that best describes it.

My Notes

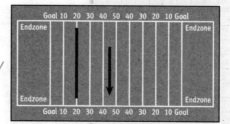

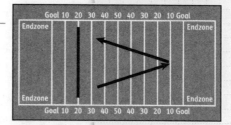

Angle

Perpendicular Lines

Parallel Lines

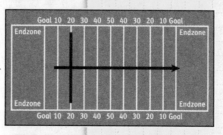

Right Angle

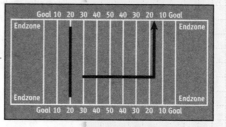

Angle Pair Relationships

Activity Focus
- Angle pair relationships
  - Complementary
  - Supplementary
  - Vertical
  - Alternate exterior
  - Alternate interior
  - Corresponding

Materials
- Whiteboard/chalkboard
- Tape (opaque color)

Chunking the Activity

#1	#9	#20–21
#2–3	#10–12	#22
#4	#13–14	#23
#5–6	#15–16	#24
#7	#17–18	
#8	#19	

TEACHER TO TEACHER This unit will allow some of the football fans in your classroom to share their knowledge of the game with the other students. Allow them to explain what the plays in the diagrams look like on the field.

1 Activating Prior Knowledge, Think/Pair/Share, Debrief, Interactive Word Wall Students need to match the play diagrams on this page with the mathematical terms for each of the play diagrams. The concepts being shown in these diagrams are concepts that students have studied in previous math courses. Make sure to debrief the class after this question so that students who have not yet mastered the material hear the names for these diagrams. These can be posted in the classroom on the interactive word wall.

2 Activating Prior Knowledge

Differentiating Instruction

Some students may need extra support when drawing these complementary angles and other angles later in the unit. If necessary, draw one ray of the set for them on the paper so they have a starting place for their work.

3 Quickwrite, Think/Pair/Share, Debrief

This is an opportunity to informally assess what students know about angle relationships. Many different terms may come out when you debrief the class after this question. It is important to discuss what each of the terms brought forth means. Be sure to bring out the idea that the term complementary applies to *pairs* of angles only. Some students may believe that the term can apply to more than two angles.

4 Visualization, Create Representations, Think/Pair/Share

Students may have an easier time coming up with the complementary angles than illustrating them. If more instruction is needed on protractor use, take a timeout from the lesson and have the students measure different size angles. Student directions for measuring angles are given on this page as a mini-lesson. When they have mastered measuring angles, have them draw angles of different sizes by first drawing one ray and using that ray for the bottom of the angle just as they did with measuring angles.

5 Quickwrite, Create Representations, Debrief

After the discussion from Question 3, the concepts in this exercise might have been refreshed for students. Have them share their sketches of supplementary angles with their partners and their groups so that they can compare the various ways that a set of supplementary angles can look.

My Notes

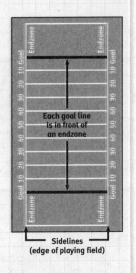

Each goal line is in front of an endzone

**Sidelines
(edge of playing field)**

ACADEMIC VOCABULARY

An **angle** is the union of two rays with a common endpoint called a vertex.

SUGGESTED LEARNING STRATEGIES: Activating Prior Knowledge, Debrief, Quickwrite, Think/Pair/Share, Visualization, Create Representations,

Coach Toose is very particular about the routes that his players run. He told his receiver that this "corner" route needed to be run at a 50° **angle** to the sideline of the end zone.

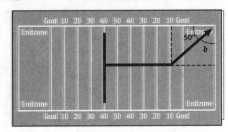

2. What is the measure of angle *b* in the diagram above?
40°

3. What is the relationship between these two angles called? Explain your choice.

These angles are complementary angles. They are called complementary because the sum of their measures is 90°.

4. Coach Toose wanted his players to run other corner routes as well. Identify the angle complementary to the one listed. Then draw and label each route.

a. 20° 70°

b. 73° 17°

Another route that Coach Toose has his players run is a "post" route. The route can be used to show supplementary angles.

5. Tell what it means for angles to be supplementary and sketch an example below.

Angles are supplementary if the sum of their angles is 180°. Sample sketch:

MINI-LESSON: Measuring Angles with a Protractor

To better illustrate this concept, the angles should be composed of two rays.

1. Put the vertex at the center of the straight side of the protractor. With the vertex in place, line up one ray of the angle with the straight side of the protractor. Call this the "base" ray. Make sure the second ray falls inside the arc of the protractor when the base ray is lined up.

2. On the curved edge of most protractors are two sets of numbers. One scale starts with zero on the left edge and increases to the right, while the other starts with zero on the right edge and increases to the left. Choose the scale that starts on the side that your base ray points towards.

3. Read off the number from this scale at the point where the second ray of the angle crosses the protractor. You may have to extend this side of your angle so that it does cross the protractor.

SUGGESTED LEARNING STRATEGIES: Activating Prior Knowledge, Visualization, Create Representations, Think/Pair/Share

6. This "post" route is seen below as it passes over the goal line. Give the measure of angle *d*.   70°

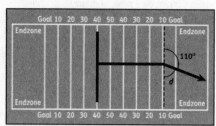

7. Coach Toose's team runs a variety of "post" routes. Draw and label the routes below and identify the angle supplementary to the one listed.

a. 20° 160°

b. 153° 27°

TRY THESE A

Give the measure of the complementary and supplementary angles of each:

a. 57° _33°_ , _123°_

b. 93° _not possible_ , _87°_

Are these angles complementary? Explain why or why not.

c. 47° and 53°   No, because 47 + 53 = 100. Complementary angles must have a sum of 90°.

d. 12° and 78°   Yes, because the sum of 12 and 78 is 90; and if the sum of two angles is 90°, they are complementary.

Are these angles supplementary? Explain why or why not.

e. 37° and 143° Yes, because the sum of 37 and 143 is 180; and if the sum of two angles is 180°, they are supplementary.

f. 118° and 52° No, because the sum of 118 and 52 is 170. Two angles must have a sum of 180° to be supplementary.

My Notes

TEACHER TO TEACHER   To help students remember complementary and supplementary and which is 90° and 180°, remind them that "c" for complementary comes before "s" for supplementary in the alphabet just as 90° comes before 180°.

6 Activating Prior Knowledge

7 Visualization, Create Representations, Think/Pair/Share, Debrief This question is similar to Question 4 but is done with supplementary, rather than complementary, angles. Debriefing the class afterwards will ensure that everyone understands what it means for angles to be supplementary.

TRY THESE A The Try These on this page act as extra practice for the concepts in the activity so far, and as informal assessment of the same.

TEACHER TO TEACHER Students will use tape on their desks (or a sheet of paper) as a manipulative for working with parallel lines cut by a transversal. The introduction begins with them using the tape to make just the parallel lines. The next step has them make the transversal and label the diagram for use on the questions that follow. The angles may be labeled with sticky notes or small pieces of tape. A pair or trio of students can use one diagram to save tape.

8 Use Manipulatives, Activating Prior Knowledge, Debriefing Debrief the class after this question. If they haven't already reached it, lead them to the conclusion that this diagram represents parallel lines cut by a transversal.

9 Use Manipulatives, Activating Prior Knowledge

10 Predict and Confirm, Quickwrite Make sure this answer is based on a prediction made without measuring.

11 Use Manipulatives, Predict and Confirm, Quickwrite, Debrief Have the students compare their predictions and the actual measures of these angles.

12 Activating Prior Knowledge, Quickwrite, Debriefing During the class discussion after this question, make sure that the word congruent comes out.

My Notes

SUGGESTED LEARNING STRATEGIES: Use Manipulatives, Activating Prior Knowledge, Predict and Confirm, Quickwrite

The coach uses a diagram like the one below to show plays to his team. Your teacher will give you tape to recreate these same play lines on your desk or on a piece of paper.

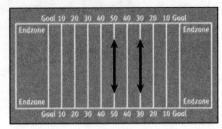

Now using the tape, add a "slant" route to your diagram and label the angles as seen below.

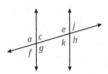

MATH TERMS

A **transversal** is a line that intersects two or more lines to form eight or more angles.

8. What mathematical term do you think Coach Toose uses for this play?
The Transversal

9. Measure angle *j* on your diagram.
Answers may vary. For the diagram shown above: 75°

10. Without measuring, predict which other angles have the same measure as angle *j* and list them below.
k, *c*, and *f*

11. Now measure these angles. Were your predictions correct?
Yes, angles *k*, *c*, and *f* are the same size as angle *j*.

12. What term is used to identify angles that have the same measure?
Angles or figures that are the same size and shape are called congruent.

Angle Pair Relationships
The Winning Angle

SUGGESTED LEARNING STRATEGIES: Use Manipulatives, Quickwrite, Group Presentation, Think/Pair/Share

My Notes

13. What is true about the measures of the remaining angles in your diagram?

The remaining angles are the same size or congruent.

14. Using the diagram that you made on your desk and your observations in the previous questions, what can you say about the angles formed by two parallel lines cut by a transversal?

Answers may vary. Sample answer: Parallel lines cut by a transversal create sets of angles having the same measure.

TRY THESE B

a. Find the missing angle measures on the diagram below.

Angle	Measure
∠RHC	125°
∠SKU	125°
∠HKO	125°
∠JHK	125°
∠RHJ	55°
∠CHK	55°
∠OKU	55°
∠SKH	55°

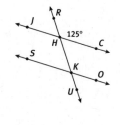

---

15. What does the term exterior mean in everyday language? Give at least two examples.

Answers may vary. Sample answer: Exterior means outside. Examples: exterior paint, exterior furniture, and exterior color on a car.

16. Which angles in the figure above do you think are exterior angles? Explain.

Exterior angles in the diagram are: ∠RHC, ∠SKU, ∠OKU, ∠RHJ

ACTIVITY 4.1 Continued

13 Use Manipulatives, Quickwrite, Debrief Students should conclude that the remaining angles are congruent.

14 Quickwrite, Debrief, Group Presentation Have the students share answers as a class, making a master list of what can be said about the angles formed by two parallel lines cut by a transversal.

TRY THESE B Try These B can be done at different levels. Some students may need to measure each of the angles with a protractor, some may measure a few of the angles and be able to discern the rest, and other students may be able to take the given measure and complete the table without using a protractor at all. Allow students to complete the exercise as they need to. When they are done, they can compare methods with the other students in the class.

Suggested Assignment

CHECK YOUR UNDERSTANDING
p. 194, #1–7

UNIT 4 PRACTICE
p. 243, #1–6

15 Quickwrite, Debrief This question refers to the everyday use of the word exterior to build vocabulary for following questions. Be sure to discuss the various examples the students have chosen.

16 Quickwrite, Think/Pair/Share Students should apply their definitions of exterior from Item 15 to defend their choice of exterior angles.

17 Quickwrite, Debrief This question refers to the everyday use of the word interior to build vocabulary for questions on the next page. As a class, discuss the various examples students have chosen.

18 Quickwrite, Think/Pair/Share Students should use their definitions of exterior from Item 17 to defend their choice of interior angles.

TEACHER TO TEACHER Before beginning the next section on alternate exterior and alternate interior angles, some students may benefit by discussing the term "alternate." Students may be able to think of real world examples for this term as well.

19 Visualization, Quickwrite, Think/Pair/Share, Debrief Students may benefit from using colored pencils to color in these angles so that the relationship is obvious. They may need guidance to come up with definitions in parts a and c. Be sure to discuss which of the angles are alternate exterior in part b and alternate interior in part d. Students should notice that the angles in each pair are congruent to each other.

My Notes

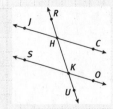

SUGGESTED LEARNING STRATEGIES: Quickwrite, Think/Pair/Share, Visualization

17. What does the term interior mean in everyday language? Give at least two examples.

Answers may vary. Sample answer: Interior means inside. Examples: interior paint, a car's interior, and interior design.

18. Which angles in the figure on the left do you think are interior angles? Explain

Interior angles in the diagram are: ∠CHK, ∠HKO, ∠JHK, ∠SKH

19. There are two pairs of angles in the diagram on the left that are referred to as **alternate exterior angles** and two pairs of angles that are referred to as **alternate interior angles**.

  a. Explain what it means for angles to be *alternate exterior angles*.

  Alternate exterior angles are on opposite sides of the transversal line, and outside the parallel lines.

  b. Name the two pairs of alternate exterior angles and tell what you notice about the measure of these angles.

  ∠RHC and ∠SKU; ∠OKU and ∠RHJ; The angles in each pair are congruent to each other. The measures of each of the angles in one pair are supplementary to the measures of each of the angles in the other pair.

  c. Explain what it means for angles to be *alternate interior angles*.

  Alternate interior angles are on opposite sides of the transversal line, and inside the parallel lines.

  d. Name the two pairs of alternate interior angles and tell what you notice about the measures of these angles.

  ∠JHK and ∠HKO; ∠SKH and ∠CHK; The angles in each pair are congruent to each other. The measures of each of the angles in one pair are supplementary to the measures of each of the angles in the other pair.

MINI-LESSON: Geometry Vocabulary

There are many geometric terms in this activity. Some students may have difficulty remembering and applying these terms. Some ideas to help with this problem are:

- Have the students design flashcards for these terms and hook them together with a shower curtain ring to keep them together for studying.
- Have the students create a bingo game with terms and definitions that can be played by the class.
- Play term charades with the students writing down their guesses on whiteboards for the term being acted out.
- Have the students make a "concentration" type game with definitions, examples, and terms as the matching items.

Angle Pair Relationships
The Winning Angle

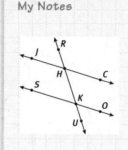

SUGGESTED LEARNING STRATEGIES: Quickwrite, Visualization, Activating Prior Knowledge, Think/Pair/Share

My Notes

20. Another type of angle found in parallel lines cut by a transversal are **corresponding angles**. What do you think is meant by the term corresponding?

Corresponding angles are angles that are at the same location at each intersection in the figure.

21. Name the pairs of corresponding angles in the diagram above and tell what you notice about the measures of these angles.

∠RHC and ∠HKO; ∠CHK and ∠OKU; ∠RHJ and ∠HKS; ∠JHK and ∠SKU; The angles in these pairs are congruent to each other.

22. Two pairs of **vertical angles** are formed when two lines intersect. List the pairs of vertical angles in the diagram above and tell what you notice about the measures of these angles.

∠RHJ and ∠CHK; ∠RHC and ∠JHK; ∠OKU and ∠HKS; ∠SKU and ∠HKO; The angles in these pairs are congruent to each other.

> **MATH TERMS**
>
> **Vertical angles** are formed when two lines intersect. A pair of vertical angles share a common vertex but no common rays.

23. Using what you now know about alternate exterior, alternate interior, corresponding and vertical angles, find the missing measures in the diagram below without using a protractor.

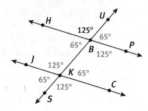

20 Quickwrite, Debrief The term "corresponding" should be familiar to students from previous courses. Discussing the term will be helpful to the students who have not mastered the idea.

21 Visualization

22 Activating Prior Knowledge, Visualization, Debrief Some students may benefit from coloring each of the vertices in the diagram with a darker color so that they see the vertex of each set of vertical angles.

23 Visualization, Think/Pair/ Share, Debrief, Group Presentation For this problem, students should be encouraged to use all of the types of angle relationships that they have been learning about to find the angle measures. The groups should share their solutions and explain how they determined their answers.

24 Quickwrite, Group Presentation Students should share their answers with the class. This would be good information to make a class set of posters for.

Suggested Assignment

CHECK YOUR UNDERSTANDING
p. 194, #8–9

UNIT 4 PRACTICE
p. 243, #7

CHECK YOUR UNDERSTANDING

1. Answers will vary. Sample answer: train tracks, double lines on the highway, lines on a page of music, etc.

2. Answers will vary. Sample answer: the letter t, the capital letter H, the goal posts on a football field, etc.

3. An angle must measure 90° to be a right angle.

4. Angles with measures of 11° and 89° are not complementary because the sum of these angles is 100°.

5. Two obtuse angles cannot be supplementary because the sum of their measures would be greater than 180°.

6. 79°

7. It is not possible to have an angle complementary to a 105° angle.

8.

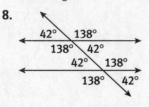

9. Answers will vary. Look for five examples of daily activities and a related math concept.

My Notes

SUGGESTED LEARNING STRATEGIES: Quickwrite, Group Presentation

24. Choose an activity you are interested in and find at least three ways in which the relationship between angles and lines are related to this activity.

Answers will vary. Students should choose an activity and describe the relationship between angles and lines and that activity.

CHECK YOUR UNDERSTANDING

Write your answers on notebook paper. Show your work.

1. Give a real-life example of parallel lines.

2. Give a real-life example of perpendicular lines.

3. What must be true for an angle to be a right angle?

4. Are angles with measures of 11° and 89° complementary? Why or why not?

5. Can two obtuse angles be supplementary? Explain why or why not.

6. What is the measure of an angle supplementary to an angle that measures 101°?

7. What is the measure of an angle complementary to an angle that measures 105°?

8. Give the missing angle measures in the diagram below.

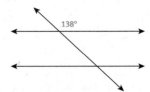

9. **MATHEMATICAL REFLECTION** Give at least five examples of how math and your daily routine are related. Explain the math concept that is related to each activity and what the relationship is.

Angles and Transformations
Down the Chute

ACTIVITY
4.2

SUGGESTED LEARNING STRATEGIES: Use Manipulatives, Visualization, Think/Pair/Share, Summarize/Paraphrase/Retell

My Notes

Chip designs games for his computer. One of his current projects is called *Down the Chute*. In the game, triangles appear at the top of a long U-shaped chute with parallel sides and slowly descend to rest at the bottom. The object of the game is to completely fill the region between the parallel sides of the chute.

Before each triangle appears, the player must provide the measure (in degrees) of one angle in the triangle. As the triangle descends down the chute, the player is allowed to transform the triangle with the following commands:

- reflect the triangle vertically
- reflect the triangle horizontally
- rotate the triangle *x* degrees clockwise

Once the triangle comes to rest

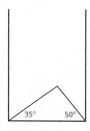

1. Use the triangular pieces given to you by your teacher to fill in the rectangular chute you have. Is there more than one way to fill the chute? Explain.
Yes. Explanations may vary.

Angles and Transformations

Activity Focus
- Rigid transformations
- Angle measure sum in a triangle

Materials
- BLMs 1: Empty chute and pre-cut triangles (1 set per pair of students)
- Dry erase boards or chart paper and markers

Chunking the Activity

#1	#6–8	#11–12
#2–4	#9	#13
#5	#10	#14–17

TEACHER TO TEACHER Each student will need a duplicate of the empty chute and triangular puzzle pieces. One set per pair of students should suffice. The black line master for the chute and puzzle pieces can be found.

Introduction Summarize/Paraphrase/Retell

1 Use Manipulatives, Visualization, Think/Pair/Share, Debrief Students use the pre-cut triangular pieces to fill in the chute. This hands-on part of the activity should help students understand the importance of reorienting (transforming) each triangle in order to fill the allotted space. A class discussion about different solutions may ensue.

2 Think/Pair/Share, Create Representations, Close Reading, Summarize/Paraphrase/Retell, Interactive Word Wall Students are given the definition of a translation and asked to translate a triangle on a coordinate grid. If students are struggling, try suggesting a translation of the vertices first. You should have a student paraphrase the definitions of *transformation* and *translation* and add these terms to the Interactive Word Wall.

3 Think/Pair/Share, Create Representations, Close Reading, Summarize/Paraphrase/Retell, Interactive Word Wall Students are given the definition of a reflection, and asked to reflect a triangle over the line $y = 4$. Students should realize that they only need to reflect the vertices of the triangle and then draw the sides.

You should have a student paraphrase the definition of *reflection*, and add this term to the Interactive Word Wall.

4 Think/Pair/Share, Group Presentation, Debrief Students are asked to list the coordinates of the vertices of the image in Item 3. This is an opportunity for you to assess student understanding of a reflection, and to stress the importance of making a precise drawing rather than just a "rough sketch." Debriefing this Item will help students with Unit Practice #9.

My Notes

> **ACADEMIC VOCABULARY**
>
> A **transformation** changes the position or size of a figure in the coordinate plane.
>
> **Translations, reflections,** and **rotations** are all types of transformations.

> **MATH TERMS**
>
> **Equidistant** means to be the same distance from a given point or line.

SUGGESTED LEARNING STRATEGIES: Think/Pair/Share, Create Representations, Close Reading, Summarize/Paraphrase/Retell, Group Presentation

2. If a triangle is not changed as it slides down the chute, this move (or **transformation**) is called a **translation**. A translation changes only a figure's position. Translate the triangle below two units down and five units to the right.

3. To perform a **reflection**, each point of a pre-image is copied on the opposite side of a given line and remains **equidistant** from the line. Sketch the reflection, called the image, of the triangle over the line $y = 4$.

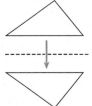

4. List the coordinates of the vertices of the image in Item 3.
(2,5), (−4,8), and (4,10)

SUGGESTED LEARNING STRATEGIES: Close Reading, Visualization, Think/Pair/Share, Create Representations, Summarize/Paraphrase/Retell

My Notes

5. If a pre-image is reflected over a horizontal line, the transformation is a **vertical reflection**. If a pre-image is reflected over a vertical line, the transformation is a **horizontal reflection**. Label each transformation below as a vertical or horizontal reflection.

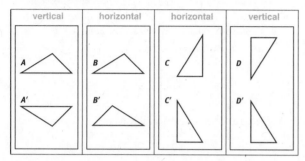

vertical	horizontal	horizontal	vertical
A / A′	B / B′	C / C′	D / D′

6. To perform a **rotation**, each point of the pre-image travels along a circle the same number of degrees. The direction of this path can be either clockwise or counter clockwise. Label each of the following rotations as 90° clockwise, 90° counterclockwise, 180°, or not a rotation.

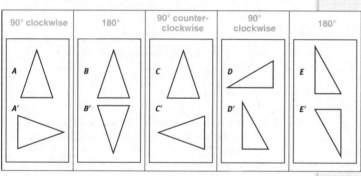

90° clockwise	180°	90° counter-clockwise	90° clockwise	180°
A / A′	B / B′	C / C′	D / D′	E / E′

> **CONNECT TO AP**
>
> Translations and reflections of figures in the coordinate plane are preparing you to successfully translate and reflect functions. This is a helpful tool for visualizing and setting up the graphs for many problems you will solve in calculus.

TEACHER TO TEACHER It is recommended to have enlarged and pre-cut versions of at least a few of the triangles from Items 5–9 for class demonstrations. This will benefit struggling students in particular, but will also help solidify the concepts for the rest of the class.

5 Close Reading, Visualization, Interactive Word Wall, Debriefing Students are given the definitions for vertical and horizontal reflections and asked to identify them in four situations. One option is to have students come to the front board and show how each triangle is reflected, using a larger cut-out version of each triangle. The terms *horizontal reflection* and *vertical reflection* should be added to the Interactive Word Wall. Students should be encouraged to edit their responses once the class discussion has ended.

6 Think/Pair/Share, Create Representations, Close Reading, Visualization, Summarize/Paraphrase/Retell, Interactive Word Wall Students are given the definition of a rotation and asked to identify 90° clockwise, 90° counterclockwise and 180° rotations. Have a student paraphrase the definition of *rotation* in addition to having a student demonstrate a reflection on the front board. *Rotation* can go on the Interactive Word Wall. Students should be encouraged to edit their responses once the class discussion has ended.

ACTIVITY 4.2 *Continued*

7 Create Representations, Group Presentation Students are given the opportunity to practice different rotations. This is a good opportunity to check for their understanding. Students should be encouraged to edit their responses after the solutions have been discussed.

8 Think/Pair/Share, Group Presentation Students are asked to use reflections to produce the same result as a 180° rotation. This item may spark a class discussion. Having an enlarged version of the triangle in this item is suggested. Students should be encouraged to edit their responses once this item has been discusssed.

My Notes

SUGGESTED LEARNING STRATEGIES: Create Representations, Group Presentations, Think/Pair/Share

7. Draw a sketch of the image of the triangle to the right when it is:

   a. rotated 180° clockwise around point *A*

   b. rotated 90° counterclockwise around point *A*

   c. rotated 90° clockwise around point *A*

   d. rotated 45° counterclockwise around point *A*

   e. rotated 45° clockwise around point *A*

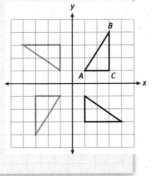

8. How many and what types of reflections would have to be performed on a pre-image to get the same image as a 180° rotation?

   A horizontal reflection and a vertical reflection combined will give the same result as a 180° rotation.

9. The grid at the left shows triangle *ABC* and a 90° clockwise rotation of *ABC* about the origin. Sketch the 180° rotation of *ABC* and the 90° counterclockwise rotation of *ABC*. How do the images compare with triangle *ABC*?

   They are congruent.

SUGGESTED LEARNING STRATEGIES: Think/Pair/Share,
Group Presentation, Quickwrite

My Notes

10. What transformation(s) would you need to perform on each
of the following right triangles so that you would end up with a
triangle that satisfies both of the following?

- Both points A and B are at the bottom of the figure.
- Point A is horizontally to the right of point B.

Answers may vary. Sample answers:

a.

rotate 180°

b.

rotate 90° clockwise

c.
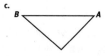
vertical reflection

d.
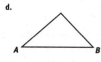
horizontal reflection

11. How do the sides of the image of a polygon after a translation,
reflection, or rotation compare with the corresponding sides of
the original figure? How do you know?

The corresponding sides are equal in length. Explanations may
vary. Possible explanation: You can slide, flip, or turn the original
figure onto the image to see that the sides match exactly.

12. In one game, Chip's first triangle
with a 90° angle came to rest and
displayed the measure of ∠CAB
to be 32°.

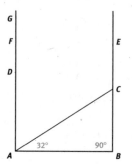

a. Determine the measure
of ∠CAD.

58°

b. Explain why the measure of
∠CAD is equal to the measure
of ∠ACB.

Answers may vary. Sample answer: If two parallel lines
are cut by a transversal then alternate interior angles are
congruent.

10 Think/Pair/Share, Group
Presentation Because it may
be difficult for students to
visualize the transformations in
this problem, you may opt to
have each group cut out their
own triangles and demonstrate
their results to the class. Students
should be encouraged to edit their
responses once this item has been
discussed.

Suggested Assignment

CHECK YOUR UNDERSTANDING
p. 202, #1–2

UNIT 4 PRACTICE
p. 243-244, #8–10

12 Think/Pair/Share,
Quickwrite, Debriefing
Students are expected to
recognize complementary angles
(∠CAD and ∠CAB) and alternate
interior angles (∠CAD and ∠ACB).
Because the sides of the chute
are parallel, the alternate interior
angles have the same measure.
It is essential that you debrief
the class before allowing them
to continue on to Items 13–15.
Students should be encouraged to
edit their responses once this item
has been discussed.

13 Identify a Subtask, Think/
Pair/Share The measure of ∠ECD
is 79° because the three angles
with vertex C must add to 180°.
Students should use congruent
alternate interior angles to find
the measure of ∠CDA. ∠FDC is
the supplement to ∠CDA.

14 Look for a Pattern, Quickwrite
Students should realize that the
three angles in △ACD have the
same measure as the three angles
whose vertex is at C.

15 Identify a Subtask, Think/
Pair/Share Students continue
to find the measure of angles
using alternate interior or
supplementary relationships. This
is an opportunity for you to check
for understanding and students
should be encouraged to edit
their responses if they initially
misunderstood.

My Notes

13. When △ACD came down the
chute, Chip selected the 58° and
the computer selected the 43° angle.
Find the measure of each of the
following angles.

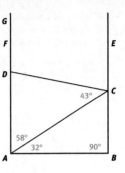

   a. ∠ECD
   79°

   b. ∠CDA
   79°

   c. ∠FDC
   101°

14. List the measures of the three angles in △ACD and list the
measures of the three non-overlapping angles whose vertex
is at C. How do the two lists compare?
Angles in triangle ACD and angles with vertex at C: 79°, 58°, and
43°. They are the same!

15. Find the measure of each of the following angles.

   a. ∠FCE
   64°

   b. ∠CFD
   64°

   c. ∠CEF
   90°

   d. ∠EFG
   90°

   e. ∠FGE
   80°

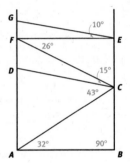

SUGGESTED LEARNING STRATEGIES: Think/Pair/Share,
Look for a Pattern, Quickwrite, Group Presentation

My Notes

16. Every triangle has three sides and three angles. Use your
responses to Items 12, 13 & 15 to complete the following table.
For each triangle, list the angle measures and find the sum of
the measures of the three angles.

Triangle Name	Angle Measures	Sum of the Angle Measures
△ABC	90°, 32°, 58°	180°
△ACD	58°, 43°, 79°	180°
△DCF	101°, 15°, 64°	180°
△ACF	64°, 58°, 58°	180°
△CEF	90°, 26°, 64°	180°
△GEF	90°, 80°, 10°	180°

17. Write a statement that appears to be true about the sum of the
measures of the angles of a triangle.
The sum of the angle measures in a triangle is 180°.

18. Determine the measure of the
unknown angle in the triangle.
42°

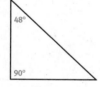

48°

90°

ACTIVITY 4.2 *Continued*

16 Think/Pair/Share Students list
the measures of the three angles
in six different triangles and find
the sum of the three angles for
each triangle.

17 Look for a Pattern,
Quickwrite, Debriefing
Students are asked to summarize
their findings for the sum of
the measures of the angles in a
triangle. It is essential that you
debrief the class to ensure that
everyone has come to the correct
conclusion.

18 Group Presentation Students
are given an opportunity to practice
finding an unknown angle in a
triangle (by adding the measures
of the two known angles and
subtracting from 180°).

19 Debrief Students write an equation using the property they discovered in Item 15 and solve for *x*. It is essential that the teacher debrief the class after this item before assigning the problems in the CYU.

Suggested Assignment

CHECK YOUR UNDERSTANDING
p. 202, #3–6

UNIT 4 PRACTICE
p. 244, #11–13

CHECK YOUR UNDERSTANDING

1. The transformed points, labeled here using he prime notation (') are:

a. *M'*(0, 1), *O'*(6, 1) and *V'*(6, 6)

b. *M'*(−2, 8), *O'*(4, 8) and *V'*(4, 3)

c. *M'*(10, −2), *O'*(4, −2) and *V'*(4, 3)

2. C

3. 68°

4. $2x + 20 + 3x + 5x = 180$;
   $x = 16$
   The measures of the angles in the triangle: 52°, 48° and 80°.

5. $m\angle F = 56°$

6. Sometimes the order matters (CYU #2), but sometimes it does not.

My Notes

19. The measures of three angles in a triangle are 44°, $3x°$, and $5x°$. Write an equation and solve for *x*. Determine the missing angles.

$44 + 3x + 5x = 180, 8x = 136, x = 17°; 51°$ and $85°$

CHECK YOUR UNDERSTANDING

Write your answers on notebook paper. Show your work.

1. Let △*MOV* have vertices: *M*(−2,−2), *O*(4,−2), and *V*(4,3). Determine the coordinates of the vertices for each image of △*MOV* after each of the following transformations are performed.

    a. △*MOV* is translated 3 units up and 2 units to the right.

    b. △*MOV* is reflected over the line $y = 3$.

    c. △*MOV* is reflected over the line $x = 4$.

2. Which transformation(s) have been performed on the pre-image to obtain the image?

Pre-image
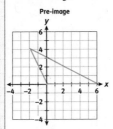

Image
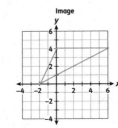

    a. Rotate 180°.

    b. Shift down two units and reflect over the line $y = 2$.

    c. Reflect over *x*-axis and shift up 4 units.

    d. Reflect over *y*-axis and shift up 4 units.

3. If one of the acute angles of a right triangle has a measure of 22°, calculate the measure of the other acute angle.

4. Suppose the measures of the angles in a triangle are $(2x + 20)°$, $3x°$, and $5x°$. Write an equation, solve for *x*, and determine the measure of each angle.

5. In △*FAR* $\angle F \cong \angle A$ and $m\angle R = 68°$. Calculate $m\angle F$. Show your work.

6. **MATHEMATICAL REFLECTION** Does the order in which multiple transformations are performed on a pre-image have an effect on the image?

Angles in Polygons
A Star Is Drawn

SUGGESTED LEARNING STRATEGIES: Activating Prior
Knowledge, Close Reading, Interactive Word Wall

Skye Gaiser loves stars, and she decorates everything with them.
She has become interested in the star patterns used in quilting
and knows they are very precisely created and also that the angle
measure is very important.

    Skye is particularly interested in stars that are inscribed inside
regular polygons. A **regular polygon** is a polygon with all sides
congruent and all angles congruent.

1. Write the name of each of the following polygons and tell which
   appear to be regular polygons.

a.

rectangle

b.

pentagon

c.

regular
square

d.

regular
triangle

e.

regular
hexagon

f.

trapezoid

2. An equilateral triangle is an example of a regular polygon.

   a. Use the definition of a regular polygon to show how to find
   the measure of each angle of an equilateral triangle.
   In a regular polygon all the angles have the same
   measure. $\frac{180}{3} = 60$ so each angle measures 60 degrees.

   b. If a triangle is equilateral it is also equiangular. Explain what
   equiangular means.
   Equiangular means all the angles have the same measure.

3. A square is also a regular polygon.

   a. Write a statement about the four sides and four angles of
   a square.
   Answers may vary. Sample answer: The four sides of a square
   are congruent and the 4 angles of a square are congruent.

   b. Tell the measure of each angle in a square.
   90°

My Notes

ACTIVITY 4.3 Investigative

Angles in Polygons

Activity Focus
- Angle measures in regular
  polygons
- Isosceles and equilateral triangles

Materials
- Protractor
- Dry erase boards or chart paper
  and markers

Chunking the Activity

#1–2	#10–12	#18
#3–5	#13–14	#19
#6–9	#15–17	#20

Introduction Close Reading,
Interactive Word Wall, Activate
Prior Knowledge Students
should carefully read the text
before Item 1 and add the term
regular polygon to the Interactive
Word Wall. You may wish to elicit
the names of *regular polygons*
with which students are already
familiar. Make sure that students
name *square* and *equilateral
triangle*, in particular.

1 Think/Pair/Share, Debriefing
Students are given the definition
of a regular polygon and asked
to pick out the regular polygons
from a group of six polygons.

2 Activating Prior Knowledge,
Think/Pair/Share Students
calculate the measure of each
angle in an equilateral (and
equiangular) triangle.

3 Activating Prior Knowledge,
Think/Pair/Share Students
should already know the
properties of a square: all sides
are congruent and all angles
measure 90°.

4 Students are given the directions for completing the 4-pointed star.

5 Think Aloud, Debriefing
Students are asked to find the measure of several angles in the figure they drew in Item 4. A mini-lesson on the relationships between sides and angles in an isosceles triangle is given below. It is important that you debrief the class on this item before continuing on with Items 6–8.

My Notes

SUGGESTED LEARNING STRATEGIES: Think Aloud

4. To draw a four-pointed star, Skye begins by drawing a square and then sketches a second, smaller square that has been rotated 45° inside the first square and has the same center as the larger square.

MATH TERMS
Congruent triangles are triangles in which all corresponding sides are congruent and all corresponding angles are congruent.

a. Complete the 4-pointed star by drawing the segment that joins each vertex of the large square to the nearest two vertices of the smaller square. The first two of these segments have already been drawn. All eight segments will be congruent and they will form two sets of congruent triangles.

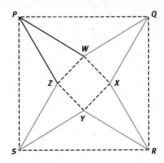

MATH TIP
An **isosceles triangle** has two congruent sides called **legs**. The angles opposite the congruent sides are congruent and are called the base angles.

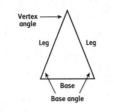

b. Which triangles formed by the four-pointed star are congruent?
△PQW, △QXR, △RYS, △SZP are congruent; △PWZ, △QWX, △RXY, △SYZ are congruent.

c. What is the best name for the triangles?
The triangles are isosceles since two of their sides are congruent.

5. If the measure of ∠QPW is 27.5° and quadrilaterals PQRS and WXYZ are squares, then find the measure of each of the following angles.

a. ∠PWQ   125°   **b.** ∠SPZ   27.5°

c. ∠WPZ   35°   **d.** ∠PWZ   72.5°

MINI-LESSON: (continued)

Practice: Triangle *GHJ* is an isosceles triangle with $\overline{GH} \cong \overline{HJ}$. Given the measure of one angle of the triangle, find the measures of the other 2 angles

1. m∠G = 36° (m∠J = 36°, m∠H = 108°)
2. m∠H = 90° (m∠J = 45°, m∠G = 45°)
3. m∠J = 25° (m∠G = 25°, m∠H = 130°)

MINI-LESSON: Isosceles Triangles

Isosceles Triangle Theorem If a triangle has two congruent sides, then the angles opposite those sides are congruent.

Converse of the Isosceles Triangle Theorem If a triangle has two congruent angles, then the sides opposite those angles are congruent

EXAMPLE 1: Triangle *ABC* is an isosceles triangle with $\overline{AB} \cong \overline{BC}$. If m∠B = 50°, find m∠A and m∠C.
180° − 50° = 130°. Since AB ≅ BC, ∠A ≅ ∠C; $\frac{130}{2}$ = 65 so each base angle measures 65 degrees.

EXAMPLE 2: Triangle *DEF* is an isosceles triangle with $\overline{DE} \cong \overline{EF}$. If m∠D = 70°, find m∠E and m∠F.
∠D and ∠F are the base angles of an isosceles triangle and have the same measure so m∠D = 70°. 70 + 70 = 140. 180 − 140 = 40° so m∠E = 40°.

SUGGESTED LEARNING STRATEGIES: Activating Prior
Knowledge, Close Reading

My Notes

6. Pentagon *ABCDE* is a regular polygon with diagonal $\overline{AC}$.

a. Explain how you know from the definition of regular
polygon that $\triangle ABC$ is isosceles.
Answers may vary. Sample answer:
All sides of the pentagon are
congruent. Two sides of the pentagon
are also sides of $\triangle ABC$, so $\triangle ABC$
must be isosceles.

b. Name the congruent angles in $\triangle ABC$.
$\angle BAC \cong \angle BCA$

c. If the measure of $\angle B$ is 108°, determine the measures of the
other two angles in $\triangle ABC$.
36°

7. To complete the 5-pointed star, draw the remaining diagonals in
the pentagon.

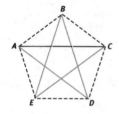

8. Use the regular pentagon and completed star above to
determine the measure for each of the following angles.

a. $\angle BAE$ 108°   **b.** $\angle DAE$ 36°

c. $\angle CAE$ 72°   **d.** $\angle CAD$ 36°

9. What kind of triangle is $\triangle BAE$? Explain how you made your
decision.
Answers may vary. Sample answer: Isosceles. An isosceles
triangle has two congruent sides. BA and AE are congruent
because *ABCDE* was given as a regular polygon.

ACTIVITY 4.3 *Continued*

TEACHER TO TEACHER   Students may need to be
reminded that a *diagonal
of a polygon* is a segment whose
endpoints are non-consecutive
vertices. In a square and a regular
pentagon, the diagonals are
congruent. That is not the case for
regular polygons with more than
5 sides. This term may be added
to the Interactive Word Wall.

6 **Activating Prior Knowledge,
Think/Pair/Share, Debriefing**
Students are asked to identify an
Isosceles triangle (two congruent
sides and two congruent angles)
and find the measure of the
congruent angles by subtracting
108° from 180° and dividing by 2.
You may need to add the isosceles
triangle terms to the Interactive
Word Wall. It is important that
you debrief the class on this item
before continuing on to Items 7–8.

7 Students are directed to
complete a 5-point star by
drawing all possible diagonals.
If needed, you can review the
definition of a diagonal.

8-9 **Think/Pair/Share** Students
are asked to determine the measure
of several angles in the figure and
identify a triangle by type.

Suggested Assignment

CHECK YOUR UNDERSTANDING
p. 210, #2–4

UNIT 4 PRACTICE
p. 244, #14

10 Think Aloud, Create Represntations, Visualization
Students draw the three diagonals from one vertex. They should notice that there is one long diagonal and that the two short diagonals are congruent.

11 Think Aloud, Create Represntations, Visualization
Students complete the 6-pointed star by drawing the long diagonals in a regular hexagon. Students should recognize that all radii and diameters of a circle are congruent. If in Part c, students are struggling to get the right answer, it may be helpful for them to work on Item 12 before returning to this question.

TEACHER TO TEACHER | Pattern blocks may be used to help convince skeptical students that a regular hexagon can be viewed as the union of six equilateral triangles. In Geometry, students will prove the triangles are congruent using the Side-Angle-Side Theorem.

My Notes

SUGGESTED LEARNING STRATEGIES: Close Reading, Think Aloud

10. Hexagon *PQRSTU* is a regular polygon.

a. List the diagonals that can be drawn containing vertex *P*.
$\overline{PT}$, $\overline{PS}$ and $\overline{PR}$

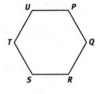

b. Are any of these diagonals congruent? Explain how you made your decision.
Yes; $\overline{PR} \cong \overline{PT}$; Answers may vary. Sample answer: measured, used tracing paper

11. When a regular hexagon is inscribed in a circle, the circle and the hexagon have the same center. The longest diagonal drawn from a vertex passes through the center of the hexagon.

a. Draw the three longest diagonals in the hexagon below.

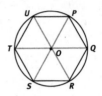

b. How can you tell $\overline{PO}$, $\overline{QO}$, $\overline{RO}$, $\overline{SO}$, $\overline{TO}$, and $\overline{UO}$ are congruent?
They are all radii of a circle.

> **MATH TIP**
> The sum of the non–overlapping angles around a point is 360 degrees.

c. When the diagonals $\overline{PS}$, $\overline{QT}$, and $\overline{RU}$ are drawn, 6 congruent triangles are formed. Are these triangles isosceles, equilateral, or scalene? Explain your reasoning.
Equilateral; Answer may vary. Sample answer: The triangles must be isosceles because the radii of a circle are congruent. The vertex angle ($vertex = \frac{360}{6} = 60°$) is 60°. This forces the two base angles to be 60° also. Only equilateral triangles have 3 congruent angles.

SUGGESTED LEARNING STRATEGIES: Visualization, Create Representations

12. Tell the measure of the following angles and explain how you determined each measure.
Explanations may vary.

a. ∠POU
∠POU = 60°; Sample explanation: The 6 triangles are given as congruent. The sum of their angles around point *O* must be 360, $\frac{360}{6}$ = 60°.

b. ∠OQP and ∠OQR
60°; Sample explanation: The two base angles of all 6 triangles are forced to be 60°. The base angles must be congruent and the vertex angle is 60°.

c. ∠PQR
120°; Sample explanation: ∠PQO + ∠OQR = 60 + 60 = 120

13. In a regular hexagon the 6 diagonals that do not pass through the center of the hexagon are congruent.

a. Complete the 6-pointed star by drawing all diagonals that are congruent to $\overline{QS}$.

b. What type of triangles are △SUQ and △TPR? Explain your reasoning.
Equilateral. Explanations may vary. Sample explanation: All the line segments drawn are congruent.

c. Tell the measure of each angle of △SUQ and △TPR.
60°

d. What kind of triangles are △TUP and △PQR? Explain your reasoning.
Isosceles. Explanations may vary. Sample explanation: The sides of the triangle are the sides of a regular polygon which makes them congruent.

My Notes

ACTIVITY 4.3 *Continued*

12 Visualization, Group Presentation, Debriefing Guide students to the math tip on the previous page if they struggle with this problem, and facilitate a discussion of non-overlapping triangles. After students find the measure of angle *POU* they should use the fact that triangle *POU* is isosceles to find the remaining angles.

13 Create Representations, Debriefing The simplest way to determine the angle measures in a regular hexagon is to consider it as being the union of six equilateral triangles.

ACTIVITY 4.3 Continued

14 Debriefing Students should understand that not only is *ABCDEF* a hexagon, it is also regular. A good way to demonstrate this is by looking at the angle measures of the six triangles that make up the tips of the 6-pointed star. Since it can be established that all six are equilateral and congruent, it follows that the hexagon they form is regular. It is important that you debrief the class on this Item before continuing on to Items 15 and 16.

TEACHER TO TEACHER In Geometry students will prove that the diagonals of a regular hexagon which do pass through the center are congruent using the Side-Angle-Side Theorem.

15 Students use their work from Items 1–14 to complete a table which helps to organize everything they've discovered so far.

16 Debriefing, Look for a Pattern, Think Aloud Students are asked to look for patterns in the table in Item 15. It would be helpful for students if the teacher leads a class discussion to get the most complete list of patterns. Lead students to create algebraic expressions for the sum of the angle measures in a polygon [$180(n - 2)$], and the measure of each interior angle in a regular polygon $\left[\frac{180(n - 2)}{n}\right]$, where *n* represents the number of sides in the polygon.

SUGGESTED LEARNING STRATEGIES: Think Aloud, Look for a Pattern

My Notes

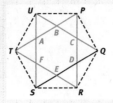

14. In hexagon *PQRSTU*, the diagonals intersect at 6 points:

A is the point where $\overline{TP}$ and $\overline{US}$ intersect;

B is the point where $\overline{TP}$ and $\overline{UQ}$ intersect;

C is the point where $\overline{PR}$ and $\overline{UQ}$ intersect;

D is the point where $\overline{PR}$ and $\overline{QS}$ intersect;

E is the point where $\overline{RT}$ and $\overline{QS}$ intersect;

F is the point where $\overline{RT}$ and $\overline{US}$ intersect.

a. Label the points of intersection.

b. What type of polygon is *ABCDEF*?

hexagon

15. Review your work in this activity and complete the table below as you review.

Name	Number of Sides	Measure of Each Interior Angle	Sum of the Measures of the Interior Angles	Sum as a Factor Times 180°
Equilateral triangle	3	60°	180°	1 • 180°
Square	4	90°	360°	2 • 180°
Regular pentagon	5	108°	540°	3 • 180°
Regular hexagon	6	120°	720°	4 • 180°

16. What patterns can you find in the above table?

Answers may vary, but students should note: As you go down each column, the number of sides increases by 1, the measure of each interior angle increases, the sum of the measures of the interior angles increases by 180° and the factor times 180° increases by 1 and is two less than the number of sides.

SUGGESTED LEARNING STRATEGIES:

My Notes

17. Use your patterns to complete the next two rows of the table.

Name	Number of Sides	Measure of Each Interior Angle	Sum of the Measures of the Interior Angles	Sum as a Factor Times 180°
Regular Heptagon	7	$128\frac{4}{7}°$	900°	$5 \cdot 180°$
Regular Octagon	8	135°	1080°	$6 \cdot 180°$

18. Use a protractor and straight edge to draw a regular octagon in the space below. Decide which diagonals should be used to draw an 8-pointed star and draw the star.

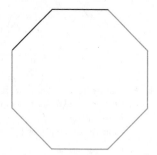

Sample stars:

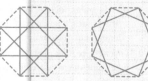

19. Make a list of the steps that would be needed to calculate the measure of one interior angle of a regular nine-sided polygon.

Step 1: Multiply 7 times 180°
Step 2: Divide the product in Step 1 by 9

When you extend the side of a polygon, an exterior angle of the polygon is formed. In the figure to the right, triangle *PQR* has exterior angle *PQS*.

20. What is the measure of angle *PQS*? How do you know?

137°; angle *PQS* is supplementary to angle *PQR*.

21. How is the measure of angle *PQS* related to the measures of angles *P* and *R*?

The measure of angle *PQS* is equal to the sum of the measures of angles *P* and *R*.

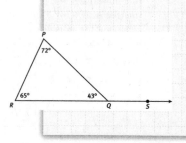

---

17 Think/Pair/Share, Debriefing, Group Presentation, Self/Peer Revision Students use the patterns listed in Item 16 to extend the table for a regular heptagon (7 sides) and octagon (8 sides).

18 Create Representations Students should use the angle measure 135° from their table in Item 17 and a protractor to complete a regular octagon. They are directed to decide which diagonals to use as they draw an 8-pointed star.

19 Look for a Pattern, Self/Peer Revision, Group Presentation, Debriefing Students are asked to make a list of the steps needed to determine the measure of an interior angle of a regular 9-sided polygon (a nonagon). It is important for the teacher to debrief the class on this item before assigning practice problems.

Suggested Assignment

CHECK YOUR UNDERSTANDING
p. 210, #1, #5–8

UNIT 4 PRACTICE
p. 245, #15–19

ACTIVITY 4.3 Continued

CHECK YOUR UNDERSTANDING

1a. False

b. True

c. True

d. False

e. True

2a. 108°

b. 18°

c. 72°

d. 36°

e. 108°

f. 50°

g. 130°

h. 14°

3a. 90°

b. 30°

c. 120°

d. 90°

e. 75°

f. 120°

4. Sample answer: Draw a regular triangle. At its center draw a smaller, inverted regular triangle. From each vertex of the larger triangle, create a point of the star using the smaller triangle.

5a. 120°

b. 60°

c. 60°

d. 60°

e. 30°

f. 120°

CHECK YOUR UNDERSTANDING

Write your answers on notebook paper. Show your work.

1. True or False? Explain your choice.

  a. As the number of sides of a regular polygon increases, the measure of the interior angles decreases.

  b. If a regular polygon has more than four sides, at least one of the diagonals is parallel to one of its sides.

  c. The sum of the measures of the interior angles of a polygon is always a multiple of 180°.

  d. As the perimeter of a regular hexagon increases, the measure of each interior angle increases.

  e. If a regular polygon has more than three sides, it has at least one pair of congruent diagonals.

2. Given the regular pentagon *PENTA*, determine the measure of each of the following angles

  a. ∠*PAT*   **b.** ∠*PAG*

  c. ∠*APG*   **d.** ∠*EPN*

  e. ∠*EPA*   **f.** ∠*EGO*

  g. ∠*EGP*   **h.** ∠*PEG*

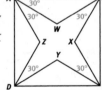

3. Given Quad *ABCD* and Quad *WXYZ* (not shown) are squares with isosceles triangles *AZD*, *ABW*, *BCX*, and *CYD*. Determine the measure of each of the following angles.

  a. ∠*ABC*   **b.** ∠*ABW*

  c. ∠*AWB*   **d.** ∠*ZWX*

  e. ∠*AWZ*   **f.** ∠*DYC*

4. Design a 3-pointed star. Write the steps needed to reproduce your design.

5. Given regular hexagon *ACFDBE*. Draw $\overline{AB}$, $\overline{AD}$ and $\overline{BC}$. Label the point of intersection of $\overline{AD}$ and $\overline{BC}$ as *X*. Determine the measure of each of the following angles.

  a. ∠*GCA*   **b.** ∠*CGB*

  c. ∠*ACB*   **d.** ∠*BDA*

  e. ∠*EAB*   **f.** ∠*BDF*

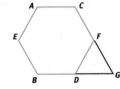

6. Use the figure in Item 5 to determine the best name for each of the following quadrilaterals (trapezoid, parallelogram, rhombus, rectangle, or square)

  a. Quadrilateral *ABDC*

  b. Quadrilateral *AEBD*

  c. Quadrilateral *AEBX*

  d. Quadrilateral *ACGD*

  e. Quadrilateral *BDFC*

7. Calculate the measure of an interior angle in a regular decagon (10-sided polygon).

8. **MATHEMATICAL REFLECTION** What is the largest possible value for the measure of an interior angle in a regular polygon?

6a. rectangle

  b. trapezoid

  c. rhombus

  d. parallelogram

  e. trapezoid

7. 144°

8. Sample answer: As the number of sides in a regular polygon increase, the measure of an interior angle will approach, but will never reach, 180°.

Lines, Angles, Transformations

SWEET HEXAGONS

Honeybees build combs in which they store honey. If you look at a slice of honeycomb, you will see hexagonal sections. Suppose all hexagons in the figure to the right are regular hexagons.

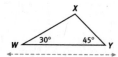

1. Determine the measure of ∠*FAB*. Show your work.

2. Draw $\overline{AD}$. Determine the measure of ∠*FAD* and ∠*ADC*.

3. Is $\overleftrightarrow{AF}$ parallel to $\overleftrightarrow{CD}$? Explain how you know.

4. If $\overrightarrow{ED}$ is extended to contain point *G*, name an angle that is corresponding to ∠*ADG*.

5. Given △*WXY* in the figure.

   a. Determine the measure of ∠*X*. Show your work.

   b. Sketch the image of △*WXY* if it is reflected over the dotted line.

6. Given isosceles △*PQR* with $\overline{PR} \cong \overline{QR}$ and m∠*R* = 30°.

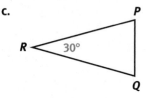

   a. Determine the measure of ∠*P*. Show your work.

   b. If side *PQ* were extended to the left through point *T*, what would be the measure of angle *RPT*?

   c. Sketch the image of △*PQR* if it is rotated 90° in a clockwise direction.

Embedded Assessment 1

Assessment Focus
- Parallel lines and special pairs of angles
- Sum of angle measures in a triangle
- Angles in a polygon (hexagon)
- Rigid transformations

Materials
- Straightedges

Answer Key

1. Students determine the measure of an angle in a regular hexagon. There are at least 2 different ways to arrive at 120°.
   $\frac{4 \cdot 180°}{6}$ or $\frac{360°}{3}$

2. $\overline{AD}$ bisects ∠*FAB* and ∠*CDE*, so m∠*FAD* = m∠*ADC* = 60°.

3. Students should use the congruent alternate interior angles from Item 2 to explain why the line segments are parallel.

4. Students will need to recognize that *AB* ∥ *ED* before they can identify the corresponding angle, ∠*HAB*. Students may also correctly name ∠*FED*.

5. Students calculate the measure of an unknown angle in a triangle and sketch the reflection of that triangle over a horizontal line.

   a. m ∠*X* = 180° − (30° + 45°) = 105°

   b.
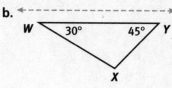

6. Students use the properties of an isosceles triangle (Base angles are congruent) and the sum of the angles in a triangle to calculate the measure of an unknown angle in a triangle. Students rotate that triangle 90° in a clockwise direction.

   a. 2x + 30° = 180°; 2x = 150°; x = 75°

   b. 105°

   c.

Embedded Assessment 1

7. Students asked to determine the measures of unknown angles given two parallel lines with a transversal.

   a. 147.5°

   b. 32.5°

   c. 107°

   d. ∠6, ∠2, and ∠7

TEACHER TO TEACHER | You may wish to read through the rubric with students and discuss the differences in the expectation levels. Make sure students understand the meanings of any terms used.

Lines, Angles, Transformations
SWEET HEXAGONS

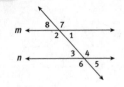

7. In the figure to the left, *m* is parallel to *n*.

   a. If $m\angle 1 = 32.5°$, then $m\angle 2 =$ _____.

   b. If $m\angle 1 = 32.5°$, then $m\angle 3 =$ _____.

   c. If $m\angle 1 = 73°$, then $m\angle 6 =$ _____.

   d. List all angles in the figure congruent to ∠4.

	Exemplary	Proficient	Emerging
Math Knowledge #1, 2, 5a, 6a, 7a–c, d	• Determines the correct measure of angle *FAB* (1) • Determines the correct measures of angles *FAD* and *ADC* (2) • Determines the correct measures of angles *X* and *P* (5a, 6a) • Determines the correct measures of angles 2, 3, and 6 (7a–c) • Lists all angles congruent to angle 4 (7d)	• Determines only one of the correct measures of the two angles • Determines the correct measure of only one of the angles • Determines the correct measures of only two of the angles • Lists only two of the angles congruent to angle 4	• Gives an incorrect measure of angle *FAB* • Determines the correct measures of neither of the angles • Determines the correct measures of neither of the angles • Determines the correct measures of fewer that two of the angles • Lists fewer than two angles congruent to angle 4
Problem Solving #3, 4	• Determines correctly whether or not segment *AF* is parallel to segment *CD*. (3) • Determines the correct angle that is corresponding to angle *ADG*. (4)		• Determines an incorrect relationship between segments *AF* and *CD* • Determines an incorrect angle
Representations #2, 5b, 6b	• Draws segment *AD* correctly. (2) • Sketches a correct reflected image of triangle *WXY*. (5b) • Sketches a correct image of a rotated triangle *PQR*. (6b)	• Sketches a partially correct reflected image. • Sketches a partially correct rotated image.	• Draws *AD* incorrectly • Sketches an incorrect reflected image • Sketches an incorrect rotated image
Communication #1, 3, 5a, 6a	• Shows correct work for the measure of angles *FAB*, *X*, and *P*. (1, 5a, 6a) • Gives a complete explanation for his/her conclusion about whether segment *AF* is parallel to segment *CD*. (3)	• Shows correct work for the measure of two of the angles. • Gives an incomplete explanation for a correct conclusion.	• Shows correct work for fewer than two of the angles • Gives an explanation for an incorrect conclusion

Proportions and Scale Drawings
Patriotic Proportions

SUGGESTED LEARNING STRATEGIES: Think/Pair/Share, Quickwrite

My Notes

Martha Rose Kennedy was watching an old black and white movie about World War II, and during the parade scene she noticed that the flags seemed to have a "funny shape." Martha did a little research and according to the *US Code, Title 4, Chapter 1*, the ratio of the **hoist** (height) to the **fly** (width) of the flag should be 1:1.9. However, in the 1950's, president Dwight D. Eisenhower eased the restrictions on the dimensions of the US Flag to accommodate current "standard" sizes such as 3×5, 4×6, and 5×8.

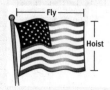

1. Without using a ruler, predict which of the following rectangles will have a ratio: $\frac{hoist}{fly} = \frac{1}{1.9}$. Explain how you made your decision.

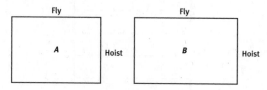

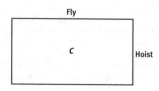

C; Answers may vary. Sample answer: The length of the fly is nearly twice the length of the hoist.

2. Explain what it means for "*two sides of a rectangle to be in the ratio $\frac{1}{1.9}$.*"

Answer may vary. Sample answer: The longer side is 1.9 times as long as the shorter side.

3. **a.** If $\frac{hoist}{fly} = \frac{1}{1.9}$ and the hoist is 1 ft, calculate the fly.

1.9 ft

b. If the ratio remains constant and the hoist of the flag is 2 ft, calculate the fly.

3.8 ft

Proportions and Scale Drawings

Activity Focus
- Proportions
- Percent increase and decrease
- Scale drawings

Materials
- Centimeter ruler
- US flag
- Dry erase boards or chart paper and markers

Chunking the Activity

#1	#9–10	#15–17
#2–3	#11	#18
#4	#12–14	#19–20
#5–8		

TEACHER TO TEACHER Most classrooms display a US flag. It is strongly recommended that students have access to a US flag for this and the next activities.

Much information is presented in the introductory text. You may choose to use several reading strategies such as Questioning the Text and Summarize/Paraphrase/Retell.

1 Think/Pair/Share Students are asked to choose which rectangle has sides that are in the ratio 1:1.9. They should realize that 1.9 is close to 2 and look for the rectangle whose width (fly) is nearly twice the height (hoist).

2 Quickwrite Students are asked to interpret the meaning of a ratio in terms of the sides of a rectangle.

3 Think/Pair/Share, Debriefing Students apply the ratio to find the fly of a flag given the hoist. Students will most likely multiply the hoist by 1.9 to determine the fly. They may also set up a proportion. It is important that you debrief the class before continuing on to Item 4.

4 Think/Pair/Share, Group Presentation, Debrief, Self/Peer Revision Students should use proportional reasoning or look for a pattern to extend the table of hoist and fly measurement.

TEACHER TO TEACHER Students are given the steps for solving a proportion. The teacher may choose to reinforce these steps with a class demonstration or the use of reading strategies.

My Notes

4. Complete the following table which displays the correct hoist and fly of the US Flag according to the *US Flag Code*. Assume that the units of measure are the same for the hoist and fly and that $\frac{\text{hoist}}{\text{fly}} = \frac{1}{1.9}$.

Hoist	Fly
1	1.9
2	3.8
3	5.7
4	7.6
5	9.5
≈8.95	17
10	19
≈13.16	25
20	38

A useful way to calculate values that are proportional to a given ratio is to set up and solve a proportion. For example, in Items 3 and 4 the proportion $\frac{1}{1.9} = \frac{2}{x}$ could have been used to find the fly of a flag whose hoist is 2 units.

EXAMPLE 1

The lengths of two sides of a rectangle are in the ratio 4:9. If the shorter side has a length of 18 cm, calculate the length of the longer side.

Step 1: Write an equation with 2 equivalent ratios. $\qquad \frac{4}{9} = \frac{18 \text{ cm}}{x}$

Step 2: Calculate the cross products. $\qquad \frac{4}{9} \diagdown \frac{18 \text{ cm}}{x}$

$\qquad\qquad\qquad\qquad 4x = 162 \text{ cm}$

Step 3: Solve for the unknown. $\qquad \frac{4x}{4} = \frac{162}{4}$

Solution: $x = 40.5$ cm

Proportions and Scale Drawings
Patriotic Proportions

SUGGESTED LEARNING STRATEGIES: Think/Pair/Share, Group Presentation, Self Revision/Peer Revision

TRY THESE A

a. Solve for a: $\frac{a}{35} = \frac{1}{1.75}$ $a = 20$

b. Solve for n: $\frac{7}{8} = \frac{n}{100}$ $n = 87.5$

c. The lengths of two sides of a rectangle are in the ratio 2:3. If the shorter side has a length of 24 in., calculate the length of the longer side.
36 in.

d. The lengths of two sides of a rectangle are in the ratio 1:2.5. If the longer side has a length of 40 mm, calculate the length of the shorter side.
16 mm

5. Suppose the hoist of a flag is 10 inches and $\frac{\text{hoist}}{\text{fly}} = \frac{1}{1.9}$. Write and solve the proportion needed to calculate the fly.
$\frac{10}{x} = \frac{1}{1.9}$; $x = 19$ in.

6. Write and solve the proportion needed to calculate the hoist of a flag whose fly is 17 inches if $\frac{\text{hoist}}{\text{fly}} = \frac{1}{1.9}$.
$\frac{x}{17} = \frac{1}{1.9}$; $x \approx 8.95$ in.

7. One of the ratios that President Eisenhower approved for the hoist and fly of the US Flag was 3:5.

a. Write this ratio as a fraction.
$\frac{3}{5}$

b. Using this ratio, determine the fly of a flag whose hoist is 3 ft.
5 ft

My Notes

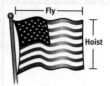

Fly — Hoist

TRY THESE A Students practice setting up and solving proportions. This skill is a prerequisite for the rest of this activity. The teacher should stress the importance of units. Possible proportions for Parts c and d are given.

c. $\frac{2}{3} = \frac{24 \text{ in}}{x}$

d. $\frac{1}{2.5} = \frac{x}{40 \text{ mm}}$

5-6 Think/Pair/Share, Group Presentation, Debrief, Self/Peer Revision Students are taken back to the context of the US flag and asked to set up and solve proportions to find a fly in Item 5 and a hoist in Item 6. These proportions both use the same ratio, $\frac{1}{1.9}$, but the variable in the second ratio appears in the denominator in Item 5 and the numerator in Item 6.

7 Think/Pair/Share, Group Presentation, Debrief, Self/Peer Revision Students are given a new ratio, 3:5, and asked to determine the length of the fly. Students may use the proportion $\frac{3}{5} = \frac{3 \text{ ft}}{x}$ or an intuitive understanding of *ratio* to determine their response.

8 Think/Pair/Share Group Presentation, Self/Peer Revision Students are given a hoist of 3 ft and asked to compare the fly of a flag whose sides are in the ratio 3:5 to the fly of a flag whose sides are in the ratio 1:1.9.

TEACHER TO TEACHER Students are given the steps for calculating percent increase or decrease. You may choose to reinforce these steps with a class demonstration or the use of reading strategies before assigning the related practice problems in Try These B.

TRY THESE B Debriefing Students practice calculating percent decrease and increase. It is important for you to debrief the class on these exercises before continuing on with Items 9 and 10.

9 Think/Pair/Share, Self/Peer Revision Students are taken back to the context of the activity and calculate a percent decrease.

My Notes

MATH TIP

A percent is written as a fraction by placing the number over 100.
$3\% = \frac{3}{100}$

8. Find the difference in the lengths of the fly for a 3:5 flag and the flag in the table in Item 4 whose hoist is 3 ft. Which flag has the longer fly?

The difference is 0.7 ft. The flag in the table has a longer fly.

EXAMPLE 2

Harry copied a drawing. The original width was 5 in., and the width of Harry's drawing was 7 in. Calculate the percent increase or decrease of the change in the width of Harry's drawing.

Step 1: *Calculate the difference between the quantities.* $7 - 5 = 2$

Step 2: *Write the difference to original as a ratio and set up a proportion to solve for the percent.* $\frac{2 \text{ in.}}{5 \text{ in.}} = \frac{p}{100}$

Step 3: *Solve for p.* $5p = 200$
$p = 40$

Solution: Since Harry's copy is larger than the original, the 2 inch difference is a 40% increase.

TRY THESE B

Solve the following problems.

a. Hillary used to deposit $40 in her savings account each month. Now she deposits $30 each month. Calculate the change in Hillary's deposits as a percent increase or decrease.

$\frac{10}{40} = 25\%$ decrease

b. Bill's dog, Buddy, gained 5 lbs. If Buddy's original weight was 60 lbs, express Buddy's weight gain as a percent increase or decrease.

$\frac{5}{60} = 8.3\%$ increase

9. Express the difference that you calculated in Item 8 as a percent increase or decrease of the fly length (for a 3 ft hoist) displayed in the table in Item 4.

$\frac{.7}{5.7} = 12.28\%$ decrease

SUGGESTED LEARNING STRATEGIES: Think/Pair/Share,
Group Presentation, Self Revision/Peer Revision

My Notes

Fly
Hoist

10. Another dimension approved by President Eisenhower was 5 by 8. Calculate the difference in the fly for a flag that is 5 ft by 8 ft and the fly of the flag in the table in Item 4 whose hoist is 5 feet. Express this difference as a percent increase or decrease of the value from the table. Show your work.

$9.5 - 8 = 1.5$; $\frac{1.5}{9.5} = 15.79\%$ decrease

11. Suppose a flag manufacturer chooses to make flags the ratio of whose hoist to fly is 3:5.

a. Express this ratio as a fraction.

$\frac{3}{5}$

b. Find the fly of one of these flags if the hoist is 12 feet. Show your work.

$\frac{3}{5} = \frac{12}{x}$, $3x = 60$, $x = 20$; 20 ft

c. Find the fly of one of these flags if the hoist is 1 foot. Show your work.

$\frac{3}{5} = \frac{1}{x}$, $3x = 5$, $x = \frac{5}{3}$; $\approx$1.67 ft

d. Write a fraction that is equal to the fraction in part a, but that has a 1 in the numerator.

$\frac{1}{1.67}$ or $\frac{1}{\frac{5}{3}}$

TRY THESE C

a. Write a fraction equal to $\frac{4}{9}$ whose numerator is 1.

$\frac{1}{2.25}$

b. Measure the dimensions of the US flag in your classroom, and write them as a ratio of the hoist to the fly with a numerator of 1.

Answers may vary but they should be close to $\frac{1}{1.6}$.

c. If the ratio of the length of a rectangle to the width is 6:5, find the width of the rectangle when the length is 15 cm.

12.5 cm

---

10 Think/Pair/Share, Group Presentation, Debriefing, Self/Peer Revision Students are given another ratio for the sides of a flag and asked to calculate the percent decrease in the fly when compared to the table in Item 4. This is an opportunity for you to assess students' understanding.

11 Think/Pair/Share, Group Presentation, Debriefing, Self/Peer Revision Students are led through the steps for rewriting the ratio 3:5 as a fraction whose numerator is 1. A class discussion may ensue as students compare this ratio to the 1:1.9 ratio from the beginning of this activity. Possible proportions for Parts b and c are:

b. $\frac{3}{5} = \frac{12\ ft}{x}$

c. $\frac{3}{5} = \frac{1\ ft}{x}$

TRY THESE C Students practice rewriting fractions so they have a numerator equal to 1. Students will need to be able to measure the dimensions of the US flag displayed in the classroom. Students will need to have a clear understanding of these problems if they are to be able to complete the Check Your Understanding and Unit 4 Practice assignment for this portion of the activity. Possible proportions for Parts a and c are:

a. $\frac{4}{9} = \frac{1}{x}$

c. $\frac{6}{5} = \frac{15\ cm}{x}$

Suggested Assignment

CHECK YOUR UNDERSTANDING
p. 220, #1–6

UNIT 4 PRACTICE
p. 245, #20–23

TEACHER TO TEACHER Important properties of the US flag that students are about to draw are given in the bullets above Item 12. You may choose to use reading strategies such as Questioning the Text or Summarize/Paraphrase/Retell at this point.

12 Think/Pair/Share, Self/Peer Revision Students are asked to express the height of one stripe as a fraction of the flag.

13 Think/Pair/Share, Self/Peer Revision Students should use their fraction from Item 12 and the third bullet in the description of the flag to determine what fraction of the height of the flag the height of the blue field is.

14 Think/Pair/Share, Group Presentation, Debriefing, Self/Peer Revision Students are asked to explain why 13 cm is a good choice for the height of a flag.

15 Think/Pair/Share, Group Presentations, Debriefing, Self/Peer Revision Students use a proportion to find the width of a flag given the height. They are directed to draw a rectangle with this height and width. It is essential that students draw an accurate right angle, so the teacher may need to remind them to use a piece of paper that they know has a right angle. Also, students will need a centimeter ruler. A proportion can be used to determine the width: $\frac{3}{5} = \frac{13\ cm}{w}$.

16 Think/Pair/Share, Group Presentation, Debriefing, Self/Peer Revision Students determine the height and width of the blue field and add them to their scale drawing. After using the information from Items 13 and 14 to find the height, students can use a proportion to determine the width of the blue field: $\frac{2}{3} = \frac{7\ cm}{x}$.

SUGGESTED LEARNING STRATEGIES: Think/Pair/Share, Self Revision/Peer Revision, Group Presentation

My Notes

MATH TERMS
A **scale drawing** of a figure is a copy of the figure with all lengths in the same ratio to the corresponding lengths in the original. If Quad *ABCD* is a scale drawing of Quad *PQRS* then $\frac{AB}{PQ} = \frac{BC}{QR} = \frac{CD}{RS} = \frac{AD}{PS}$.

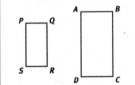

Creating a Scale Drawing

Martha Rose decides to investigate further by creating a **scale drawing** of the US Flag including the thirteen stripes and the blue field for the stars. She chooses the following characteristics for her flag.

- $\frac{height}{width} = \frac{3}{5}$.
- There are 7 red and 6 white stripes, all of which have the same height (hoist).
- The height of the blue field equals the height of seven stripes.
- $\frac{height\ of\ blue\ field}{width\ of\ blue\ field} = \frac{2}{3}$

12. The height of one stripe is what fraction of the height of the entire flag?

$\frac{1}{13}$

13. The height of the blue field is what fraction of the height of the flag?

$\frac{7}{13}$

14. Since all of the information concerning the dimensions of the flag and its parts are given in terms of the height, Martha decides to begin her scale drawing by choosing 13 cm for the height. Explain why 13 cm is a good choice for the height.

Answers may vary. Sample answer: The height of each stripe and blue field are fractions with 13 in the denominator. 13 is the smallest multiple of 13.

15. Determine the width of Martha's flag if $\frac{height}{width} = \frac{3}{5}$. On a plain piece of paper, draw the rectangle with this width and a height of 13 cm.

$w \approx 21.67$ cm; Check students' drawings.

16. Use the information given above to calculate the dimensions of the blue field. Show your work. Add the rectangle that represents the blue field to your scale drawing of the flag.

$\frac{7}{13} \cdot 13 = 7$, $h = 7$ cm; $\frac{2}{3} = \frac{7}{w}$, $2w = 21$, $w = 10.5$ cm; Check students' drawings.

SUGGESTED LEARNING STRATEGIES: Think/Pair/Share, Group Presentation, Self/Peer Revision

17. The stripes have the same height but two different widths.

   a. Find the dimensions for each of the six longer stripes and add them to your scale drawing.
   1 cm by ≈ 21.67 cm; Check students' drawings.

   b. Find the dimensions for each of the seven shorter stripes and add them to your scale drawing.
   1 cm by ≈ 11.2 cm; Check students' drawings.

18. Create a scale drawing for a US flag with a height of 13 cm that has the following specifications:

   • $\dfrac{\text{height}}{\text{width}} = \dfrac{1}{1.9}$

   • There are 7 red and 6 white stripes, all of which have the same height.

   • The height of the blue field is the height of 7 stripes.

   • $\dfrac{\text{height of blue field}}{\text{width of blue field}} = \dfrac{2}{3}$ Student samples may vary but should be scale drawings.

19. At the beginning of this activity, you were asked to choose the rectangle whose dimensions were in the ratio 1:1.9. Compare the scale drawings of the two flags that you have drawn to the rectangles presented in Item 1.

   a. Which of the rectangles in Item 1 looks most like the flag you drew in Items 12–17?   B

   b. Which of the rectangles in Item 1 looks most like the flag you drew in Item 18?   C

   c. Which of the rectangles in Item 1 is most similar to the flag in your classroom?   Answers may vary.

20. If you owned a company that manufactures US flags, which would you prefer: flags with the ratio $\dfrac{\text{hoist}}{\text{fly}} = \dfrac{1}{1.67}$ or flags with the ratio $\dfrac{\text{hoist}}{\text{fly}} = \dfrac{1}{1.9}$? Explain your answer.

Answers may vary. Sample answer: I would choose the flag with the ratio $\dfrac{\text{hoist}}{\text{fly}} = \dfrac{1}{1.67}$ because the fly is shorter and it would take less material to make each flag and cost less money.

My Notes

Fly — Hoist

---

17 Think/Pair/Share, Group Presentation, Debriefing, Self/Peer Revision Students calculate the dimensions of the long and short stripes. They should see that the width of the short stripe is the width of the flag minus the width of the blue field.

18 Think/Pair/Share, Group Presentation, Debriefing, Self/Peer Revision Students are asked to create a second scale drawing, this time the ratio of the sides is 1:1.9. They should follow the same steps as in Items 15–17. This is an opportunity for the teacher to assess students' understanding.

19 Think/Pair/Share Students are asked to compare their scale drawings to the rectangles in Item 1.

20 Think/Pair/Share, Group Presentation, Debriefing, Self/Peer Revision Students are asked to explain why it might be advantageous to make flags whose sides are in the ratio 3:5 (1:1.67) as opposed to flags whose sides are in the ratio 1:1.9. If they are struggling, encourage them to think of the problem practically: Less material is needed for the 3:5 flag with the same height as a 1:1.9 flag, so it would be cheaper to produce.

Suggested Assignment

CHECK YOUR UNDERSTANDING
p. 220, #7–11

UNIT 4 PRACTICE
p. 245–246, #24–26

CHECK YOUR UNDERSTANDING

1a. $x = 14$

b. $x = 81.25$

c. $x \approx 1.39$

d. $x = 0.72$

2. Thomas is 15 yrs old.

3. $h = 17.5$ mm

4. 12.5% increase

5. 11.1% decrease

6a. $\frac{1}{1.25}$

b. $\frac{1}{1.4}$

c. $\frac{1}{2}$

7. 15 in.

8. 44 mm

9. Check students' drawings, which should show a rectangle in which $w = 9.375$ in. and $h = 2.5$ in.

10. 48.75 cm

11. Answers may vary. Sample answer: $\frac{p}{100}$ accounts for the percent. The proportion allows you compare "difference is to original as p is to 100."

CHECK YOUR UNDERSTANDING

Write your answers on notebook paper. Show your work.

1. Solve for x.

   a. $\frac{x}{20} = \frac{52.5}{75}$

   b. $\frac{13}{16} = \frac{x}{100}$

   c. $\frac{18}{25} = \frac{1}{x}$

   d. $\frac{25}{18} = \frac{1}{x}$

2. The ratio of Thomas' age to his sister's age is 3:2. Find Thomas' age if his sister is 10 years old.

3. The ratio of the altitude of a triangle to the length of its base is 5:12. Calculate the altitude if the length of the base is 42 mm.

4. Sarah's hourly wage went from $4.00 per hour to $4.50 per hour. Calculate the difference in Sarah's wages as a percent increase or decrease.

5. Todd's hourly wage went from $4.50 per hour to $4.00 per hour. Calculate the difference in Todd's wages as a percent increase or decrease.

6. Write a fraction that is equal to each of the given fractions and has a numerator of 1.

   a. $\frac{4}{5}$

   b. $\frac{5}{7}$

   c. $\frac{3.15}{6.3}$

7. Kenyatta is creating a scale drawing of a rectangle whose height is 3 cm and width is 10 cm. Find the width of the rectangle in his drawing if the height is 4.5 inches.

8. Mariela is creating a scale drawing of a triangle such that $\frac{\text{altitude}}{\text{length of the base}} = \frac{1}{1.75}$. Find the altitude of Mamie's triangle if the length of the base is 77 mm.

9. Create a scale drawing of the rectangle below. The height of the scale drawing should be 2.5 inches.

2 cm

7.5 cm

10. Find the width of the rectangle that is a scale drawing of the rectangle above if the height is 13 cm.

11. **MATHEMATICAL REFLECTION** When solving for a percent increase or decrease, you set up a proportion. Explain why the ratio $\frac{p}{100}$ is one of the ratios used in that proportion.

Percents & Circle Graphs
Red, White, & Blue

SUGGESTED LEARNING STRATEGIES: Think/Pair/Share,
Create Representations, Close Reading

John Abraham Roosevelt is running for student government. He plans to create posters with a patriotic theme: red, white, and blue. John also wants his colors to be proportional to those of the US Flag.

Before John can buy paint or markers for the posters, he needs to know the ratio of the number of red markers to the number of blue markers. John has a flag hanging in his bedroom with the dimensions pictured below.

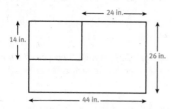

1. Find the total area of the US Flag. Show your work.
   1144 in²

2. Draw in the thirteen stripes: 7 "short" and 6 "long" and label each stripe as "red" or "white."
   Check students' drawing and labeling of stripes.

My Notes

ACTIVITY 4.5 Guided

Percents & Circle Graphs

Activity Focus
- Percents
- Circle graphs

Materials
- US flag
- Protractors (1 per student)
- Dry erase boards or chart paper and markers

Chunking the Activity

#1–3	#8–9	#13
#4–5	#10	#14
#6–7	#11–12	

1 Think/Pair/Share Students calculate the area of a rectangle. You may need to remind them to express their answers using proper units: square inches.

TEACHER TO TEACHER Items 2 and 3 refer to "long" and "short" stripes. It may be helpful for students if you (or a student) point these out on the US flag displayed in the classroom.

2 Think/Pair/Share, Create Representations, Close Reading Students draw and label the thirteen stripes on the flag. The top and bottom stripes are red.

3 Think/Pair/Share, Group Presentation, Debrief, Self/Peer Revision Students are led through the steps for calculating the total area of the 7 red stripes.

4-5 Activating Prior Knowledge, Think/Pair/Share, Group Presentation, Debrief, Self/Peer Revision Students express a ratio as a fraction in lowest terms and convert that fraction to a decimal and percent.

6 Think/Pair/Share, Group Presentation Students calculate the sum of the areas of the 6 white stripes. The teacher may elect to use a reading strategy such as Marking the Text or Summarize/Paraphrase/Retell to help students process the information given in Part b.

My Notes

SUGGESTED LEARNING STRATEGIES: Group Presentation, Self Revision/Peer Revision, Activating Prior Knowledge, Think/Pair/Share

3. There are four "short" red stripes and three "long" red stripes.

   a. List the dimensions of each "short" stripe and find the area.
24" by 2"; 48 in²

   b. List the dimensions of each "long" stripe and find the area.
44" by 2"; 88 in²

   c. Find the total area of the 7 red stripes. Show your work.
$4 \cdot 48 + 3 \cdot 88 = 192 + 264 = 456$; 456 in²

4. Write the ratio of the sum of the areas of the red stripes to the total area of the flag. Express your answer as a fraction reduced to lowest terms.
$\frac{57}{143}$

5. Express your answer from Item 4 as a decimal and as a percent.
0.4; 40%

6. The total area for white on the US Flag can be found by adding the areas of the three "short" stripes, three "long" stripes and fifty stars.

   a. Calculate the sum of the areas of the 6 white stripes. Show your work.
$3 \cdot 48 + 3 \cdot 88 = 144 + 264 = 408$; 408 in²

   b. John researched flag dimensions and estimated that there was as much red as there is white on the US Flag. Calculate the total area of the fifty stars. Be sure to include units and show your work.
$x + 408 = 456$, $x = 48$; 48 in²

SUGGESTED LEARNING STRATEGIES: Think/Pair/Share, Self Revision/Peer Revision, Group Presentation

7. What percent of this flag is white? Round your answer to the nearest whole percent.
40%

8. Calculate the area of the US Flag that is blue. Include units and show your work.
$x = 1144 - (456 + 456)$, $x = 232$; 232 in²

9. What percent of this flag is blue?
20%

10. Recall that John Abraham Roosevelt wanted to calculate the number of red or blue markers needed for his campaign posters, and his color scheme would be proportional to those in the US Flag.

a. How does the area of the blue region on the US Flag in this activity compare to the sum of the areas of the red stripes?
Answers may vary. Sample answer: The area of the blue region is slightly more than half the area of the red region.

b. If John has enough money to buy 24 red and blue markers, how many of each should he buy? Explain your answer.
16 red and 8 blue; Explanations may vary. Sample explanation: The total is 24 markers and there are half as many blue markers as red markers.

My Notes

7 Debriefing, Self/Peer Revision

8 Think/Pair/Share, Group Presentation, Debriefing
Students may calculate the area of the blue field by subtracting the red and white areas from the area of the flag, and finding an area of 232 in.² They may also find the area by subtracting the percent of the flag that is red or white from 100%, finding that 20% of the flag is blue, and finding 20% of the total area (20% · 1144 in.² = 228.8 in.²). The slight difference in the answers is due to the fact that the percents were rounded. Students would benefit from a class discussion about the two different solutions.

9 Think/Pair/Share, Group Presentation, Debriefing, Self/Peer Revision Students determine the percent of the area of the flag that is blue. They can either write a ratio of the areas and convert to a percent, or they can subtract the red and white percentages from 100%.

10 Think/Pair/Share, Group Presentation, Debriefing, Self/Peer Revision Students are asked to compare the area of the red on a US flag to the area of the blue, which is roughly 2:1. They will use this information to proportionally divide the 24 markers. You may elect to use a reading strategy such as Summarize/Paraphrase/Retell to help students understand this item.

TRY THESE A Think/Pair/Share, Group Presentation, Self/Peer Revision Students practice converting fractions to percents and determining the percent of the area of a region.

Suggested Assignment

CHECK YOUR UNDERSTANDING
p. 228, #1, 2, 4, 5

UNIT 4 PRACTICE
p. 246, #27–29

TEACHER TO TEACHER | Vocabulary is presented in the text at the bottom of this page as an introduction to Item 11. You may elect to use a reading strategy, such as Shared Reading, to help students process these terms. These terms can be added to the interactive Word Wall.

SUGGESTED LEARNING STRATEGIES: Think/Pair/Share, Group Presentation, Self Revision/Peer Revision

My Notes

TRY THESE A

a. Express $\frac{3}{8}$ as a decimal and a percent.
0.375 = 37.5%

John has a lot of socks. 6 pairs are white, 6 pairs are brown, 4 pairs are green, and 8 pairs are black.

b. What percent of John's socks are brown?
25%

c. What percent of John's socks are black?
33.3%

d. What percent of John's socks are black and green?
50%

e. The area of the triangular region is what percent of the rectangle's area?
20%

(Rectangle: 5 ft top, 2 ft left side, 2 ft bottom with a diagonal line forming a triangle)

MATH TERMS

A **sector** of a circle is formed by two radii and an arc of the circle.

A **central angle** is an angle whose vertex is the center of the circle.

Circle Graphs

Circle graphs are used to display data by representing each portion of the whole as a **sector** of a circle. The size of the sector is determined by the measure of the **central angle**.

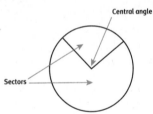

Central angle

Sectors

SUGGESTED LEARNING STRATEGIES: Think/Pair/Share, Self Revision/Peer Revision, Group Presentation

My Notes

11. Use a protractor to measure the central angle in each of the sectors.

A: 120°, B: 90°, C: 150°

12. Find the sum of the measures of the three central angles above.
360°

John has to deliver a campaign speech. He has decided to spend his allotted time as follows.

- 40% talking about dances and pep rallies
- 25% talking about the food in the cafeteria
- 20% talking about the canned food drive for the community food bank
- 15% talking about recycling on campus

13. John is a "visual" person, so he creates a circle graph that represents the four parts of his speech. Calculate the measure of each central angle for each sector in his circle graph by finding a percent of 360°. Show your work.
In order: 144°, 90°, 72°, and 54°

> **MATH TIP**
> To find a percent of a number, convert the percent to a decimal (divide by 100) and multiply.
> *Example:*
> 35% of 150 = 0.35(150) = 52.5

---

11 Think/Pair/Share, Self/Peer Revision

12 Think/Pair/Share, Debrief Students should already know that the sum of the three sectors is 360°.

13 Think/Pair/Share, Group Presentation, Debriefing, Self/Peer Revision Students are asked to convert percents to the degree measure of the central angles. You will need to employ a reading strategy in order to emphasize the bulleted information above this item.

14 Group Presentation, Debriefing Students are given directions for creating a circle graph for the information given in Item 13. You may want to have students use chart paper and have group presentations. Students will see that not all groups will choose to place their sectors in the same place and, yet, their circle graph is still correct. You will need to use a reading strategy such as Shared Reading and Summarize/ Paraphrase/Retell to help students understand the steps for creating their own circle graph. You may elect to have a larger circle available that students can use to model the steps in front of the rest of the class.

SUGGESTED LEARNING STRATEGIES: Group Presentation

My Notes

14. Use a protractor and the circle below to complete a circle graph that represents the four parts of John's speech.

- Refer to your responses to Item 13 and draw an angle with the first degree measure. The vertex of the angle should be the center of the circle. One side of this angle has already been drawn. Draw the other side of this sector and label this sector.
- Draw the second central angle such that it has a side in common with the first angle. Label this sector.
- Draw the third central angle such that it has a side in common with the second angle. Label this sector.
- Label the remaining sector. Use a protractor to make sure it has the correct measure.
- Create a title for your circle graph.

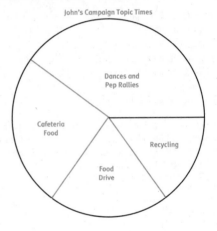

John's Campaign Topic Times

SUGGESTED LEARNING STRATEGIES: Think/Pair/Share,
Group Presentation, Self Revision/Peer Revision

TRY THESE B

a. Match each central angle measure of a circle graph to its corresponding percent.

Central Angle Measure		Percent			
a. 270°	**b.** 180°	41.7% h		10% g	
c. 30°	**d.** 216°	50% b		75% a	
e. 108°	**f.** 60°	16.7% f		8.3% c	
g. 36°	**h.** 150°	30% e		60% d	

b. Create a circle graph that represents the area of red, white and blue on the US Flag in this activity. Use your responses to Items 5, 7, and 9.

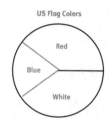

US Flag Colors

c. For his science class, John counted the trees in the woods behind his house:

- 120 maple trees
- 84 oak trees
- 24 pine trees
- 12 other trees

Trees Behind My House

Create a circle graph that represents the number of each kind of tree behind John's house.

d. Use the My Notes space to make a list of the steps needed to create the circle graph above.

Step 1:   Calculate the central angle measure for each sector.

Step 2:   Use a protractor to draw a central angle for each sector.

Step 3:   Create a title.

My Notes

ACTIVITY 4.5 *Continued*

TRY THESE B Think/Pair/Share, Group Presentation, Self/Peer Revision Students practice by matching percents to degree measure of central angles and creating two circle graphs, one of which reflects the percents found in Items 5, 7, and 9.

Suggested Assignment

CHECK YOUR UNDERSTANDING
p. 228, #3, 6–10

UNIT 4 PRACTICE
p. 246, #30–32

1a. 50%

b. 62.5%

c. 90%

d. 45%

2a. 35%

b. 46%

c. 19%

3. DDE Middle School Enrollment

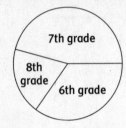

4. 24%

5. ≈ 64.2%

6a. $24

b. $52

c. $30

d. $96

7a. 43.2°

b. 90°

c. 30.6°

d. 216°

8. 55%

9.

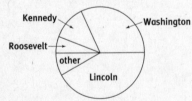

10. The measure of the central angle would be greater than 180°.

CHECK YOUR UNDERSTANDING

Write your answers on notebook paper.
Show your work.

1. Express each ratio as a percent.

  a. $\frac{1}{2}$

  b. $\frac{5}{8}$

  c. $\frac{9}{10}$

  d. $\frac{9}{20}$

2. At DDE Middle School, there are 280 6th graders, 368 7th graders, and 152 8th graders.

  a. What percent of the students at DDE Middle School are 6th graders?

  b. What percent of the students at DDE Middle School are 7th graders?

  c. What percent of the students at DDE Middle School are 8th graders?

3. Create a circle graph to represent the number of 6th, 7th, and 8th graders at DDE Middle School from #2 above.

4. The area of rectangle *ABCD* is what percent of the area of rectangle *BCEF*?

5. The radius of the circle is 5 mm and the length of one side of the inscribed square is 7.1 mm. What percent of the area of the circle is occupied by the square? The area of a circle is $A = \pi r^2$. Use 3.14 for π.

6. Find each of the following percents of $80.

  a. 30%

  b. 65%

  c. 37.5%

  d. 120%

7. Find each of the following percents of 360°.

  a. 12%

  b. 25%

  c. 8.5%

  d. 60%

8. In a recent football game, the offense was on the field for 26.4 minutes out of a total of 48 minutes. For what percent of the game was the offense on the field?

9. In a recent survey, Shayla asked her classmates to name their favorite president. The results are displayed below. Create a circle graph to represent the results from Shayla's survey.

Favorite US President	
George Washington	16
Abraham Lincoln	21
Theodore Roosevelt	3
John F. Kennedy	6
Other	4

10. **MATHEMATICAL REFLECTION** What is true about the measure of the central angle of any sector that represents more than 50% of the circle?

Similar Triangles
Tunnel to a Parallel Dimension

SUGGESTED LEARNING STRATEGIES: Create Representations

Carl found an old journal in which the science fiction author documented his adventures to parallel universes through different tunnels.

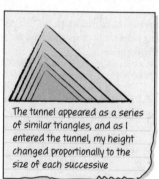

The tunnel appeared as a series of similar triangles, and as I entered the tunnel, my height changed proportionally to the size of each successive

The triangles below represent two of the triangles described in the journal.

1. Use the lengths of the three pairs of **corresponding sides** to create three ratios in the form $\dfrac{\text{side length in small triangle}}{\text{corresponding length in large triangle}}$.

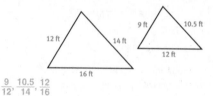

$$\frac{9}{12}, \frac{10.5}{14}, \frac{12}{16}$$

My Notes

ACTIVITY 4.6 Guided

Similar Triangles

Activity Focus
- Similar triangles
- Dilations

Materials
- Dry erase boards or chart paper and markers

Chunking the Activity

#1–3	#7	#11–13
#4–6	#8–10	

TEACHER TO TEACHER You may elect to begin a KWL Chart as you are debriefing the class on Item 1, and complete this chart as part of the Day 1 wrap-up. Based on the "K," you may want to model several examples of corresponding parts.

1 Create Representations, Debriefing Students are asked to create ratios using the corresponding sides in two triangles. This is very similar to the corresponding angles and sides students worked with in Activity 4.1. In this case, corresponding sides are in "corresponding positions" such as the bottom, left, and right sides. The importance of units should be stressed. In this item, the 16 ft (longest) side in the large triangle corresponds to the 12 ft (longest) side in the small triangle. The 12 ft (shortest) side in the large triangle corresponds to the 9 ft (shortest) side in the small triangle. Lastly, the 14 ft side in the large triangle corresponds to the 10.5 ft side in the small triangle.

2 Think/Pair/Share Students should look for a pattern and realize that all ratios are equal to $\frac{3}{4}$. You may elect to lead a class discussion on how to identify equivalent fractions.

3 Think/Pair/Share, Debriefing, Interactive Word Wall, Quickwrite Students are given the definition of similar triangles and asked to apply this definition to the triangles in Item 1. The term *similar figures* may be added to the Interactive Word Wall as part of the discussion of this item. After students read and discuss Item 3, ask them to explain why the two triangles in Item 1 are similar triangles.

4 Think/Pair/Share Students are given the similarity notation rules and asked to label the vertices using corresponding parts in the similarity statement.

5 Think/Pair/Share, Group Presentation, Debriefing, Self/Peer Revision, Identify a Subtask, Create Representations Students identify corresponding sides (they are in the same proportion 4:5). Group Presentations can be used to launch a class discussion concerning the way in which the triangles are named, and there are, actually, 6 possible correct responses: $\triangle COR$, $\triangle PTS$, $\triangle CRO$, $\triangle PST$, $\triangle ORC$, $\triangle TSP$.

My Notes

MATH TiP

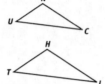

Notation Alert!
The notation for similar is ~.
The similarity notation for two triangles is $\triangle UNC \sim \triangle THL$ where the following sides and angles are corresponding.

$\angle U \longleftrightarrow \angle T$ $\overline{UN} \longleftrightarrow \overline{TH}$
$\angle N \longleftrightarrow \angle H$ $\overline{NC} \longleftrightarrow \overline{HL}$
$\angle C \longleftrightarrow \angle L$ $\overline{UC} \longleftrightarrow \overline{TL}$

The symbol, $\longleftrightarrow$, means corresponding.

ACADEMIC VOCABULARY

Similar figures

SUGGESTED LEARNING STRATEGIES: Think/Pair/Share, Create Representations, Identify a Subtask, Simplify the Problem, Quickwrite, Self Revision/Peer Revision

2. Compare the ratios that you created in Item 1.
Answers may vary. Sample answers: They are all equal to $\frac{3}{4}$. The ratios are equivalent.

3. **Similar figures** are figures in which the lengths of the corresponding sides are in proportion and the corresponding angles are congruent.
All three pairs of corresponding sides are equivalent to $\frac{3}{4}$ so they are in proportion.

4. If $\triangle ABC \sim \triangle DEF$, label the missing vertices in the triangles below.

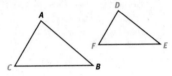

5. The triangles below are similar.

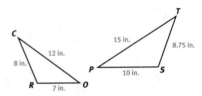

a. What transformation would help you identify the corresponding parts of the triangles?
rotation

b. Use similarity notation to identify all the similar parts of the triangles.
$\angle C \sim \angle P$, $\angle O \sim \angle T$, $\angle R \sim \angle S$
$CO \sim PT$, $CR \sim PS$, $OR \sim TS$,
$\triangle COR \sim \triangle PTS$

SUGGESTED LEARNING STRATEGIES: Create Representations, Identify a Subtask, Simplify the Problem, Self Revision/Peer Revision, Group Presentation

6. Consider the three triangles below.

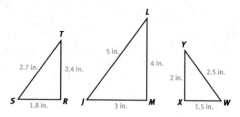

a. Compare ratios to identify the similar triangles.

$\frac{2.7}{1.8} \neq \frac{5}{3}, \frac{2.7}{1.8} \neq \frac{5}{4}, \frac{2.7}{1.8} \neq \frac{4}{3}, \frac{5}{3} = \frac{2.5}{1.5}, \frac{4}{3} = \frac{2}{1.5}, \frac{5}{4} = \frac{2.5}{2}$

b. Identify the similar triangles using similarity notation.

$\triangle MJL \sim \triangle XWY$

7. The ratio of two corresponding sides of similar triangles is called the **scale factor**. Find the scale factors for the similar triangles in Items 1, 5, and 6.

Sample answers: Item 1: $\frac{3}{4}$; Item 5: $\frac{4}{5}$; Item 6: $\frac{2}{1}$

EXAMPLE 1

Solve for x if $\triangle AIM \sim \triangle LOW$.

Step 1: Find the scale factor using known corresponding lengths.

The scale factor is $\frac{20 \text{ cm}}{16 \text{ cm}}$ or $\frac{5}{4}$

Step 2: Write a proportion using the scale factor.

$\frac{5}{4} = \frac{15 \text{ cm}}{x}$

Step 3: Solve the proportion.

$5x = 60$

$x = 12$

Solution: 12 cm

My Notes

TEACHER TO TEACHER Students may not be familiar with the quotation mark notation for feet and inches. It may be worthwhile to have them make a note in their notebooks that the double quotation mark is shorthand for inches, and the single quotation mark is shorthand for feet.

6 Group Presentation, Debriefing, Self/Peer Revision, Create Representations Only two of the three triangles are similar. Students must realize that they should compare the ratio of a pair on sides in one triangle to the ratio of all pairs of sides in the other triangle, not just the pair of sides that seem to correspond. Again, group presentations will bring out several of the possible correct responses.

7 Debriefing, Interactive Word Wall, Self/Peer Revision Students are given the definition of *scale factor* and asked to find the scale factors for the pairs of triangles in Items 1, 5 and 6. Some students' ratios may be the reciprocals of other student responses. A class discussion may be needed to assure the students that their responses are correct as long as they are consistent with where they place corresponding lengths in their ratios. The term *scale factor* may be added to the Interactive Word Wall as part of the class discussion on this item.

TEACHER TO TEACHER You may want to model the example on this page and employ a reading strategy such as Questioning the Text or Summarize/Paraphrase/Retell to call attention to the steps for finding the length of an unknown side in one of two similar triangles.

TRY THESE A Students practice finding the scale factor of two similar triangles and solving for unknown lengths using a proportion.

Suggested Assignment

CHECK YOUR UNDERSTANDING
p. 234, #1–4

UNIT 4 PRACTICE
p. 246, #33–35

8 Think/Pair/Share, Create Representations Given a similarity statement, students are asked to write the three pairs of congruent angles. This is an opportunity to assess students' understanding of correct congruence notation. A class discussion may ensue concerning how many vertices are needed to name the angles (three or one). It is simpler and appropriate for this item to use one vertex when naming these angles.

9 Activating Prior Knowledge, Visualization, Think/Pair/Share Students use the properties: the sum of the measures of the three angles in a triangle is 180° and corresponding angles are congruent in similar triangles.

10 Group Presentation, Debriefing, Self/Peer Revision, Create Representations, Identify a Subtask Students find the measure of the unknown angle in each triangle and write two similarity statements. It is important that students understand by now that the vertices in their similarity statements are corresponding.

My Notes

MATH TIP

Congruent triangles are similar triangles with a scale factor of 1:1.

MATH TIP

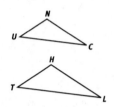

The notation for congruent is ≅. The congruency notation for angles is ∠U ≅ ∠T

TRY THESE A

Given △TIN ~ △CAN

a. Find the scale factor.

$\frac{8}{15}$

b. Solve for x and y.

x = 4.8; y = 12

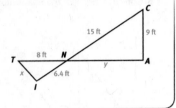

8. If two triangles are similar, then corresponding angles are congruent. If △BIG ~ △SKY, then list three pairs of congruent angles.

∠B ≅ ∠S, ∠I ≅ ∠K, ∠G ≅ ∠Y

9. Suppose △DOG ~ △CAT Find the measure of each of the following angles.

a. ∠C   71°

b. ∠D   71°

c. ∠A   90°

d. ∠G   19°

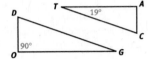

10. If the three angles of one triangle are congruent to the three angles of another triangle, the triangles are similar. Use similarity notation to state which triangles are similar.

△LOG ~ △PIN and △ARM ~ △BET

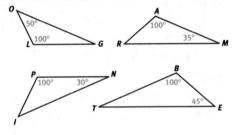

ACTIVITY 4.6 Continued

My Notes

11. A **dilation** is a transformation where the image is similar (but not congruent) to the pre-image. Given the pre-image of $\triangle PQR$ below, sketch the image of $\triangle PQR$ if it is dilated:

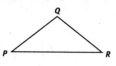

a. by a factor of 2.

b. by a factor of $\frac{1}{2}$.

> **MATH TERMS**
> To **dilate** an image by a factor means to multiply the length of each side by that factor.

12. Given the similar triangles below.

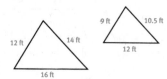

> **CONNECT TO AP**
> Graphs of functions can also be dilated. For example, the graph of $y = 2x$ is a dilation of the graph of $y = x$. In later math courses, you will learn to dilate the graphs of more complicated functions.

a. The larger triangle is a dilation of the smaller triangle. By what factor is the smaller triangle enlarged?

$\frac{4}{3}$

b. By what factor is the larger triangle reduced?

$\frac{3}{4}$

c. What is the relationship between the two scale factors?

They are reciprocals.

You can sketch the dilation of a polygon on the coordinate plane by multiplying the coordinates of each vertex by the dilation factor and connecting the new vertices.

13. Sketch the image of $\triangle RST$ to the right if it is dilated by a factor of 2.

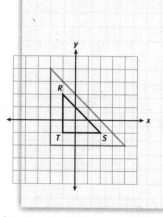

11 Group Presentation, Debriefing, Interactive Word Wall, Create Representations, Self/Peer Revision Students are given the definition of a dilation and asked to dilate a given triangle by a factor of 2, and then by a factor of $\frac{1}{2}$. The term *dilation* may be added to the Interactive Word Wall as part of the class discussion of this item.

12 Debriefing, Self/Peer Revision, Look for a Pattern Students should recognize that the two scale factors are reciprocals.

TEACHER TO TEACHER Testing tip: students need to be aware of the order when responding with a scale factor. It should be clear to them that it makes a difference if you are scaling from a larger to a smaller figure or vice versa. Many multiple choice items include the reciprocal of the correct response as a distractor.

Suggested Assignment

CHECK YOUR UNDERSTANDING
p. 234, #5–10

UNIT 4 PRACTICE
p. 247, #36–38

Connect to AP

In Algebra 2 and Precalculus, students will dilate functions as they learn to quickly sketch them using transformations. The dilations usually occur in one direction only. For example, the graphs of $y = f(x)$ and $y = 2f(x)$ are shown to the right.

At each x-value, notice the y-coordinates of $y = 2f(x)$ are those of function f multiplied by two. The ability to quickly anticipate what the graph of a function will look like by analyzing its equation is a valuable skill for future calculus students.

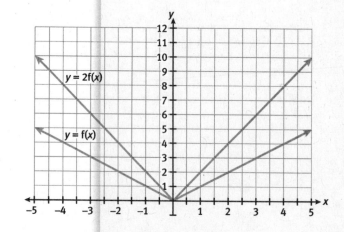

CHECK YOUR UNDERSTANDING

1a. △ALT ∼ △DIM

b. $\frac{6}{4}$ or $\frac{3}{2}$ or $\frac{12}{8}$ or $\frac{9}{6}$

2a. △AGE ∼ △NGL

b. $\frac{8}{12}$, $\frac{10}{15}$, $\frac{6}{9}$, or $\frac{2}{3}$

c. h = 4.8"

d. The ratio of the perimeters is equal to the scale factor.

3. a = 3.75; b = 8

4. p = 3"; q = 2.6"

5a. 82°

b. 37°

c. 61°

d. 61°

6a. 20°

b. 80°

c. 80°

d. 80°

7. △JAF ∼ △DCE and △CLH ∼ △GKB

8. Check students' drawings.

9a. increase

b. decrease

10. Explanations may vary. Sample answer: The ratio of the perimeters of two similar triangles will always be equal to the scale factor, because each perimeter is the sum of 3 numbers that are in proportion to the 3 sides of the other triangle.

CHECK YOUR UNDERSTANDING

Write your answers on notebook paper. Show your work.

1. Given the triangles to the right,
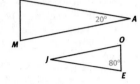
   a. use similarity notation to identify the two triangles as similar.
   b. find the scale factor.

2. Given the triangles below,
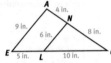
   a. use similarity notation to identify the two similar triangles.
   b. find the scale factor.
   c. If the height of △AGE is 7.2" find the height of the smaller triangle.
   d. How does the ratio of the perimeters of the triangles compare to the scale factor?

3. If △SIX ∼ △TEN then solve for a and b.
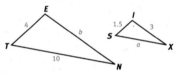

4. If △CAN ∼ △CYR then solve for p and q.
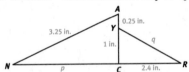

5. △MON ∼ △WED, m∠M = 37° and m∠E = 82°. Find the measure of each of the following angles.
   a. ∠O   **b.** ∠W   **c.** ∠N   **d.** ∠D

6. If △JOE ∼ △AMY find the measure of each of the following angles.
   a. ∠J
   b. ∠O
   c. ∠Y
   d. ∠M
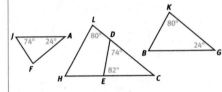

7. Compare ratios and use similarity notation to state which triangles are similar.

8. Sketch the image of the figure below once it is dilated by a factor of $\frac{2}{3}$.

9. Does the size of a pre-image increase or decrease when
   a. dilated by a factor greater than 1?
   b. dilated by a factor between 0 and 1?

10. **MATHEMATICAL REFLECTION** If two triangles are similar, how does the ratio of their perimeters compare to the scale factor. Justify your answer.

Unit Conversion
Presto Chango!

SUGGESTED LEARNING STRATEGIES: Think/Pair/Share, Group Presentation, Self Revision/Peer Revision

Ramon was excited when he won tickets to see the Great Howie Dudat, an illusionist. One of the Great Howie Dudat's best tricks is to raise a 7.5 ton truck into the air 15 meters.

1. One ton is equal to 2000 pounds. Calculate the weight of the truck in pounds. Show your work.

$7.5 \cdot 2000 \text{ lbs} = 15{,}000 \text{ lbs}$

2. The average student at Ramon's school weighs 125 pounds. Find the number of students whose combined weights equal the weight of the truck. Show your work.

$15{,}000 \text{ lbs} \div \frac{125 \text{ lbs}}{\text{student}} = 15{,}000 \text{ lbs} \cdot \frac{1 \text{ student}}{125 \text{ lbs}} = 120 \text{ students}$

3. One meter is approximately 39.4 inches. Calculate the height that the Great Howie levitates the truck in inches.

591 in.

4. Convert your response from Item 3, which is given in inches, into feet.

$591 \text{ in} \div \frac{12 \text{ in}}{1 \text{ foot}} = 591 \text{ in} \cdot \frac{1 \text{ foot}}{12 \text{ in}} = 49.25 \text{ ft}$

5. a. Which of the Items 1–4 required multiplication?

1 and 3

b. Which of the Items 1–4 required division?

2 and 4

c. When converting units, explain how you know which operation to use: multiplication or division.

Answers may vary. Sample answer: Divide when converting to a larger unit, and multiply when converting to a smaller unit.

My Notes

Unit 4 • Proportional Relationships **235**

TEACHER TO TEACHER If students are struggling with Items 1–4, you may choose to get them started by walking them through how to create and solve one or more of the proportions below.

1. $\dfrac{1 \text{ ton}}{2000 \text{ lbs}} = \dfrac{7.5 \text{ tons}}{x}$

2. $\dfrac{1 \text{ student}}{125 \text{ lbs}} = \dfrac{x}{15000 \text{ lbs}}$

3. $\dfrac{1 \text{ meter}}{39.4 \text{ in.}} = \dfrac{15 \text{ meters}}{x}$

4. $\dfrac{12 \text{ in}}{1 \text{ ft}} = \dfrac{591 \text{ in.}}{x}$

ACTIVITY 4.7 Guided

Unit Conversion

Activity Focus
- Unit conversion
- Dimensional analysis

Materials
- Dry erase boards or chart paper and markers
- Optional materials for stunt that is discussed in Items 9–14: 4 matching glasses with at least 2 inches of water, cookie sheet with an edge, 4 congruent cylinders, and 4 eggs.
- Calculator (optional)

Chunking the Activity

#1–5	#7–8	#11–12
#6	#9	#13–15
	#10	

TEACHER TO TEACHER As the class progresses through this activity, it is suggested that the class keep a list of measurement conversions that the students are expected to remember. Students should be encouraged to mark the text throughout this activity.

1-4 Think/Pair/Share Students convert tons to pounds either by multiplication or by using a proportion. Students convert pounds to tons either by division or by using a proportion. Students convert meters to inches either by multiplication or by using a proportion. Students convert inches to feet either by division or by using a proportion.

5 Group Presentation, Debriefing, Self/Peer Revision Students are asked to generalize which operation, multiplication or division, to use when converting units.

TEACHER TO TEACHER | Students will need Internet access or a newspaper to complete Try These A. See comment below.

TRY THESE A Think/Pair/Share Students practice 1-step conversions. If they do not have Internet access in the classroom, you may have to research the currency exchange rates for US dollar to the Japanese yen and Mexican peso.

6 Group Presentation, Debriefing Students are asked to convert 107 cubic feet to gallons in two steps: convert cubic feet to cubic inches by multiplying, and convert cubic inches to gallons by dividing.

My Notes

TRY THESE A

a. Convert 80 inches to feet. 6.67 ft or $6\frac{2}{3}$ ft

b. There are 8 ounces in one cup. How many ounces are in 3.5 cups?
28 ounces

c. Find the latest foreign currency conversions and convert $50 (US) to yen (Japanese currency), pesos (Mexican currency) and Canadian dollars.
Answers will vary depending upon the exchange rates.

d. Ray needs 25.5 feet of wire to complete a project. Wire is sold by the yard, so he ordered 78.5 yards. Did Ray calculate his order correctly? Explain your answer.
No; Answers may vary. Sample answer: He should have divided 25.5 by 3 to get 8.5 yards. Even if he did multiply, the correct product is 76.5.

On the way to the performance, Ramon passes by a dam, and on the side of the road there is a sign that posts the rate at which water passes over the spillway.

Water Volume:
107 cubic feet
(Per Minute)

6. One cubic foot is equal to 1,728 cubic inches and one gallon is equal to 231 cubic inches. How many gallons are in 107 cubic feet? Round to the nearest hundredth. Show your work.

800.42 gallons

SUGGESTED LEARNING STRATEGIES: Group Presentation,
Think/Pair/Share

My Notes

7. Calculate the number of gallons that pass over the spillway in a day. Explain how you got your answer.

1,152,604.8 gallons each day; Explanations may vary.

8. The speed of the river that flows from the base of the dam is approximately 705 feet per minute. Convert the speed of the river to miles per hour. Explain the steps you used to get your answer.

8.01 mph; Multiply 705 times 60 to get 42,300 $\frac{ft}{h}$ and divide by 5,280 to get 8.01 mph.

> **MATH TIP**
> 1 mile = 5,280 feet

TRY THESE B

a. Convert 1.5 cubic feet to gallons.

11.22 gallons

b. Ramona is thinking about getting a 50-gallon fish tank. How many cubic feet of space will this tank take up?

6.68 cubic feet

c. An ant can cover 22 feet in a minute. Convert this speed to miles per hour.

0.25 mph

d. Jack rabbits have been clocked at speeds as high as 36 mph. At this speed, how far can a jack rabbit travel in one second?

52.8 ft

e. One square yard of carpeting costs $4.50 and 1 square yard = 9 square feet. Calculate the cost of carpeting an area of 945 square feet.

$472.50

---

9. John determined that his house has $1.3 \cdot 10^8$ square inches of living space.

a. Choose a more appropriate unit of area for John to use.

Answers may vary: Sample answer: square feet

b. Find the approximate area of living space in John's house using the unit you chose for part a.

Using square feet, approximately $9.03 \cdot 10^2$, or 903

ACTIVITY 4.7 *Continued*

7 Think/Pair/Share, Debriefing Students use their response to Item 6 and write it as gallons per minute. They should multiply this by 60 to get gallons per hour and then multiply by 24 to get gallons per day.

8 Group Presentation, Debriefing Students should multiply the 705 feet per minute by 60 to get feet per hour and then divide by 5280 to get miles per hour. This is a good place to introduce dimensional analysis as an alternate way to solve to this item.

$$\frac{705\ \cancel{ft}}{minute} \cdot \frac{60\ \cancel{minutes}}{hour} \cdot \frac{1\ mile}{5280\ \cancel{ft}} =$$

$$8.01\ \frac{miles}{hour}$$

TRY THESE B Students practice 2-step conversions.

Suggested Assignment

CHECK YOUR UNDERSTANDING
p. 240, #1–4

UNIT 4 PRACTICE
p. 247, #39–42

TEACHER TO TEACHER ▸ The understanding of how this trick works does not influence the mathematics. However, it may increase student interest if the teacher can model the set-up. It is not necessary that you perform the egg trick, but if you do:

- Practice ahead of time using golf balls.
- The glasses should be identical.
- The cylinders should be identical. Penny wrappers work very well.
- As you pull the tray, keep it level and at a steady rate. The edge of the tray knocks the cylinders out of the way and the eggs fall into the glasses.
- Have extra eggs and paper towels ready for clean-up.

Side View of Egg Trick Set Up

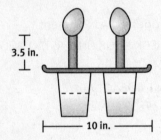

3.5 in.

10 in.

10 Predict and Confirm
Answers will vary depending on whether students consider 74 in./sec as being fast or slow. They will revisit this question once they have converted this rate to mph.

11 Think/Pair/Share It is important that students understand that this fraction is equal to 1, and multiplying a value by 1 does not change the value.

My Notes

SUGGESTED LEARNING STRATEGIES: Predict and Confirm Think/Pair/Share

During the show, the Great Howie Dudat performs a trick with four raw eggs. A tray is set on four glasses and each egg is placed on a cylinder and on the tray above each glass. As Howie pulls the tray, the eggs drop into the glasses. Ramon is sure he can learn to do this trick, too. Of course, he will practice with golf balls, and before he begins, he calculates the speed at which he needs to pull the tray to be 74 inches per second.

Egg trick set up

Each egg lands in a glass!

10. Does Ramon have to be "lightning fast" or "slow and steady" as he pulls the tray? Explain your answer.
    Answers will vary.

Since "miles per hour" are more common as a unit for speed than "inches per second", it may be necessary to convert units before responding to Item 9. Another way to think about the problem of changing a rate expressed as $\frac{\text{inches}}{\text{second}}$ to a rate expressed as $\frac{\text{miles}}{\text{hour}}$ is to multiply the first rate by ratios that are equal to 1.

11. Explain why $\frac{60 \text{ seconds}}{1 \text{ minute}}$ is equal to 1.
    Explanations may vary. Sample answer: When the numerator of a fraction is equal to the denominator of a fraction, the fraction is equal to 1. 60 seconds is equal to 1 minute.

MINI-LESSON: How Ramon Calculates 74 in./sec

This is an opportunity for the class to review literal equations.

1. Given the formula $s = \frac{1}{2}gt^2$ where s represents the height of the cylinder in feet, g represents the gravitational constant, 32 ft/sec², and t represents the time it takes the egg to fall in seconds. Solve the equation for t. $\left(t = \sqrt{\frac{2s}{g}}\right)$

2. Given the formula $d = rt$ in which r which represents the rate (speed), d represents the distance that the edge of the tray travels in order to clear all 4 eggs, and t represents the time calculated in Step 1. Solve the equation for r. $\left(r = \frac{d}{t}\right)$

SUGGESTED LEARNING STRATEGIES: Debrief, Think/Pair/Share, Self Revision/Peer Revision, Group Presentation, Discussion Group

My Notes

12. Multiply $\frac{74 \text{ inches}}{\text{second}}$ by $\frac{60 \text{ seconds}}{\text{minute}}$ and simplify the answer, including units.

$\frac{4440 \text{ in.}}{\text{min}}$

13. Multiply your response in Item 11 by the appropriate ratio that is equal to 1 so the units of the product are $\frac{\text{inches}}{\text{hour}}$ and simplify your answer.

$\frac{266{,}400 \text{ in.}}{\text{hour}}$

14. Multiply your response in Item 13 by two ratios, each of which is equal to 1, so the units of the product are $\frac{\text{miles}}{\text{hour}}$ and simplify your answer.

$\frac{185 \text{ miles}}{44 \text{ hours}}$ or $\frac{4.2 \text{ miles}}{\text{hour}}$

15. Revisit your response to Item 10. Does Ramon have to be "lightning fast" or "slow and steady" as he pulls the tray? Explain your answer.

slow and steady; Answers may vary. Sample answer: He only needs to pull the tray at 4.2 mph. Most people can walk at that pace.

ACTIVITY 4.7 Continued

12 Debriefing Students should multiply 74 by 60 and the seconds simplify to 1 leaving in./min.

13 Think/Pair/Share, Self/Peer Revision Students should multiply their response to Item 12 by 60 min/hr to get in./hr.

14 Group Presentation, Debriefing, Self/Peer Revision Students are asked to multiply their response to Item 13 by two ratios: $\frac{1 \text{ ft}}{12 \text{ in.}}$ and $\frac{1 \text{ mile}}{5280 \text{ ft}}$ to get mi/hr.

15 Discussion Group Students are given the opportunity to revisit Item 9 and change their answer if they wish. 4.2 mph does not sound as fast as 74 in./sec! The "trick" to this stunt is pull the tray smoothly and level. Do not worry about being fast.

MINI-LESSON: Dimensional Analysis "Short Cut"

In the summary for Day 2 of this activity, you may elect to model for students how converting the 74 in./sec given before Item 9 to "miles/hour" in Item 13 can be accomplished in one step as follows:

$$\frac{74 \text{ in.}}{\text{sec}} \cdot \frac{60 \text{ sec}}{1 \text{ min}} \cdot \frac{60 \text{ min}}{1 \text{ hr}} \cdot \frac{1 \text{ ft}}{12 \text{ in.}} \cdot \frac{1 \text{ mile}}{5280 \text{ ft}} = \frac{4.2 \text{ miles}}{\text{hour}}$$

TRY THESE C Students are given an opportunity to practice conversions using dimensional analysis.

TEACHER TO TEACHER — As a summary, you may elect to lead a class discussion on the unit conversions that students are expected to know and make a composite list for students to copy into the My Notes region in their textbook.

Suggested Assignment

CHECK YOUR UNDERSTANDING
p. 240, #5–10

UNIT 4 PRACTICE
p. 247, #43–44

CHECK YOUR UNDERSTANDING

1. 104 km

2. 3.8 miles; 20,064 feet

3. 168 hours

4a. 2.11 quarts

   b. $0.89 for 1 liter

5. $\dfrac{5.68 \text{ miles}}{\text{hour}}$

6. 3.11 miles

7. $91.25

8. $\dfrac{9.375 \text{ gal}}{\text{month}}$

9. Answers may vary. Sample answer: 6 cm per year

10. Explanations may vary. Sample answer: Yes. $\dfrac{3 \text{ hours}}{180 \text{ minutes}}$ is equivalent to 1, so her answer will be equivalent to a mile a minute.

My Notes

TRY THESE C

a. Convert $\dfrac{60 \text{ miles}}{\text{hour}}$ to $\dfrac{\text{inches}}{\text{second}}$. $\dfrac{1056 \text{ in.}}{\text{second}}$

b. Ramona's coffee maker drips coffee at a rate of 4 ounces per minute. Given 1 cup = 8 ounces, 1 quart = 4 cups, and 1 gallon = 4 quarts, convert $\dfrac{4 \text{ ounces}}{\text{minute}}$ to $\dfrac{\text{gallons}}{\text{hour}}$. $\dfrac{1.875 \text{ gal}}{\text{hour}}$

c. Ralene's car averages 25 mpg (miles per gallon). Given 1 km = 0.6 mi, 1 gallon = 3.8 liters and 1 km = 1000 meters, convert $\dfrac{25 \text{ miles}}{\text{gallon}}$ to $\dfrac{\text{meters}}{\text{liter}}$. $\dfrac{10{,}964.91 \text{ meters}}{\text{liter}}$

d. The Raymonds estimate that they create 200 ounces of trash each day. At this rate, how many tons of trash will they create in a year? 1 ton = 2000 lbs and 1 pound = 16 ounces. $\dfrac{2.28 \text{ tons}}{\text{year}}$

CHECK YOUR UNDERSTANDING

Write your answers on notebook paper. Show your work.

1. Given 1 mile is about 1.6 kilometers, change 65 miles to kilometers.

2. Given 1 mile = 1,760 yards, convert 6,688 yards to miles. Now convert it to feet.

3. How many hours are in a week?

4. Given 1 gallon = 3.8 liters and 1 gallon = 4 quarts:

   a. Convert 2 liters to quarts.

   b. Which is a better buy: $0.89 for 1 liter or $0.89 for 1 quart?

5. Convert $\dfrac{500 \text{ feet}}{\text{minute}}$ to $\dfrac{\text{miles}}{\text{hour}}$.

6. Given 1 meter = 39.4 inches, 1 kilometer = 1000 meters and 1 mile = 5,280 ft, convert 5 kilometers to miles.

7. If a special hen can lay two eggs each day, and each dozen is sold for $1.50, how much money can be earned by selling all of the hen's eggs for a year?

8. If a pipe is leaking at a rate of 5 cups per day, how many gallons will leak in a month?
   1 quart = 4 cups, 1 gallon = 4 quarts, 1 month = 30 days

9. Over the past three years, Gerry has grown at the rate of $6 \cdot 10^{-1}$ meters per year. Estimate Gerry's growth rate using a more appropriate unit.

10. **MATHEMATICAL REFLECTION** Annise wanted to convert 60 miles per hour into miles per minute. She multiplied: $\dfrac{60 \text{ miles}}{\text{hour}} \cdot \dfrac{3 \text{ hours}}{180 \text{ minutes}}$. Will she end up with the right answer? Explain.

Proportions, Similarity, and Conversions

GOLDEN RECTANGLES

Early mathematicians marveled at rectangles whose sides were in the ratio 1:1.618. They went so far as to call them *Golden Rectangles*.

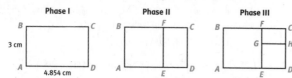

1. Verify that the lengths of the sides of the rectangle in Phase I are in the ratio 1:1.618.

2. In Phase II, Quadrilateral *ABFE* is a square.

   a. Calculate the length of $\overline{FC}$ and $\overline{ED}$. Show your work.

   b. The length of $\overline{FC}$ is what percent of the length of $\overline{BC}$? Show your work and round to the nearest tenth of a percent.

   c. Is Quadrilateral *CDEF* a golden rectangle? Show the work that supports your answer and round to three decimal places.

3. If Quadrilateral *DEGH* is a square, identify the smallest golden rectangle in Phase III. Show your work and round to three decimal places.

4. Draw the figure that would appear in Phase IV of this pattern.

5. Draw $\overline{AC}$ in Phase I and $\overline{DF}$ in Phase II.

   a. Use a triangle from Phase II that completes the similarity statement
   $\triangle ACD \sim$ _____.

   b. Find the scale factor.

   c. Calculate $\overline{DF}$ if $\overline{AC} = 5.706$ cm. Round to three decimal places.

6. A rod was a common unit for measuring distances until the mid 1800's. Today, a rod is used to approximate the length of a 2-person canoe. Let the length of one side of a rectangle be 4 rods. Given 1 rod = 16.5 feet, calculate the length of the known side of the rectangle in yards.

7. 1 furlong = 40 rods and 1 mile = 5280 feet. If a race horse can run 4 furlongs in a minute, calculate the speed of this horse in miles per hour (mph).

Embedded Assessment 2

Assessment Focus

- Ratios and proportions
- Percents
- Similarity and scale factors
- Unit conversion

Materials

- 4 function calculators
- Straightedges

TEACHER TO TEACHER In order for students to recognize a pattern, it is essential that they round all responses to the nearest 0.001.

Answer Key

1. Students need to verify that two ratios are equal using cross products or showing that one of the ratios reduces to the other.
   $\frac{3 \text{ cm}}{4.854 \text{ cm}}$ reduces to $\frac{1}{1.618}$

2. Students use $BC - BF$ to determine *FC*. $\overline{FC} = \overline{ED}$ as they are opposite sides of a rectangle. Students then set up a ratio and change it to a percent. They also verify that a rectangle is golden by identifying the sides that must be in the ratio 1:1.618 and showing the ratios are equal.

   a. 4.854 cm − 3 cm = 1.854 cm

   b. $\frac{1.854 \text{ cm}}{4.854 \text{ cm}} = 38.2\%$

   c. *CDEF* is a golden rectangle.
   $\frac{1.854 \text{ cm}}{3 \text{ cm}}$? $\frac{1}{1.618}$
   The cross products are 3 and 2.9998 ≈ 3. Since the cross products are equal, the ratios are equal.

TEACHER TO TEACHER The actual Golden Ratio involves irrational numbers: $2:(1 + \sqrt{5})$. In order to make this assessment accessible for the students, this ratio was converted to a decimal approximation. If the students round too much, the rectangles will lose their "gold." This is why approximations to the nearest ten thousandth should be required.

3–7. See page 242.

Embedded Assessment 2

3. Students identify another rectangle in the figure whose sides are in the ratio 1:1.618.

CHGF is the smallest golden rectangle because $\dfrac{1.146 \text{ cm}}{1.854 \text{ cm}} = \dfrac{1}{1.618}$.

4. Students extend the pattern to Phase IV.

Phase IV

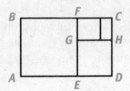

5. Students identify similar triangles and determine the scale factor. They must use the scale factor to determine the length of an unknown side using a proportion.

a. $\triangle FDE$

b. $\dfrac{3}{1.854}$ or $\dfrac{4.854}{3}$

c. $\dfrac{3}{1.854} = \dfrac{5.706}{x}$; $x = 3.526$

6. Students convert 4 rods to yards. Some will multiply 4 by 16.5 and divide that product by 3. Some students may calculate the response using dimension analysis:
$\dfrac{4 \text{ rods}}{1} \cdot \dfrac{16.5 \text{ ft}}{1 \text{ rod}} \cdot \dfrac{1 \text{ yd}}{3 \text{ ft}} = 22 \text{ yd}$

7. See below right.

8. This item addresses percents, ratios and circle graphs.

a. $16\dfrac{2}{3}\%$

b. $12\dfrac{1}{2}\%$

c. 25%

---

8. Shaleetra met with the guidance counselor to plan her high school curriculum and learned that to graduate she would need to take 4 English, 4 math, 4 science, 3 foreign language, 2 Fine Arts classes, 1 Physical Education, and 6 elective classes.

a. What percent of her classes will be Math?

b. What percent of her classes will be Foreign Language?

c. What percent of her classes will be Electives?

d. Make a circle graph that represents Shaleetra's high school curriculum.

	Exemplary	Proficient	Emerging
Math Knowledge #5c	Correctly calculates the measure of segment *DF* and rounds correctly. (5c)	Correctly calculates the measure of *DF*, but does not round or rounds incorrectly	Does not calculate the correct measure of *DF*
Problem Solving #2a–c, 3, 5a, b; 6, 7, 8a–c	• Calculates the correct lengths of segments *FC* and *ED* (2a) • Finds the correct percent and rounds correctly (2b) • Answers correctly whether or not *CDEF* is a golden rectangle (2c) • Identifies the correct smallest golden rectangle in Phase III (3) • Completes the similarity statement correctly (5a) • Finds the correct scale factor (5b) • Finds the correct length of the side of the rectangle in yards (6) • Correctly calculates the speed of the horse in miles per hour (7) • Correctly calculates the three percents (8a, b, c)	• Calculates the correct length of either *FC* or *ED* • Finds the correct percent, but rounds incorrectly • Uses a correct method to identify the smallest rectangle, but makes a computational error • Uses a correct method to find the scale factor, but makes a computational error • Finds the correct length of the side of the rectangle in feet • Correctly calculates the speed of the horse in feet per minute • Correctly calculates only two percents	• Calculates the correct length of neither *FC* nor *ED* • Does not find the correct percent • Answers incorrectly whether or not quadrilateral *CDEF* is a golden rectangle • Does not identify the correct rectangle • Completes the statement incorrectly • Finds an incorrect scale factor • Finds an incorrect side length • Finds an incorrect speed • Correctly calculates only one of the percents
Representations #4, 5, 8d	• Draws the correct figure that would appear in Phase IV of the pattern. (4) • Draws segments *AC* and *DF* correctly. (5) • Makes a circle graph that correctly represents the curriculum. (8d)	• Draws a partially correct figure • Draws segment *AC* or *DF* correctly • Makes a circle graph that has some, but not all correct sectors	• Draws an incorrect figure. • Draws neither segment correctly • Makes a circle graph at least two correct sectors
Communication #1, 2a–c, 3	• Correctly verifies that the lengths are in ratio 1:1.618. (1) • Shows the correct work in finding the lengths of segments *FC* and *ED*. (2a) • Shows the correct work in finding the percent. (2b) • Shows work that adequately supports the answer. (2c) • Shows correct work that supports the identification. (3)	• Uses a correct method of verification, but makes a computational error • Shows a correct method to find the lengths, but makes a computational error • Shows a correct method to find the percent, but makes a computational error • Shows incomplete work that contains no errors • Shows a correct method to support the identification, but makes a computational error	• Does not verify the ratio • Shows work that contains conceptual errors • Shows work that contains conceptual errors • Shows work that includes a conceptual error • Shows work that contains conceptual errors

---

7. $\dfrac{4 \text{ fur}}{1 \text{ min}} \cdot \dfrac{60 \text{ min}}{1 \text{ hr}} \cdot \dfrac{40 \text{ rods}}{1 \text{ fur}} \cdot \dfrac{16.5 \text{ ft}}{1 \text{ rod}} \cdot \dfrac{1 \text{ mile}}{5280 \text{ ft}} = 30 \text{ mph}$

8d. Students' circle graphs should show $16\dfrac{2}{3}\%$ for English, for math, and for science; $12\dfrac{1}{2}\%$ for foreign language; $8\dfrac{1}{3}\%$ for fine arts; $4\dfrac{1}{6}\%$ for physical education; and 25% for electives.

TEACHER TO TEACHER — You may wish to read through the rubric with students and discuss the differences in the expectation levels. Make sure students understand the meanings of any terms used.

ACTIVITY 4.1

1. What must be true for lines to be parallel?

2. What must be true for lines to be perpendicular?

3. Give a real life example of a right angle.

4. What has to be true for two angles to be complementary?

5. Are angles with measures of 40° and 50° complementary?

6. What is the measurement of the angle that is supplementary to a 58° angle?

7. Give the missing measurements in the diagram below.

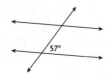

57°

ACTIVITY 4.2

8. Complete the following table.

Pre-Image	Image	Transformation
△	◁	
	◺	Vertical reflection
◹	◺	
◺	◹	

9. Determine the coordinates of the vertices for each image of △GEO after each of the following transformations are performed. For example, if △GEO is translated up 1 unit the coordinates of the vertices would become (0, 5), (3, 1), and (0, 1).

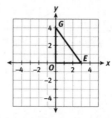

a. Rotate △GEO 180° around the origin.

b. Rotate △GEO 90° counterclockwise around the origin.

c. Rotate △GEO 90° counterclockwise around point E.

d. Translate △GEO 3 units to the left and reflect over the x-axis.

e. Reflect △GEO over the x-axis and translate 3 units to the left.

f. Translate △GEO 2 units to the right and reflect over the y-axis.

g. Reflect △GEO over the y-axis and translate 2 units to the right.

9a. G′(0, −4), E′(−3, 0) and O′(0, 0)

b. G′(−4, 0), E′(0, 3) and O′(0, 0)

c. E′(3, 0), O′(3, −3) and G′(−1, −3)

d. O′(−3, 0), G′(−3, −4) and E′(0, 0)

e. O′(−3, 0), G′(−3, −4) and E′(0, 0)

f. E′(−5, 0), O′(−2, 0) and G′(−2, 4)

g. E′(−1, 0), O′(2, 0) and G′(2, 4)

UNIT 4 PRACTICE

Activity 4.1

1. For lines to be parallel they must never intersect and they must be in the same plane.

2. For lines to be perpendicular they must be in the same plane and intersect at 90° angles.

3. Answers will vary. Examples include: the corner of the page of a book, the corner of a wall, etc.

4. For two angles to be complementary the sum of their measures must be 90°.

5. Angles with measures of 40° and 50° are complementary because the sum of these angles is 90° and two angles with a sum of 90° are complementary.

6. The measure of the angle that is supplementary to an angle that measures 58° is 122°.

7.

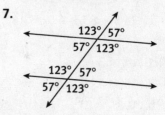

123° / 57°
57° / 123°

123° / 57°
57° / 123°

Activity 4.2

8. from top to bottom: 90° counter clockwise rotation, 180° rotation, Horizontal reflection,

Pre-image	Image	Transformation
△	◁	90° counter clockwise rotation
◹	◺	Vertical reflection
◺	◹	180° rotation
◺	◹	Horizontal reflection

10 i. Rotate 90° counter clockwise around the origin

ii. Rotate 90° counter clockwise around the origin and translate 5 units to the right.

iii. Reflect over the *y*-axis and translate right 4 units or reflect over *x* = 4 and translate left 4 units or reflect over *x* = 2.

iv. Reflect over *y* = 3 and translate down 3 units or reflect over the *y*-axis and translate up 3 units.

11. B

12a. 50°

b. 72°

c. 116.5°

d. 110°

13a. 55 + 107 + 3*x* = 180; *x* = 6; 18°

b. 57 + 87 + 8*x* = 180; *x* = 4.5; 36°

c. 36.5 + 83.5 + 5*x* = 180; *x* = 12; 60°

Activity 4.3

14a. 90°

b. 108°

c. 72°

d. 18°

e. 54°

f. 36°

g. 36°

h. 72°

10.

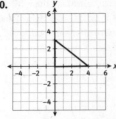

Each triangle in i–iv is an image of the triangle above. Make a list of the transformations that were performed.

i.

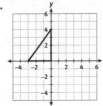

ii.

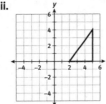

iii.

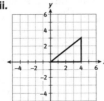

iv.

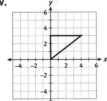

---

11. Find the measure of the unknown angle.

a. 42°   **b.** 48°

c. 98°   **d.** 132°

12. In each of the following, the measures of two angles in a triangle are given. Find the measure of the third angle in each triangle.

a. 98° and 32°

b. 83.5° and 24.5°

c. 23° and 40.5°

d. 12.25° and 57.75°

13. In each of the following, the measures of the three angles in a triangle are given. Write an equation, and solve for *x*. Give the measure of the third angle.

a. 55°, 107°, and 3*x*

b. 57°, 87°, and 8*x*

c. 36.5°, 83.5°, and 5*x*

ACTIVITY 4.3

14. Given Quadrilateral *FOUR* is a square and *PENTA* is a regular pentagon. Determine the measure of each of the following angles.

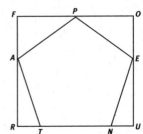

a. ∠*R*   **b.** ∠*ATN*

c. ∠*ATR*   **d.** ∠*RAT*

e. ∠*FAP*   **f.** ∠*FPA*

g. ∠*ETN*   **h.** ∠*ETA*

15. Given regular hexagon *HEXAGN* and right triangle *ARX*. Determine the measure of each of the following angles.

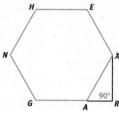

a. ∠*GAX*   **b.** ∠*XAR*

c. ∠*AXR*   **d.** ∠*NXR*

e. ∠*AXG*   **f.** ∠*XGN*

16. Given regular octagon *DEFGHJKL*. Determine the measure of each of the following angles.

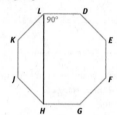

a. ∠*EFG*   **b.** ∠*FEG*

c. ∠*DEG*   **d.** ∠*DHL*

e. ∠*JHL*   **f.** ∠*GHD*

g. ∠*HDL*   **h.** ∠*JHD*

17. Use the regular octagon in Question 16 to answer each of the following.

   a. Is $\overline{KJ}$ parallel to $\overline{LH}$? Explain how you know.

   b. Is $\overline{EG}$ parallel to $\overline{LH}$? Explain how you know.

   c. Is $\overline{EG}$ parallel to $\overline{DH}$? Explain how you know.

18. Calculate the measure of an interior angle in a regular dodecagon (12-sided polygon).

19. Which of the following could be the measure of an interior angle in a regular polygon?

   30°, 45°, 60°, 75°, 90°, 100°, 120°, 125°, 135°

ACTIVITY 4.4

20. The ratio of students to teachers at a middle school is 24:1. Calculate the number of teachers if there are 1080 students.

21. Suppose $\dfrac{\text{radius of circle A}}{\text{radius of circle B}} = \dfrac{4}{3}$. Determine the radius of circle A if the radius of circle B is 36 cm.

22. Jimmy scored a 75 on his first math test and an 80 on the second test. Calculate the difference in Jimmy's test scores as a percent increase or decrease.

23. Rewrite $\dfrac{25}{67}$ as a fraction with a numerator of 1.

24. Rosalind is creating a scale drawing of the triangle below. Calculate the height of Rosalind's triangle if the length of the base is 180 cm.

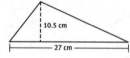

15a. 120°

   b. 60°

   c. 30°

   d. 90°

   e. 30°

   f. 90°

16a. 135°

   b. 22.5°

   c. 112.5°

   d. 22.5°

   e. 45°

   f. 67.5°

   g. 67.5°

   h. 67.5°

17a. Yes, same side interior angles are supplementary.

   b. No, same side interior angles are not supplementary.

   c. Yes, same side interior angles are supplementary.

18. 150°

19. 60°, 90°, 120°, 135°

Activity 4.4

20. 45 teachers

21. 48 cm

22. 6.7% increase

23. $\dfrac{1}{2.68}$

24. 70 cm

25. Check students' drawings, which should be in a ratio of 8 in.:1.6 m, or 5 in.:1 m, to the original figure.

26. $h = 7$ m

Activity 4.5

27. 56.25%

28a. 25%

b. 20%

c. 31.25%

d. 50%

e. 93.75%

f. 68.75%

29. 50%

30. B

31. 167.4°

32. **Betsy's Activities**

Activity 4.6

33a. △RTO ~ △ATI

b. $\frac{5}{3}$

c. $h = 2.7''$

34. $x = \frac{25}{12}$ or $2.083''$;

$y = \frac{65}{12}$ or $5.417''$

35. △TAM ~ △AHM ~ △THA

---

25. Create a scale drawing of the figure below. The width of your drawing should be 8 inches.

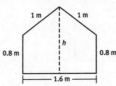

26. If the height, *h*, in the figure above is 1.4 meters, calculate the height of the figure in the scale drawing that you created.

ACTIVITY 4.5

27. Express $\frac{9}{16}$ as a percent.

28. James needs to save $160 to purchase a new amplifier. For the amounts shown below, calculate what percent each is of his total cost.

   a. $40   b. $32
   c. $50   d. $80
   e. $150   f. $110

29. The area of the rectangle is what percent of the area of the triangle in the figure below?

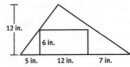

30. Zack is recording songs on a disk with space for 110 minutes of music. His computer says he has 40% of the space remaining on a disk. How much time does Zack still have available on the disk?

   a. 40 min   b. 44 min
   c. 66 min   d. 70 min

---

31. Calculate 46.5% of 360°.

32. A chart showing the amount of time Betsy spends on her activities is given below.

Activity	Hours
practice the piano	10.5 hrs
walk the dog	7 hrs
homework	21 hrs
chores	3.5 hrs

Create a circle graph to represent the time Betsy spends on each activity.

ACTIVITY 4.6

33. Given the triangles below.

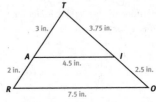

   a. Use similarity notation to identify the two similar triangles.
   b. Find the scale factor.
   c. If the height of △RTO is 4.5", determine the height of the smaller triangle.

34. If △MAH ~ △ATH, then solve for *x* and *y*.

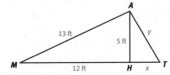

35. Use the figure above to complete the following similarity statement:

   △TAM ~ △_____ ~ △_____

---

36. If △*TOM* ~ △*VAL*, determine the measure of each of the following angles.

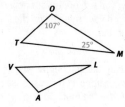

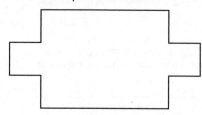

a. ∠*T*   b. ∠*L*
c. ∠*V*   d. ∠*A*

37. Tell the measure of each angle of △*ABC* and △*PQR* if △*ABC* ~ △*PQR*, *m*∠*A* = 90°, and *m*∠*B* = 56°,

38. Sketch the image of the figure below once it is dilated by a factor of 1.5.

ACTIVITY 4.7

39. Given 1 pound = 16 ounces, convert 88 ounces to pounds.

40. If $1 US = $0.92 Canadian, convert $25 US to Canadian currency and $25 Canadian to US currency.

41. Given 1 inch = 2.54 centimeters, convert 1 yard to centimeters.

42. Given 1 mile = 5280 feet and 1 rod = 16.5 feet, how many miles are equal to 800 rods?

43. Convert $\frac{432 \text{ miles}}{\text{hour}}$ to $\frac{\text{feet}}{\text{second}}$.

44. Water is flowing over a dam at a rate of $\frac{462 \text{ cubic feet}}{\text{minute}}$. Covert this rate to $\frac{\text{gallons}}{\text{hour}}$. 1 gallon = 231 cubic inches and 1 cubic foot = 1728 cubic inches

---

UNIT 4 PRACTICE *Continued*

36a. 48°

  b. 25°

  c. 48°

  d. 107°

37. *m*∠*A* = 90°, *m*∠*B* = 56°, *m*∠*C* = 34°, *m*∠*P* = 90°, *m*∠*Q* = 56°, *m*∠*R* = 34°,

38. Check students' drawings.

Activity 4.7

39. 5.5 lbs

40. $25 US = $23 Canadian; $25 Canadian = $27.17 US

41. 91.44 cm

42. 2.5 miles

43. $\frac{633.6 \text{ ft}}{\text{sec}}$

44. $\frac{207,360 \text{ gal}}{\text{hour}}$

Reflection

Student Reflection

Discuss the essential questions with students. Have them share how their understanding of the questions has changed through studying the concepts in the unit.

Review the academic vocabulary. You may want students to revisit the graphic organizers they have completed for academic vocabulary terms and add other notes about their understanding of terms.

Encourage students to evaluate their own learning and to recognize the strategies that work best for them. Help them identify key concepts in the unit and to set goals for addressing their weaknesses and acquiring effective learning strategies.

Teacher Reflection

1. Of the key concepts in the unit, did any present special challenges for students?

2. How will you adjust your future instruction for students/activities?

3. Which strategies were most effective for facilitating student learning?

4. When you teach this unit again, what will you do differently?

Reflection

An important aspect of growing as a learner is to take the time to reflect on your learning. It is important to think about where you started, what you have accomplished, what helped you learn, and how you will apply your new knowledge in the future. Use notebook paper to record your thinking on the following topics and to identify evidence of your learning.

Essential Questions

1. Review the mathematical concepts and your work in this unit before you write thoughtful responses to the questions below. Support your responses with specific examples from concepts and activities in the unit.

   - How is proportional reasoning used to solve real-world problems?
   - What are transformations and how are they useful in solving real-world problems?

Academic Vocabulary

2. Look at the following academic vocabulary words:

   - angle
   - similar figures
   - tranformations (geometric)

   Explain your understanding of each word and why each is important in your study of math.

Self-Evaluation

3. Look through the activities and Embedded Assessments in this unit. Use a table similar to the one below to list three major concepts in this unit and to rate your understanding of each.

Unit Concepts	Is Your Understanding Strong (S) or Weak (W)?
Concept 1	
Concept 2	
Concept 3	

   a. What will you do to address each weakness?

   b. What strategies or class activities were particularly helpful in learning the concepts you identified as strengths? Give examples to explain.

4. How do the concepts you learned in this unit relate to other math concepts and to the use of mathematics in the real world?

Additional Notes

1. What is the measure of ∠*DEF* in the right triangle *DEF*?

    F. 22°

    G. 32°

    H. 68°

    I. 158°

2. Lines *ℓ* and *m* are parallel. What is the value of *x*?

3. Isaiah's little brother likes to copy everything Isaiah does. They decide they will fly kites together. Isaiah uses 14 feet of string to fly his kite 8 feet horizontally from where he is standing. If his brother imitates him, as shown below, how much kite string will he need to get his kite 6 feet away horizontally? Explain your reasoning.

Read

Solve

Explain

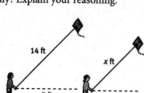

14 ft

x ft

8 ft

6 ft

Solve and Explain

$\frac{14}{8} = \frac{x}{6}$, $x = 10.5$

The two brothers flying their kites create similar angles.

We can use the properties of similar figures to set up

a proportion and solve for the missing dimension.

1. Ⓕ Ⓖ Ⓗ Ⓘ

2.

UNIT 4 Math Standards Review

These two pages provide practice with four standardized test question formats that are used in many national and state high-stakes tests:

- Multiple choice
- Gridded response
- Short response
- Extended response

These items also provide practice with the mathematics content of this unit.

1 Multiple choice
- Sum of the measures of the angles in a triangle

2 Gridded response
- Measures of angles formed when parallel lines are cut by a transversal

3 Short Response
- Similar triangles

4 Extended response
- Rates
- Solving proportions
- Measurement conversion

TEACHER TO
TEACHER You might read through the extended-response item with students and discuss your expectation levels. Make sure students understand the meanings of any terms used.

Read
Solve
Explain

4. Driver Krista Osborne won the 2008 Ultimate Speed Challenge for soap box derby. She drove down the 989-foot hill in 27 seconds.

Part A: Find Krista's speed in feet per minute.

Answer and Explain

$$\frac{989}{27} = \frac{x}{60}$$

2197.8 ft per minute

Part B: Convert her speed to meters per minute.

Answer and Explain

$$\frac{1}{3.28} = \frac{m}{2197.8}$$

$m \approx 670.1$

She travels 670.1 meters per minute

Part C: Scott Mackley won the 2008 Gasparilla 5K by completing the course in 15 minutes. A 5K race is 5 kilometers. Find Scott's speed in meters per minute.

Answer and Explain

$$\frac{5000}{15} = \frac{m}{1}$$

$m \approx 333.3$

He travels 333.3 meters per minute.

Part D: Compare Krista's speed with Scott's speed.

Solve and Explain

Krista was traveling much faster than Scott. She can travel about 336.8 meters farther in a minute.

In prior levels, students have learned to calculate probabilities and plot data in various forms. This unit continues the study of probability with the discussion of theoretical versus experimental probability, independent versus dependent events, and the concept of mutually exclusive events. The study of statistics is continued with discussion of univariate versus bivariate data, measures of central tendency, and displaying data in stem-and-leaf plots, box-and-whisker plots, and scatterplots.

Academic Vocabulary

Blackline masters for use in developing students' vocabulary skills are located at the back of this Teacher's Edition. Encourage students to explore the meanings of the academic vocabulary words in this unit, using graphic organizers and class discussions to help students understand the key concepts related to the terms. Encourage students to place their vocabulary organizers in their math notebooks and to revisit these pages to make notes as their understanding of concepts increases.

Embedded Assessments

The two Embedded Assessments for this unit follow Activities 5.2 and 5.4.

CollegeBoard
inspiring minds™

Algebra AP/College Readiness

Unit 5 extends student understanding of probability and statistics by:

- Providing contextual situations where probabilities can be calculated and data can be graphed in multiple ways.

- Visualizing patterns and probabilities in a variety of ways: tree diagrams, Venn diagrams, and categorical variable tables.

- Giving students opportunities to work with statistics in a variety of ways: measures of central tendency, box-and-whisker plots, stem-and-leaf plots, and scatterplots.

- Modeling a set of a bivariate data with a line of good fit.

- Allowing students to communicate mathematics and explain experimental results both verbally and in written sentences.

- Using technology to solve problems, experiment, interpret results, and support conclusions.

- Introducing and reinforcing the vocabulary of probability and statistics.

Embedded Assessment 1 | **How Much Off?**

- Counting Principle
- Independent/dependent events
- Complement of an event
- Outlier's effect on measures of center and the range
- Representations: tree diagram, box-and-whisker plot

Embedded Assessment 2 | **Field Day Results**

- Histogram
- Five-number summary
- Population of the sample
- Assign labels to population of center and the range

- SRS from random number table
- Scatterplot
- Line of good fit
- Predictions using a model
- Outlier

Suggested Pacing

The following table provides suggestions for pacing either a 45-minute period or a block schedule class of 90 minutes. Space is left for you to write your own pacing guidelines based on your experiences in using the materials.

	45-Minute Period	90-Minute Period	Comments on Pacing
Unit Overview	$\frac{1}{2}$	$\frac{1}{4}$	
Activity 5.1	4	2	
Activity 5.2	3	$1\frac{1}{2}$	
Embedded Assessment 1	1	$\frac{1}{2}$	
Activity 5.3	3	$1\frac{1}{2}$	
Activity 5.4	3	$1\frac{1}{2}$	
Embedded Assessment 2	1	$\frac{1}{2}$	
Total	$15\frac{1}{2}$	$7\frac{3}{4}$	

Unit Practice

Practice Problems for each activity in the unit appear at the end of the unit.

Math Standards Review

To help accustom students to the formats and types of questions they may encounter on high stakes tests, additional problems are provided at the end of the unit. These problems are constructed for multiple choice, short response, extended response, and gridded responses.

Probability and Statistics

Unit Overview
In this unit you will investigate independent and dependent probabilistic situations and compare theoretical and experimental probability. You will practice displaying, summarizing, interpreting, and communicating univariate and bivariate data.

Academic Vocabulary
Add these words to your vocabulary notebook.

- categorical variables
- experimental probability
- numerical data
- outlier
- range
- simple random sample (SRS)
- theoretical probability

Essential Questions

? How do different displays help you interpret data?

? Why is it important to know if events are dependent or independent when calculating probabilities?

EMBEDDED ASSESSMENTS

This unit has two Embedded Assessments, after Activity 5.2 and 5.4. These embedded assessments allow you to demonstrate your understanding of probability, box plots, finding the mean, data displays, and random samples.

Embedded Assessment 1

Probability, Box Plot, Mean
p. 271

Embedded Assessment 2

Data Displays and Random Samples
p. 291

251

UNIT 5 OVERVIEW

Unit Overview
Ask students to read the unit overview and relate examples of probability with which they are familiar. Ask them to recall methods they have used to present data in previous courses.

Essential Questions
Read the essential questions with students. Remind students to think about these questions as they work through the unit.

Materials
- Index cards
- Blue, green markers
- Graph paper or chart graph paper
- Hula-hoop (or loop of rope big enough to step through)
- Stopwatch
- Number cubes
- Coins
- Random number generator

Academic Vocabulary
As students develop fluency with new terms encourage them to use precise mathematical language in discussions and writing. Continue to monitor their vocabulary logs for completeness.

UNIT 5 GETTING READY

You may wish to assign some or all of these exercises to gauge students' readiness for Unit 5 topics.

Prerequisite Skills
- Simple probability (Item 1)
- Experimental, theoretical probability (Items 2, 3)
- Mean (Items 5, 7)
- Median (Items 5, 7)
- Mode (Items 5, 7)
- Range (Items 5, 7)
- Numerical and categorical data (Item 4)
- Dot plots, scatter plots, histograms (Items 6, 8)

Answer Key

1a. $\frac{2}{4}$ or $\frac{1}{2}$

b. $\frac{1}{4}$

2a. $\frac{26}{40}$

b. $\frac{20}{40}$

3a. categorical

b. categorical

c. numerical

d. numerical

e. categorical

4a. mean: 13

b. mode: 11

c. median 12

d. range: 5

Write your answers on notebook paper. Show your work.

red	blue
blue	green

1. In the spinner pictured above, what is the probability of landing on each color?
   a. blue
   b. green

2. Jackie tossed a penny 40 times and the penny landed on heads 26 times.
   a. What was the experimental probability of landing on heads in Jackie's trial?
   b. What was the theoretical probability of landing on heads in Jackie's trial?

3. Tell whether each of the following is numerical or categorical data.
   a. eye color
   b. types of fruit
   c. height of students in the class
   d. weight of textbooks
   e. favorite sport

4. Garrett enrolled in a fitness program and followed a power walking plan. For the first nine days his progress chart showed his time in minutes for walking a mile were: 16, 15, 15, 14, 12, 12, 11, 11, 11. Find each of the following for Garrett's power walking data:
   a. mean
   b. mode
   c. median
   d. range

The list below shows the number of hours the students in Ms. Gandera's class spent on homework in one week.

6, 3, 0, 1, 3, 5, 5, 2, 3, 6, 6, 5, 7, 2, 6

5. Make a dot plot of the data.

6. Give the mean, median, mode, and range of the homework data.

7. Ms. Gandera created a histogram of the absentee rate of her students.

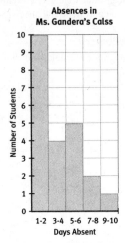

Absences in Ms. Gandera's Calss

(y-axis: Number of Students, 0–10; x-axis: Days Absent, 1-2, 3-4, 5-6, 7-8, 9-10)

   a. How many students are in Ms. Gandera's class?
   b. In which class interval is the median data?

5.

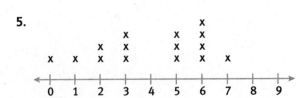

6. mean: 4, median: 5, mode: 6, range: 7

7a. 22 students in the class

   b. 3–4 day category (the median is between 11th and 12th)

Probability
Rock, Paper, Scissors

SUGGESTED LEARNING STRATEGIES: Marking the Text, Role Play, Summarize/Paraphrase/Retell, Predict and Confirm, Create Representations, Quickwrite

Rock, Paper, Scissors (RPS) is a fun two-person game. Some sources say that more people have played Rock, Paper, Scissors than any other game in the world.

To play RPS, each player taps a fist in his or her palm twice. Then both players simultaneously extend their hands in the shape of a rock, piece of paper, or pair of scissors.

The winner of a round is decided based on the following rules: rock beats scissors, scissors beats paper, and paper beats rock. If both players show the same shape, the round results in a tie.

My Notes

Rock breaks scissors. Scissors cut paper. Paper covers rock.

1. Predict which will occur more often: a win for Player 1, a win for Player 2, or a tie. Explain your reasoning.

   All three are equally likely. Explanations will vary.

2. Play 30 rounds of Rock, Paper, Scissors with a partner, and write the frequency of wins in the table below.

   Answers will vary.

Frequency Table		
	Tally	Frequency
Player 1 wins		
Player 2 wins		
Tie		

ACTIVITY 5.1 Investigative

Probability

Activity Focus
- Counting principle
- One-stage probability experiment
- Independent, dependent events
- Complement of an event
- Mutually exclusive events
- Venn and tree diagrams

Materials
- Index cards
- Blue, green markers

Chunking the Activity

Intro	#8	#22
#1	#9	#23–24
#2–3	#10–11	#25
#4	#12–14	#26
#5	#15–16	#27–28
#6	#17	#29
#7	#18–21	

TEACHER TO TEACHER The game of Rock, Paper, Scissors provides the context for students to investigate a one-stage probability experiment. The introduction explains the rules of the game.

1 **Predict and Confirm, Quickwrite** Students predict and explain which of three events is more likely in this probability setting.

2 **Create Representations** Students get an opportunity to collect their own data by playing thirty rounds of the game. The collected data can give evidence to support or refute their predictions in Item 1.

ACTIVITY 5.1 Continued

3 Create Representations, Predict and Confirm Students will use the vocabulary for a one-stage probability experiment. In the RPS game, every play of the game is a trial. The possible results of the trial (win for Player 1, win for Player 2, or tie) are called outcomes.

4 Think/Pair/Share, Debrief Part a has students recall and calculate the experimental probability for each of the possible outcomes of the game based on the data from the thirty trials they conducted. Answers for part b should reflect whether students used the experimental probability, the theoretical probability, or some other method to compute their answers. Ask students to share their methods of computation so that the whole class might gain insight into the thinking of their classmates.

SUGGESTED LEARNING STRATEGIES: Predict and Confirm, Debrief, Think/Pair/Share, Create Representations

My Notes

MATH TERMS

An **outcome** is a possible result in a probability experiment.

An **event** is any outcome or group of outcomes from a probability experiment.

MATH TIP

The notation used to denote the probability of a tie is $P(\text{tie})$.

ACADEMIC VOCABULARY

experimental probability

MATH TIP

To play using a *random strategy* means that a player's choices are without a pattern and unpredictable.

One possible result of a round of Rock, Paper, Scissors (RPS) is an example of an **outcome**. A set of outcomes from playing the game forms an **event**.

3. List the possible outcomes from a round of RPS.
   Player 1 wins, Player 2 wins, tie

When playing the RPS game, you were experimenting with probability by playing several rounds of the game and calculating how many times each outcome occurred. Calculating **experimental probability** involves conducting numerous trials of an experiment and comparing the number of times a particular outcome occurs to the total number of outcomes. For example, the experimental probability of a tie is written as a ratio comparing the number of times a tie actually occurs to the total number of times the game is played:

$$P(\text{tie}) = \frac{\text{the number of times a tie occurs}}{\text{the number of times the game is played}}$$

4. Use the data collected in the table for Question 2.

   a. Write the experimental probability for each of the possible outcomes of RPS.
   Answers will vary.

   b. If Player 2 were to play using a random strategy for 60 rounds of RPS play, how many times should she expect to win?
   Answers will vary. Students should indicate if they came to their answers via experimental or theoretical probability.

SUGGESTED LEARNING STRATEGIES: Think/Pair/Share, Create Representations, Quickwrite

5. Collect data for all games of RPS from your classmates.

a. Summarize the class data in the following table.
   Answers will vary.

Class Results for RPS Game		
Result from a Round	Number of Rounds When the Result Actually Occurred	Experimental Probability
Player 1 Wins		
Player 2 Wins		
Tie round		

b. Considering the experimental results gathered in Questions 4 and 5a, which set of results do you think is closer to the actual probability? Explain.
   Sample answer: 5a because there is more data.

Theoretical probability is the likelihood of an event based on expected results. *Theoretical probability* gives an ideal value of how likely events are to occur.

6. For each round of play, both players have the option to extend their hand in the shape of a rock, paper, or scissors.

a. List all the possible outcomes of RPS in the form (Player 1, Player 2) that are possible for a round of play. For example, if Player 1 chooses rock and Player 2 chooses paper, list the ordered pair as (R, P).
   (R, P), (R, R), (R, S), (P, R), (P, P), (P, S), (S, R), (S, P), (S, S)

b. How many possible outcomes are there when two players are involved in a round of RPS? How can you answer this question without counting the members of your list in part a?
   9; Sample answer: I multiplied 3 • 3 because each of the two players has three choices.

c. Is the probability that Player 2 makes a choice **independent** of the choice that Player 1 makes? Explain.
   Yes; Sample answer: Player 1's choice doesn't limit or influence Player 2's choice. Or vice versa.

My Notes

ACADEMIC VOCABULARY
theoretical probability

MATH TERMS
Two events are **independent** if the occurrence of one does not alter the probability that the second event will occur.

ACTIVITY 5.1 Continued

5 Quickwrite, Create Representations By gathering all the data from the class into one chart, the experimental probabilities should more closely approximate the theoretical probabilities for the game. The question in Part b asks students to reflect on whether their individual results or those gathered from the entire class will more closely approximate the actual probabilities of the situation.

6 Think/Pair/Share Students are asked to revisit the RPS game. First, they consider each outcome based on the choices made by the two players and express the outcome as a pair of letters. Second, they consider how many different outcomes this will indicate, and how students could have found this result without counting each of the unique results from Part a. By the end of the question, students should understand that the choices of Player 1 and Player 2 are independent of each other.

Suggested Assignment

CHECK YOUR UNDERSTANDING
p. 264, #2

UNIT 5 PRACTICE
p. 294, #2

7 Look for a Pattern, Create Representations A tree diagram works well for this scenario as the number of possible outcomes is relatively small. As the number of possible outcomes for a game increases, students need to have more efficient methods for finding the number without the tedium of making an exhaustive list. The counting principle and a graphic organizer like a tree diagram are good tools for students to know and use with confidence when finding the number of possible outcomes for an experiment along with their associated probabilities.

8 Debrief, Think/Pair/Share Students determine probabilities and reflect on the patterns and relationships that they see.

My Notes

A **tree diagram** can be used to organize the list of possible outcomes.

7. Complete the tree diagram below for a round of RPS. In the column labeled Outcome, write "P1" if Player 1 would win the round, "P2" if Player 2 would win the round, or "T" if the round would be a tie.

Possible plays by Player 1	Possible plays by Player2	Ordered Pairs (P1, P2)	Outcome
R	R	(R, R)	Tie
	P	(R, P)	2
	S	(R, S)	1
P	R	(P, R)	1
	P	(P, P)	Tie
	S	(P, S)	2
S	R	(S, R)	2
	P	(S, P)	1
	S	(S, S)	Tie

8. Each set of branches produces a letter pair that determines an outcome for the game. (R, P) indicates that Player 1 chooses a rock and Player 2 chooses paper. This results in a win for Player 2.

   a. What is the probability that Player 1 chooses rock?
   $\frac{1}{3}$

   b. What is the probability that Player 2 chooses paper?
   $\frac{1}{3}$

   c. What is the probability that the letter pair (R, P) occurs?
   $\frac{1}{9}$

   d. How are the probabilities for these results related?
   $\frac{1}{3} \cdot \frac{1}{3} = \frac{1}{9}$

SUGGESTED LEARNING STRATEGIES: Marking the Text, Debrief, Think/Pair/Share, Quickwrite

The theoretical probability of a tie is written $P(\text{tie})$. This theoretical probability is the ratio of the number of outcomes resulting in a tie to the total number of outcomes that can occur in a round.

9. Consider the tree diagram in Question 7.

a. What is $P(\text{tie})$ for the game Rock, Paper, Scissors? Explain how you arrived at your answer.

$\frac{1}{3}$; Sample answer: Because 3 out of the 9 outcomes result in a tie.

b. Calculate the theoretical probability that each player wins the game.

$\frac{1}{3}$

c. Do you consider this a fair game? Explain your thinking.

Answers will vary.

d. Compare and contrast the theoretical probabilities from this question with the experimental probabilities found in Question 5.

Answers will vary.

e. If Player 1 were to play RPS using a random strategy for 150 rounds, how many times could he expect to win? Explain.

50 times; Sample answer: $\frac{1}{3} = \frac{x}{150}$, $x = 50$

My Notes

ACTIVITY 5.1 *Continued*

9 Quickwrite, Think/Pair/Share, Debrief, Marking the Text Students calculate theoretical probabilities for the game based on their work, and they evaluate whether RPS constitutes a fair game. Students are asked to compare the theoretical probabilities that they found using the tree diagram with their experimental results from the beginning of the activity. They are also asked to give an expected value of wins for Player 1 with justification if the game were played 150 times.

TEACHER TO TEACHER ▸ The context of the problem shifts from the traditional RPS game to a card game variant so that additional probability concepts can be addressed.

RPS cards for each group of students can be created using the index cards and colored markers. There are six cards per deck. Each of the three blue cards contains a different word: rock, paper, or scissors. Similarly, each of the three green cards contains a different word: rock, paper, or scissors.

10-11 Marking the Text, Role Play, Create Representations, Use Manipulatives, Quickwrite These questions check for student understanding of the card game context.

12-14 Interactive Word Wall, Think/Pair/Share Students describe the complement of an event in the context of the problem and calculate its probability. Students are also asked to reflect on the relationship between the probability of an event and its complement. They should conclude that their sum is always 1.

Suggested Assignment

CHECK YOUR UNDERSTANDING
p. 264, #1, #4

UNIT 5 PRACTICE
p. 294, #1, #5

My Notes

SUGGESTED LEARNING STRATEGIES: Quickwrite, Use Manipulatives, Create Representations, Think/Pair/Share, Debrief, Role Play, Marking the Text, Interactive Word Wall

The Rock, Paper, Scissors game can be used as a method to select a person randomly for some purpose. However, unlike a truly random selection, if players play each other often, patterns of behavior in an opponent can be recognized. To create a truly random game of Rock, Paper, Scissors that will not result in a tie, Jason has designed a deck of cards with pictures of a rock, paper and scissors on them. In the deck there is 1 card for each shape in two different colors of paper: blue and green.

10. How many cards are in the deck that he designed? Explain.
6; Sample answer: There are three blue cards and three green cards.

11. What is the probability of choosing a scissors card from the deck? Explain how you know.
$\frac{1}{3}$

12. Describe the **complement** of choosing a scissor card.
Choosing a rock or paper card.

13. What is the probability of the *complement* of choosing a scissor card?
$\frac{4}{6} = \frac{2}{3}$

14. Consider the sum of the probabilities of choosing a scissor card and its complement.

a. What do you notice about the value of the sum?
The sum is 1.

b. Why do you think this is so?
Sample answer: The complement of one event is everything else in the set.

> **MATH TERMS**
> **Complementary events** are events that have no outcomes in common and that together contain all of the outcomes of the experiment.
> For example, the complement of rolling a 1 on a number cube would be rolling a 2, 3, 4, 5, 6 on a number cube.

> **CONNECT TO AP**
> In AP Statistics, binomial experiments and binomial probabilities rely on the probability of an event and the probability of its complement.

Connect to ▸ AP

In AP Statistics, binomial experiments, binomial probabilities, and the binomial probability distribution rely on the probability of an event and the probability of its complement to describe and make predictions regarding an independent event that is repeated a specific number of times. For example, what is the probability of rolling a 1 five times out of 8 rolls of a six-sided number cube? The sample space for this event is huge because there are so many possible combinations of 8 consecutive rolls of a number cube. However, the basic probabilities involved in a solving a problem like this are $P(\text{rolling a } 1) = \frac{1}{6}$ and its complementary event, $P(\text{not rolling a } 1) = \frac{5}{6}$.

SUGGESTED LEARNING STRATEGIES: Summarize/Paraphrase/Retell, Group Presentation, Think/Pair/Share, Create Representations, Look for a Pattern

To avoid an outcome of a tie in his card-playing version of Rock, Paper, Scissors, Jason has decided that blue cards beat green cards. In other words, in the event that both players draw a card with the same shape the player with the blue cards wins.

15. Jason decides that Player 1 should choose a card first. List all the possible outcomes Player 1 could choose.

blue rock, blue paper, blue scissors, green rock, green paper, green scissors

16. Complete the tree diagram using the outcomes from Question 15 above. Label each branch in your tree diagram with the probability of each event.

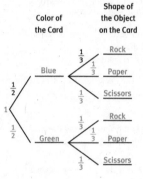

My Notes

ACTIVITY 5.1 *Continued*

15-16 Summarize/Paraphrase/ Retell, Think/Pair/Share, Look for a Pattern, Create Representations, Group Presentation Students work within the context of the RPS card game to determine the possible outcomes. In Item 16, students organize the possible outcomes of drawing the first card using a tree diagram.

17 Debrief, Think/Pair/Share, Quickwrite Students look for patterns in the probabilities given in the tree diagram to determine if each outcome is equally likely. By reflecting on the information in the tree diagram, students should recognize the multiplication principle at work in a variety of ways here.

Students may express that:

- 2 colors × 3 types of cards = 6 possible types of cards. Therefore, the probability of getting each of the six cards is $\frac{1}{6}$

(the probability of selecting a particular color) × (the probability of getting a particular RPS shape in that color) = (the probability of each of the outcomes or cards in the deck). Expressed numerically as: $\frac{1}{2} \times \frac{1}{3} = \frac{1}{6}$

18-21 Discussion Group, Create Representations Students classify cards by categories – either shapes or colors. Students recognize that scissor cards can come in both colors so that there is an overlap in the categories of blue cards and scissor cards. This leads to the term mutually exclusive: Scissor cards and rock cards are mutually exclusive, but scissor cards and blue cards are not mutually exclusive.

Suggested Assignment

CHECK YOUR UNDERSTANDING
p. 264, #3

UNIT 5 PRACTICE
p. 294, #3–4

My Notes

17. Consider the preceding tree diagram.

   a. Is the probability of selecting each card from the deck equally likely? Explain.
   Yes; Sample answer: Each card has the same chance of being picked.

   b. What do you think $P(BR)$ indicates?
   the probability of picking the blue rock card

   c. Determine $P(BR)$. Explain how you arrived at your answer.
   $\frac{1}{6}$; Sample answer: There is one blue rock card out of the six cards.

18. How many cards in the deck are blue? Describe each by the color of the card and the shape on the card.
3; blue rock, blue paper, blue scissors

19. How many cards in the deck have scissors on them? Describe them by color and shape.
2; blue scissors, green scissors

20. How many cards in the deck fit into both categories: blue and scissors?
1

21. Complete the Venn diagram to show the relationship between the blue cards and the scissor cards.

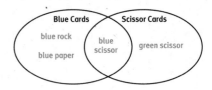

Probability
Rock, Paper, Scissors

SUGGESTED LEARNING STRATEGIES: Interactive Word Wall, Discussion Group, Think/Pair/Share, Quickwrite

22. Because the list of blue cards and the list of scissor cards have outcomes in common they are not **mutually exclusive**.

   a. What is the probability that Player 1 will choose a blue card or scissor card? Explain your answer.

   $\frac{2}{3}$; Sample answer: there are 3 blue cards and 1 green scissor card which is 4 cards out of 6.

   b. What is the probability of choosing a scissor card or a paper card?

   $\frac{2}{3}$

   c. Are choosing a scissor card and choosing a paper card mutually exclusive?

   no

For Jason's RPS game, Player 1 will draw a card and hold it while Player 2 chooses from the remaining cards in the deck.

23. Given that Player 1 chooses a blue scissor card,

   a. What are the possible outcomes for Player 2's choice?

   blue paper, blue rock, green rock, green scissors, green paper

   b. What is the probability that Player 2 will choose a green paper card?

   $\frac{1}{5}$

24. Are the events that Player 2 chooses a green paper card and Player 1 chooses a blue scissor card independent or **dependent events**? Explain.

   dependent; Sample answer: Player 1's choice changed the number of possible outcomes for Player 2.

25. In the two-player card game for RPS, how many different outcomes are there? (Recall that there are no ties in this version of the game.) Justify your answer.

   30 choices; Sample answer: Player 1 is choosing from 6 cards and player 2 is choosing from 5 cards, 6 times 5 = 30.

My Notes

MATH TERMS
Two events are **mutually exclusive** if they have no outcomes in common.

MATH TERMS
Dependent events are events for which knowing that one of them has occurred affects the probability that the other event occurs.

ACTIVITY 5.1 Continued

22 Interactive Word Wall, Think/Pair/Share Students identify types of events that are and are not mutually exclusive and find the probability of the events.

23-24 Discussion Group, Quickwrite Describes an RPS card game where the card chosen by the first player is not replaced in the deck. This situation permits the discussion of dependent events and probabilities.

25 Think/Pair/Share Students explain what is different about the selection of two cards, since order will matter in determining the winner of a round of the card game version RPS.

26 Create Representations, Look for a Pattern Provides a tree diagram for students to complete. The assumption is that the card chosen by Player 1 is not returned to the deck. This way the probability of a tie becomes zero because (per the rules already established) the blue version of a figure will trump the green version of that figure, and the blue version can only be drawn once if you don't replace cards.

While all students should have the opportunity to find the results necessary to complete the chart, different groups can be assigned portions of the tree to present to the class for reporting purposes. This way the amount of writing required of each group may be reduced.

My Notes

SUGGESTED LEARNING STRATEGIES: Look for a Pattern, Create Representations

26. Complete the tree diagram below by labeling the remaining outcomes, giving the probabilities of each outcome, and listing the results from the round (write P1 if Player 1 would win the round and P2 if Player 2 would win the round).

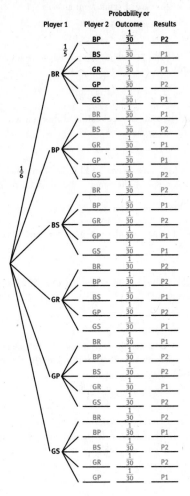

SUGGESTED LEARNING STRATEGIES: Think/Pair/Share, Debrief,
Group Presentation, Quickwrite

27. What is the probability that Player 1 chooses a blue scissors
card and Player 2 chooses a green paper card? Explain.

$\frac{1}{30}$; It is $\frac{1}{6}$ times $\frac{1}{5}$.

28. Use the tree diagram to determine the probability that
Player 1 will win. Explain.

$\frac{1}{2}$. Sample answer: There are 15 out of 30 scenarios where
Player 1 wins.

29. Recall that Jason created the card game version of RPS so
that it would be random, and so that there was no possible way
for the game to result in a tie. Determine another way to make
Rock, Paper, Scissors random.

Answers will vary.

My Notes

ACTIVITY 5.1 *Continued*

27-28 Think/Pair/Share, Debrief,
Group Presentation, Quickwrite
Students apply their previous work
and tools to find the probabilities
requested. Student justifications
will reveal their understanding.

29 Group Presentation Students
have the opportunity to create
their own version of the RPS
game. Perhaps they can come up
with a more fair or more random
version of the game.

Suggested Assignment

CHECK YOUR UNDERSTANDING
p. 264, #5–6

UNIT 5 PRACTICE
p. 294, #6

ACTIVITY 5.1 Continued

1. $\frac{4}{5}$

2a. $P(\text{heads}) = \frac{7}{10}$, $P(\text{tails}) = \frac{3}{10}$

b. $\frac{1}{2}$; Sample answer: Heads is 1 possible outcome out of 2.

c. 15; Sample answer: $\frac{3}{10}$ is equivalent to $\frac{15}{50}$

3a. $\frac{1}{6}$

b. $\frac{1}{3}$

4a. Check students' tree diagrams. Possible outcomes: (H, 1), (H, 2), (H, 3), (H, 4), (H, 5), (H, 6), (T, 1), (T, 2), (T, 3), (T, 4), (T, 5), (T, 6). They all have a probability of $\frac{1}{12}$.

b. independent; Sample answer: The outcome of rolling the number cube is not influenced at all by the outcome of tossing the coin.

c. $\frac{1}{12}$

d. $\frac{1}{4}$

5a.

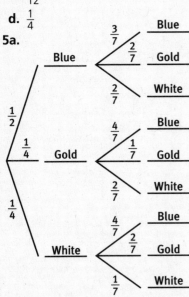

b. dependent event; Sample answer: The probabilities for the second marble are affected by the outcome of the first marble.

c. $\frac{3}{14}$

d. $\frac{2}{14}$

My Notes

CHECK YOUR UNDERSTANDING

Write your answers on notebook paper. Show your work.

1. Victoria has a spinner on which the probability of spinning a 2 is $\frac{1}{5}$. What is the probability of not spinning a 2?

2. Cheri tossed a fair coin ten times and recorded her results in the table below.

Coin-Tossing Experiment	
Heads	**Tails**
~~HHH~~ II	III

a. Write the experimental probability for each of the possible outcomes of Cheri's coin-tossing experiment.

b. What is the theoretical probability of a fair coin landing on heads? Explain.

c. Cheri used her experimental data to determine how many times she should expect the coin to land on tails in 50 tosses. What was her answer? Explain.

3. Suppose a fair number cube has sides labeled 1 to 6.

a. What is the probability that when rolled the top face will show a one?

b. What is the probability that when rolled the top face will show a one or a four?

4. Suppose you perform an experiment in which you toss a fair coin and then roll a fair number cube, in that order.

a. Draw a tree diagram to show all of the possible outcomes and their probabilities.

b. Are the events toss a head and roll a 2 independent or dependent events? Explain.

c. Calculate the theoretical probability that the coin will show heads and that the number cube will show a three.

d. Determine the theoretical probability of tossing a tail and rolling an even number.

5. Joe has a bag containing 8 marbles in it: four blue, two gold, and two white. Without looking, he draws two marbles out of the bag one at a time without replacing the first marble before drawing the second.

a. Draw a tree diagram to show all of the possible outcomes and their probabilities.

b. Are the events second marble is gold and first marble is blue independent or dependent events? Explain.

c. What is the probability that exactly two blue marbles are selected?

d. What is the probability that the first marble is blue and the second marble is gold?

6. **MATHEMATICAL REFLECTION** Why are tree diagrams useful graphic organizers when studying independent and dependent probability situations?

6. Sample answer: They allow you to neatly collect and organize information so that it may be analyzed closely when you choose.

Measures of Central Tendency
Game Day

SUGGESTED LEARNING STRATEGIES: Activating Prior Knowledge, Interactive Word Wall, Marking the Text, Summarize/Paraphrase/Retell, Think/Pair/Share

Matthew is a student reporter for the Culliver A.Tomas Middle School newspaper. His assignment for the next issue is to write an article about the fans who attend school basketball games.

To begin, Matthew decides to investigate the ages of the people who attend the next game. On game day, he randomly selects 21 fans and asks their age. The numerical data he collects is listed in the chart below.

Age of Fans						
42	12	11	12	43	13	9
13	12	12	31	11	36	3
13	40	39	10	14	30	36

The mean, median, and mode of a numerical data set are called **measures of central tendency**. Since these measures are usually located in the middle of the data, they are chosen as representatives of the entire data set.

1. Recall that the **mean** is the sum of the data values divided by the number of data items. Determine the mean age of fans who attended the basketball game.

   mean ≈ 21.05

2. The **mode** is the value or values that occur most often. What is the mode of the age of fans who attended the basketball game?

   mode = 12

3. The **median** divides the data into two sets of data with the same number of elements in each set. Follow the steps below to find the median of the age of fans in the data set.

   a. Arrange all the data items in order from smallest to largest.
   3, 9, 10, 11, 11, 12, 12, 12, 12, 13, 13, 13, 14, 30, 31, 36, 36, 39, 40, 42, 43

   b. Determine the number that divides the ordered list of data into two equal halves.
   median = 13

My Notes

MATH TERMS
Measures of central tendency—the mean, median, and mode—describe what is near the middle of a distribution of numbers; for example, the average age of middle school students (mean).

MATH TIP
If a data set has an odd number of data items, the *median* is the middle element of the ordered list. If the list has an even number of data items, the *median* is the average of the middle two data items in the ordered list.

ACTIVITY 5.2 Investigative

Measures of Central Tendency

Activity Focus
- Numerical data – outliers
- Measure of spread – range
- Box-and-whisker plot
- Quartiles
- Interquartile range

Materials
- Graph paper or chart graph paper

Chunking the Activity

Intro	#6–9	#14–16
#1–2	#10	#17
#3	#11	#18–19
#4–5	#12–13	#20–22

TEACHER TO TEACHER Students benefit from the support of an interactive Word Wall when reconnecting with the vocabulary of statistics. While most students will have been exposed to the measures of center, maximum, minimum, numerical, and categorical data, the activity reminds students of these words.

The paragraphs that begin the activity introduce the context of a student reporter collecting data on the ages of fans who attend middle school basketball games.

1-3 Activating Prior Knowledge, Interactive Word Wall, Think/Pair/Share Students calculate the measures of center for the data collected on 21 fans.

4-5 Discussion Group A different data set is provided for students to calculate the measures of central tendency.

6 Interactive Word Wall

7 Debrief, Quickwrite

8 Discussion Group, Debrief Students are asked to explain which of the measures of central tendency best represent the data set. Some data sets have no mode. The mean is a strong representative measure for a data set with no strong outliers because each data element contributes to the arithmetic average. The median is not affected to the same extent as the mean when a data set contains strong outliers. In this instance, all three measures are fairly close to one another, so students may take into account which ones are least likely to be affected by an outlier when formulating their answers.

9-10 Interactive Word Wall Students determine the measure of central tendency most affected by the outlier, and the one that must be a member of the data set.

Suggested Assignment

CHECK YOUR UNDERSTANDING
p. 270, #1–3

UNIT 5 PRACTICE
p. 294–295, #7–8

MINI-LESSON: Numerical Data Sets With Outliers

The following data represent the time in seconds it took for individuals from two different schools to solve a puzzle.

Data Set A – {29, 32, 33, 36, 40, 43, 45, 48, 91}

Data Set B – {7, 31, 33, 35, 36, 39, 42, 43, 46, 47}

1. Calculate the mean and median for each data set. Explain which measure of central tendency better describes the data. mean A–44.111, median A –40;

My Notes

SUGGESTED LEARNING STRATEGIES: Debrief, Discussion Group, Quickwrite

ACADEMIC VOCABULARY

Numerical data is quantitative. It is a collection of numbers.

Categorical variables are qualitative. Gender and eye color are examples of categorical data.

MATH TERMS

Outliers are individual data points that do not fit the overall pattern of the data set.

The ages of the cheerleaders on the middle school cheerleading squad are given below.

Ages of Cheerleaders									
11	11	12	12	12	13	13	13	13	14	14

4. Do these numbers represent **numerical data** or **categorical variables**? Explain.
   numerical data; Sample answer: Age is expressed as a number, it is quantitative.

5. Determine all three measures of central tendency for the ages of the cheerleaders on the squad.
   Mean ≈ 12.55; Median = 13; Mode = 13

The cheerleading squad has decided to have a cheerleader mascot. She is the little sister of one of the cheerleaders on the squad, and she is 3 years old.

6. Determine the mean, median, and mode of the cheerleaders if the age of their mascot is included.
   Mean = 11.75; Median = 12.5; Mode = 13

7. Describe how this **outlier** affects the mean, median, and mode of the data set.
   Sample answer: The mode didn't change but the mean and median did change.

8. Which single measure serves as the best representative of the data with the outlier? Explain.
   Sample answer: The mode. It was unaffected by the addition of the outlier, and it is very close to the mean of the data before the outlier was added.

9. Which of the measures of central tendency is the most affected by the inclusion of the outlier? Explain.
   mean

10. Which measure of central tendency: mean, median, or mode must be a value in the data set? Explain.
    mode

---

mean B −35.9, median B −37.5; The median is better for both because it is less influenced by the outliers.

2. Circle the outlier in each data set. Calculate the mean and median for each data set without the outlier. Explain which measure of central tendency best describes the average of the data. mean A −38.25, median A −38; mean B −39.111, median B −39; The mean is better since it considers all the values in the set, but in this case the median is not much different from the mean.

3. How were the mean and median affected after the outlier was removed? When the outlier from Set A was removed, the mean and median decreased. When the outlier from Set B was removed, the mean and median increased. Removing the outliers revealed that Group A generally solved the puzzle faster. This was not what the data suggested with the outliers included.

SUGGESTED LEARNING STRATEGIES: Interactive Word Wall, Debrief, Discussion Group, Think/Pair/Share

For Matthew's article, he has decided to include a **box-and-whisker plot** to represent the numerical data he collected regarding the age of the fans who attend the game. The data he collected is shown below.

Age of Fans						
42	12	11	12	43	13	9
13	12	12	31	11	36	3
13	40	39	10	14	30	36

11. List the data in the table from least to greatest, and circle the median.

3, 9, 10, 11, 11, 12, 12, 12, 12, 13, (13), 13, 14, 30, 31, 36, 36, 39, 40, 42, 43

The median of the lower half of the data is called the **lower quartile**, and the median of the upper half is called the **upper quartile**.

12. Find the lower and upper quartiles of your data list.

lower quartile: 11.5; upper quartile: 36

13. Graph the values of the lower quartile, median, and upper quartile as points above the number line below.

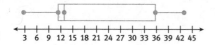

3 6 9 12 15 18 21 24 27 30 33 36 39 42 45

14. Use the number line in Question 13 for the following:

a. Create a rectangle using the lower quartile and the median as the midpoint of the sides of the rectangle.

b. Now, create another rectangle using the upper quartile and the median as the midpoints of the sides of the rectangle.

c. Finally, graph the values of the maximum and the minimum as points above the number line given above. Connect the lower quartile to the minimum with a line segment. Connect the upper quartile to the maximum with a line segment.

My Notes

MATH TERMS

A **box-and-whisker plot** is a diagram that summarizes data by dividing it into four parts, each representing 25% of the data entries. Box-and-whisker plots have the following shape:

MATH TIP

A five-number summary consists of the five numbers needed to make a box-and-whisker plot: minimum, lower quartile, median, upper quartile, maximum.

ACTIVITY 5.2 *Continued*

11-14 Think/Pair/Share, Discussion Group, Interactive Word Wall, Debrief Students are guided through the process of creating a box-and-whisker plot for the age-of-fans data collected by the student reporter.

TEACHER TO TEACHER As students work to create the box-and-whisker plot, stress that the elements of the display should be created above the number line and not on the number line.

MINI-LESSON: Box-and-Whisker Plot

Gather data from students in the classroom by having each student provide a piece of data. The data collected should be univariate.

Possible measures to collect:

- Height in inches
- Letters in their full name
- Minutes they spent on homework last night

Once the data is collected have students:

- Write the data in ascending order
- Calculate the five-number summary
- Create the box-and-whisker plot

ACTIVITY 5.2 *Continued*

15 Think/Pair/Share Students analyze and describe the data distribution for the age of the fans.

16 Interactive Word Wall The term interquartile range (IQR) is introduced along with how it is determined and what portion of the data set it represents.

TEACHER TO TEACHER The interquartile range can be used to determine numerically if a data value should be classified as a statistical outlier. Relatively large data values that fall more than 1.5 × IQR above the upper quartile or relatively small data values that fall below the lower quartile by 1.5 × IQR are considered statistical outliers.

17 Debrief, Quickwrite

My Notes

SUGGESTED LEARNING STRATEGIES: Interactive Word Wall, Debrief, Think/Pair/Share, Quickwrite

15. Use percentages to describe the distribution of the data represented by the box-and-whisker plot.
   25% of the data is between 3 and 11.5, 25% of the data is between 11.5 and 13, 25% of the data is between 13 and 36, and 25% of the data is between 36 and 43.

16. The **interquartile range (IQR)** is the difference between the lower and upper quartiles.

   a. Determine the interquartile range for the age of the fans.
      24.5

   b. What percent of the data set is represented by the IQR?
      50%

17. Explain why you cannot determine the mean or the mode of the data set by looking at a box-and-whisker plot.
   Sample answer: Because the actual numbers in the data set cannot be determined by looking at the box-and-whisker plot.

MINI-LESSON: Calculating if Extreme Values Are Statistical Outliers

The following data represent the time in seconds it took for individuals from two different schools to solve a puzzle.

Data Set A – {29, 32, 33, 36, 40, 43, 45, 48, 91}

Data Set B – {7, 31, 33, 35, 36, 39, 42, 43, 46, 47}

Statistical outliers are: *values* > (1.5 × *IQR*) + *upper quartile*

   OR   *values* < *lower quartile* − (1.5 × *IQR*)

Calculate whether the 91 in Set A, and the 7 in Set B are statistical outliers.

In set A, the upper quartile is 46.5 and the *IQR* is (46.5 − 32.5) = 14. So, 1.5 × IQR = 1.5 × 14 = 21, so 21 + 46.5 = 67.5, since 91 > 67.5, 91 is a statistical outlier for Set A.

In Set B, the lower quartile is 33 and the IQR = (43 − 33) = 10. So, 1.5 × IQR = 1.5 × 10 = 15, so 33 − 15 = 18, since 7 < 15, 7 is a statistical outlier for Set B.

SUGGESTED LEARNING STRATEGIES: Interactive Word Wall, Debrief, Think/Pair/Share, Quickwrite, Discussion Group

The box-and-whisker plot below shows the average number of points scored per game by each player on the basketball team this season.

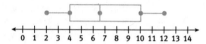

18. What is the median number of points scored by a player?
6.5

19. What is the lower quartile?
4

20. What percent of the players have average scores that are below 10 points?
75%

21. What is the **range** of the average number of points scored in a game as displayed in the box-and-whisker plot above?
10

22. Two box-and-whisker plots have the same median and equally long whiskers. If the box of one plot is longer than the box of the other, what can you say about the two data sets?

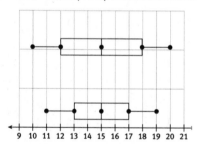

Sample answer: The data set with the longer box is more spread out so its range will be bigger.

My Notes

ACADEMIC VOCABULARY

As a measure of central tendency, the **range** of data is the difference between the minimum and maximum values of the data set.

ACTIVITY 5.2 Continued

18-21 Think/Pair/Share, Discussion Group, Interactive Word Wall Students are provided with an opportunity to interpret a box-and-whisker plot of team scoring data.

22 Quickwrite, Debrief Students describe differences between two data sets based on a display of side-by-side box-and-whisker plots.

Suggested Assignment

CHECK YOUR UNDERSTANDING
p. 270, #4–6

UNIT 5 PRACTICE
p. 295, #9–10

ACTIVITY 5.2 Continued

CHECK YOUR UNDERSTANDING

1a. ≈ 4.8

b. 4

c. 4

d. 10; Sample answer: The mean changes by about 0.65, and the mode and median don't change.

e. Answers may vary. Sample answer: The median and mode would both be appropriate since half the data is split in half by 4.

2. median

3. c

4a. See art below right.

b. 50%

c. 10

d. 17

e. 7

5. Answers may vary. Sample answer: The data have the same range, but the data with the longer rectangle is more spread out.

6. Answers will vary. Sample answer: The measures of central tendency and the range provide the statistical mean of a data set while a box-and-whisker plot does not. A box-and-whisker plot gives a visual model of how the data are dispersed.

CHECK YOUR UNDERSTANDING

Write your answers on notebook paper. Show your work.

1. Kylie surveyed 9 of her friends about how many people lived in their households. Her results are shown in the table below.

Number of People Living in a Household								
3	4	3	5	2	8	10	4	4

a. What is the mean of Kylie's data set?

b. What is the median of Kylie's data set?

c. What is the mode of Kylie's data set?

d. Give the outlier for this data set. Describe how the outlier affects the mean, median and mode of the data.

e. Which measure of central tendency is most representative of this data set? Explain.

2. The values in a data set are 10, 7, 9, 5, 13, 10, 7, 14, 8, and 11. Which measure of central tendency gives the answer 9.5 for this data set?

3. Which is not a measure of central tendency for the data set: 4, 6, 6, 7, 9, 10, 11, 11?

  a. 6   **b.** 8   **c.** 9   **d.** 11

4. Consider the data set: 14, 8, 13, 20, 15, 17, 1, 12, 18, 10

  a. Make a box-and-whisker plot of the data set.

  b. What percent of the data is greater than 13.5?

  c. What is the lower quartile?

  d. What is the upper quartile?

  e. What is the interquartile range?

5. Two box-and-whisker plots have the same median and lower and upper extremes. If the box of one plot is longer than the box of the other, what can you say about the two data sets?

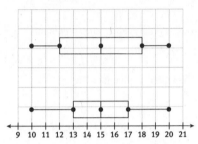

6. **MATHEMATICAL REFLECTION** Compare using measures of central tendency and the range to describe data to using a box-and-whisker plot to describe data. Discuss the strengths and weaknesses of both.

4.

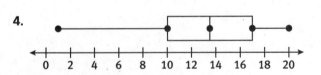

Probability, Box Plot, Mean

HOW MUCH OFF?

Playtone Records has decided to run a holiday promotion. They have printed twenty cards, each containing a discount amount. A customer randomly chooses a card and pays the price of the CD minus the discount amount. The discounts on the cards are listed in the table below.

Discount Amount Data									
$1	$1.50	$3	$2	$5	$6	$5	$2	$7	$10
$3	$4	$5	$6	$9	$8	$12	$6	$9	$6

Write your answers on notebook paper. Show your work.

1. If you are buying one CD, what is the probability that you will get exactly $5 off the price of your CD?

2. Write the complement of the event, "chooses a card with a discount of at most $5," and find the probability of the event you have written.

3. You are buying two CDs, and you have already chosen a $5 discount card:

   a. Explain the probability of the event that you will choose a $6 off card if you replace the one you have already drawn.

   b. Explain the probability of the event that you will choose a $6 off card if you do not replace the one you have already drawn.

4. Find the measures of central tendency and the range for this data set. Be sure to identify each measure by name. Then, justify which measure you believe best represents this data set.

5. Draw a box-and-whisker plot for the discount amount data. Describe the distribution of the discount amount data using your box-and-whisker plot.

6. If one special card for $100 is added to the discount amount data, how are the measures of central tendency and range affected?

To stay competitive, the store Music to My Ears decides to run a holiday promotion. Each customer chooses one card from two different bowls, and then replaces them in the bowls. The first card contains a number and the second card contains a dollar amount. The customer multiplies the dollar amount by the number to find the total amount of the discount.

Numbers: 1, 2, 3, 4
Dollar Amounts: $0.50, $1, $2, $3, $4

7. How many different pairs of cards can be drawn? Explain how you found your answer.

Embedded Assessment 1

Assessment Focus
- Counting Principle
- Independent/dependent events
- Complement of an event
- Outlier's effect on measures of center and the range
- Representations: tree diagram, box-and-whisker plot

Materials
- None

1-3 Students are asked for a one-stage independent probability, a complement, and the probability of independent and dependent events.

4-5 Students are asked about the measures of central tendency and range for the numeric data set and the box-and-whisker display that represents the data.

6 An outlier is added to the data and students are asked to determine how the introduction of this extreme value affects the measures of central tendency and the range.

Answer Key
1. $\frac{3}{20}$

2. The complement is the event choosing a discount greater than $5. The probability of the complement $= \frac{10}{20}$

3. with replacement $= \frac{4}{20} = \frac{1}{5}$
   without replacement $= \frac{4}{19}$

4. mean = 5.525, median = 5.5, mode = 6, range = 11

   Either the mean or the median could be used to represent the data because half of the data is less than those values and half is greater than those values.

5.

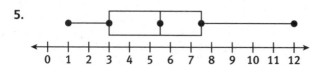

   25% of the data is between 1 and 3.
   25% of the data is between 3 and 5.5.
   25% of the data is between 5.5 and 7.5.
   25% of the data is between 7.5 and 12.

6. mean = 10.0, median = 6, mode = 6, range = 99; Only the mode remained unaffected.

Embedded Assessment 1

Students are given an opportunity to analyze a two-stage probability experiment. They calculate probabilities and create an organized representation that can enumerate all possible outcomes.

9 Students calculate the probability of an event whose description is satisfied by several of the enumerated outcomes of the two-stage experiment.

TEACHER TO TEACHER You may wish to read through the rubric with students and discuss the differences in the expectation levels. Make sure students understand the meanings of any terms used.

7. 4 times 5 = 20

8.

Numbers	Dollar Amounts	Discount

9. $\frac{3}{20}$. Explanations will vary. One student may respond that there are 3 ways to get a $4 discount out of 20.

Probability, Box Plot, Mean
HOW MUCH OFF?

8. Create a representation to illustrate the different discounts that result using the Music to My Ears two-card discount plan.

9. What is the probability that a customer's total discount will be $4 using the two-card discount plan? Explain how you arrived at your answer.

	Exemplary	Proficient	Emerging
Math Knowledge #2, 3a, b; 4, 7	• Finds the correct probability (2, 3a, b) • Finds the correct measures of central tendency and the range. (4) • Fins the correct number of different pairs of cards (7)	• Finds the correct probability for only two of the events • Finds some correct measures of central tendency and the range • Finds more than half of the correct number, but not all	• Finds the correct probability for only one of the events • Finds the correct measures of central tendency or the range • Finds half or fewer of the correct number
Problem Solving #1, 6, 9	• Finds the correct probability (1, 9) • Correctly finds how the addition to the discount amount affects the measures of central tendency and the range (6)	• Uses a correct method to find the probability, but makes a computational error • Correctly finds how the addition to the discount amount affects the measures of central tendency or the range	• Does not find the correct probability. • Does not find how the addition affects the range or the central tendency measures
Representations #5, 8	• Draws a correct box-and-whisker plot (5) • Creates a relevant representation of the two-card discount plan (8)	• Draws a box-and-whisker plot that has some, but not all correct features • Creates a representation of the plan that contains some, but not all, correct parts	• Draws an incorrect box-and-whisker plot. • Creates an incorrect representation of the plan
Communication #2, 3a, b; 4, 5, 7, 9	• Writes the correct complement (2) • Writes a correct explanation of the probability (3a, b) • Correctly identifies the measures of central tendency (4) • Writes a relevant justification for the measure that best represents the data (4) • Correctly describes the distribution of the discount amount based on the box-and-whisker plot (5) • Writes an explanation for the number of different pairs of cards (7) • Writes an explanation for the probability of getting a $4 discount (9)	• Writes a correct explanation of one of the probabilities, but not both • Correctly identifies one of the measures • Writes an incomplete justification for the measure • Writes a partial description of the distribution of the discount amount • Writes an incomplete explanation for the number of different pairs • Writes an incomplete explanation for the probability	• Writes an incorrect complement • Writes a correct explanation for neither of the probabilities • Correctly identifies none of the measures • Writes an incorrect justification for the measure • Describes an incorrect distribution • Writes an explanation for an incorrect number of different pairs • Writes an explanation for an incorrect probability

Data Displays
Strike or Spare

SUGGESTED LEARNING STRATEGIES: Activating Prior
Knowledge, Summarize/Paraphrase/Retell, Think/Pair/Share,
Look for a Pattern

My Notes

Mr. Morrow, the physical education teacher and bowling coach
at College Board Middle School, asks the bowling team manager
to gather the team averages for the ten games last season. The
manager provides Mr. Morrow with the following information.

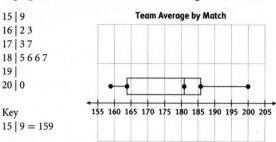

```
15 | 9
16 | 2 3
17 | 3 7
18 | 5 6 6 7
19 |
20 | 0

Key
15 | 9 = 159
```

Team Average by Match

155 160 165 170 175 180 185 190 195 200 205

1. When comparing the two displays, Mr. Morrow needs to
   determine several things.

   a. What information does the stem-and-leaf plot tell the coach?

   Sample answer: The stem plot tells the coach all of the data
   points, as well as how far apart they are spread out.

   b. What information does the box plot tell the coach?

   Sample answer: The box plot tells the coach the minimum,
   Q1, median, Q3, and maximum of the data set (five-number
   summary), as well as the spread of the data. It does not
   show the individual data points.

   c. Which display reveals more about the team's performance
      last season? Justify your answer.

   Either graph can be correct here as long as the explanation
   is well thought-out.

> **MATH TIP**
>
> Stem plot and stem-and-leaf plot
> refer to the same data display.
> Also, box plot and box-and-whisker
> plot refer to the same data display.

ACTIVITY 5.3 Investigative

Data Displays

Activity Focus
- Univariate data
- Data displays: line graph,
  double bar graph
- Outlier
- Prediction
- Two-way tables

Materials
- Hula-hoop (or loop of rope big
  enough to step through)
- Stop watch
- Graph paper

Chunking the Activity

Intro	#8–9	#16
#1	#10–11	#17
#2–4	#12	#18
#5	#13	#19
#6–7	#14–15	#20–21

1 Think/Pair/Share, Look for a
Pattern As a way to activate prior
knowledge, students are given
two different representations, a
stem plot and a box plot, in order
to compare the information that
can be found by studying them.

Since the context involves a coach
and the bowling team, it may be
necessary to allow students who
know about bowling to explain
how the game is played, and the
bowling specific terms that are
involved (i.e., strike, spare, anchor,
lane).

2 Discussion Group Based on scores in tabular format, students are asked to predict which bowler should be named as team anchor.

3 Create Representations Students make a back-to-back stem-and-leaf plot. While students have made stem plots in earlier grades, an example is provided for the back-to-back stem plot, as its creation may not be intuitive.

My Notes

CONNECT TO **BOWLING**

The *anchor* on the bowling team is the last player to roll in team competition and is usually the best bowler on the team.

At the beginning of this season, Coach Morrow has a dilemma. While his current anchor for the team, Mike, has served the team well for the last three years, a new student, George, has moved to town and proves to be an excellent "striker." Following are the scores for each player from the last ten games they bowled.

Game	1	2	3	4	5	6	7	8	9	10
Mike	212	222	237	300	167	239	145	205	170	210
George	190	189	224	257	205	267	220	205	212	218

2. Who should Coach Morrow select as the anchor for the team in the next match? Explain your reasoning.

Either player can be correct here as long as the explanation is well thought-out.

In a **back-to-back stem-and-leaf plot**, the stem goes down the center and the leaves come off both sides. For example, given Data A ={24, 31, 32, 34, 45}, and Data B = {23, 26, 33, 34, 37, 37, 46} the back-to-back stem-and-leaf plot is:

$$\text{Data A} \quad \text{Data B}$$
$$4\ |2|\ 3\ 6$$
$$4\ 2\ 1\ |3|\ 3\ 4\ 7\ 7$$
$$5\ |4|\ 6$$

3. Make a back-to-back stem-and-leaf plot for Mike's scores and George's scores from last season.

Mike		George
5	14	
	15	
7	16	
0	17	
	18	9
	19	0
5	20	55
20	21	28
2	22	04
97	23	
	24	
	25	7
	26	7
	27	
	28	
	29	
0	30	

TEACHER TO TEACHER Have a student record the predictions for the class from Item 5b.

Use this numerical data set to ask students to:

• find the measures of central tendency for the data
• select which measure best represents this data set
• find the range of the data

The students can repeat this process after Item 7 and again after Item 11a. The data set of student predictions should show a trend toward greater accuracy and less spread. This exercise also provides an opportunity to apply prior statistical terms and skills in another contextual situation.

Data Displays
Strike or Spare

SUGGESTED LEARNING STRATEGIES: Marking the Text, Summarize/Paraphrase/Retell, Create Representations, Predict and Confirm, Debrief, Look for a Pattern, Quickwrite, Self/Peer Revision

4. How does this display confirm or refute your decision in Question 2?

Answers may vary. All answers should show an application of logic.

Mr. Morrow loves to have his bowling team warm up with an activity known as "The Hula Hoop Cha Cha." In The Hula Hoop Cha Cha, students hold hands and pass a hula-hoop down the line without breaking the chain. Imagine your classmates standing in a row, grasping hands. The first person has a hula-hoop in the left hand and the hula-hoop is passed all the way to the end of the group, without letting go of hands, until the hula-hoop successfully reaches the right hand of the last person.

5. Consider The Hula Hoop Cha Cha to make the following predictions.

   a. How long will it take for one person to perform The Hula Hoop Cha Cha?

   Sample answer: 5–10 seconds

   b. How many seconds do you predict it will take for a row containing all the students in your class to pass the hula hoop from one end to the other?

   Students should multiply their answer from part a by the number of students in the class.

6. Team up with classmates to gather data about The Hula Hoop Cha Cha. Record how long it takes to pass the hula-hoop in the table. *Sample data:*

Number of Students	1	2	4	7	8	10	15
Time (seconds)	8	13	29	50	57	72	110

7. Based on the data collected, how would you revise your estimate in Question 5b?

Here students should see how long it actually took them to pass the hula-hoop and then keep or alter their answer based on the class's data.

My Notes

ACTIVITY 5.3 *Continued*

4 Quickwrite, Look for a Pattern, Debrief Based on the display created in Item 3, students are asked to confirm or refute their earlier prediction of which bowler should be named anchor.

5 Predict and Confirm Students make predictions before gathering data using members of the class. This begins a Predict and Confirm arc of questions that initially focus on graphing the data and the creation of an analytical model, both of which can be used for prediction. The confirmation comes in Item 12b when the entire class actually does "The Hula-Hoop Cha-Cha."

6 Create Representations Depending on the accuracy of the stopwatch available, times for passing the hula-hoop can be taken to the nearest tenth or hundredth of a second.

7 Debrief, Look for a Pattern, Self/Peer Revision Students are given an opportunity to revise their estimates for how long it will take the entire class to pass the hula-hoop.

"The Hula-Hoop Cha Cha" provides a context for gathering bivariate data to create displays, models, and make predictions. Students can recalculate the measures of center and the range to see how these values have changed since they were first collected after Item 5b.

Suggested Assignment

CHECK YOUR UNDERSTANDING
p. 280, #4–6

UNIT 5 PRACTICE
p. 296, #14–16

ACTIVITY 5.3 Continued

8-9 Create Representations, Think/Pair/Share, Look for a Pattern Students graph the bivariate data so that visual patterns can emerge.

10-11 Create Representations, Self/Peer Revision Students are given the opportunity to choose and to draw their own line of good fit, and to make a prediction based on the placement of the line.

After Item 11a, students have a third opportunity to gather their predictions into a data set to analyze using the measures of central tendency and the range (as suggested in the Teacher to Teacher note from p. 274). Students will then have three summaries taken over time for which to note the trend.

Item 11b asks students to actually pass the hula-hoop through the entire class to create an actual value to compare to their previous predictions.

TEACHER TO TEACHER *"Line of good fit" versus "Line of best fit"* When students are asked to visualize where a line should be placed to model the trend of two variables based on a scatter plot, this is a "line of good fit." A good goal to have when creating one is to try to fit approximately half the data points above the line and half below the line so that as many points as possible are as close to the line as possible. There are other techniques, like a median-median line, that also give a good approximation for a linear model. However, the "line of best fit" is reserved for a model that minimizes the distances (or the square of the distances) from the points in the data set to the line. One such line of best fit is the least squares regression line that can be found using a graphing calculator.

My Notes

Mike's and George's bowling scores are **univariate data** because only one measurement is taken, the score. The data you collect doing The Hula Hoop Cha Cha is **bivariate data** because two measurements are taken, the number of students (x) and the time to pass the hula-hoop (y).

8. Graph the data you gathered from The Hula Hoop Cha Cha on the coordinate grid. Answers may vary. Sample shown.

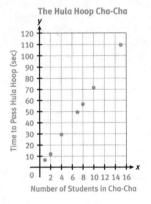

The Hula Hoop Cha-Cha

MATH TIP

When placing a line of good fit on a scatter plot, approximately half of the points should be above your line, and half of the points should be below your line.

9. What do you notice about the pattern on the scatter plot? Sample answer: It's a graph of a positive association, and the points come close to forming a straight line.

A **line of good fit** is placed on a scatter plot to note the trend and to make predictions from the data.

10. Draw a line of good fit on the scatter plot. Approximately half the points should be above the line, and half the points should be below the line. Check that student graphs have a line that is basically in the middle of the data.

11. Recall your earlier prediction for how long in seconds it will take to pass the hula-hoop through everyone in the entire class.

  a. Use your line of good fit to make a prediction for the same event. Answers may vary.

  b. Time how long it takes to pass the hoop through the entire class. How does this measurement compare to your predictions? Answers may vary.

SUGGESTED LEARNING STRATEGIES: Debrief, Discussion Group, Think/Pair/Share, Create Representations, Work Backward

My Notes

12. Use the line to predict how many people can pass the hoop in a given amount of time.

a. According to your line of good fit, how many people should be able to pass the hoop in 25 seconds? Explain.
    Answers may vary.

b. How does this prediction compare to the measurements taken when the hula-hoop was actually passed?
    Usually it will be close, but answers may vary.

Coach Longevity vs. Match Wins

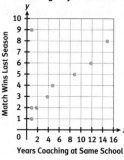

The scatter plot at left displays the number of years of experience (longevity) at the same school as a bowling coach with the number of match wins that the coach had last season.

13. What is the equation in slope-intercept form of a line of good fit for this scatter plot? Explain.
    Answers may vary. Sample answer: $y = 0.5x + 1$, I used the points (2, 2) and (4, 3) to create my line because that put four points below the line and three points above the line.

14. How many years would you expect a coach to have been at a school if the team won 7 out of 10 matches last season? Explain.
    12 years

15. How many matches would you expect a coach to win in a season if the coach had been at the same school for 3 years? Explain.
    2 or 3 wins since the sample model predicts 2.5 wins

16. Which point of the scatter plot appears to be an **outlier**? How can this data point be explained? (1, 9) is the outlier. Sample answer: The coach could have been exceptional.

ACADEMIC VOCABULARY

An **outlier** is a data point in a set of data that does not fit the overall pattern in the data set.

ACTIVITY 5.3 Continued

12 Debrief, Think/Pair/Share, Work Backward Students are asked to use the line of good fit to predict the number of people who can pass the hoop in a specified time. They then compare this result with actual data.

13-15 Create Representations, Discussion Group Students are given the opportunity to find a line of good fit for the scatter plot given. Students are asked to make predictions and to explain their method. When making these predictions, some students may choose to use the scatter plot, while others may choose to use the line of good fit.

16 Think/Pair/Share Students are asked to identify an outlier in the data set and to provide a possible explanation for the point that deviates from the pattern. Possible explanations for the point (1, 9) might be that the previous coach was very good and left the new coach with very experienced and skilled players. Another explanation might be that the coach was a very good coach who came to this school after coaching many years at another school.

Suggested Assignment

CHECK YOUR UNDERSTANDING
p. 280, #1–3

UNIT 5 PRACTICE
p. 295, #11–13

ACTIVITY 5.3 *Continued*

17 Quickwrite, Look for a Pattern, Group Presentation, Debrief, Create Representations Students are given an opportunity to create a line graph in order to consider performance trends and make predictions.

18 Discussion Group Students are given an opportunity to recall and name categorical and numerical variables that can be used to describe the school.

My Notes

MATH TIP

An example of a *line graph* shows the high temperatures in degrees over 7 days in January for Nashville, Tennessee.

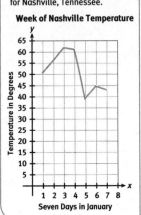

Week of Nashville Temperature

In a **line graph**, the ordered pairs are connected to show *a trend over time*.

17. The table displays the bowling team's rank throughout last year's season.

Week Number	1	2	3	4	5	6	7	8
Rank in the League	3	4	4	5	3	2	2	1

a. Make a line graph for the game number from last season and the bowling team's rank in the league. Label the graph.

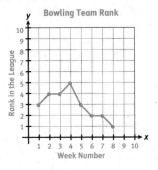

Bowling Team Rank

b. What does the graph tell you about the bowling team's performance over time?

Sample answer: While the team was in fifth place halfway through the season, the team finished in first place.

c. How did the team finish the season? Explain.

They finished in first place because the *y*-value is 1 for the last data point.

Bivariate data can be categorical or numerical. Numerical data, like bowling scores and number of wins, can be plotted using a scatter plot. However, if the two types of data being compared are categorical, a **double bar graph** is a better choice. Examples of categorical variables are gender, race, and colors of shirts.

18. What are two categorical and two numerical variables to describe your school?

18. Sample answers. Categorical: public or private; rural or urban; large, medium, or small sized. Numerical: the number of students in the school, the rank in academics in the district, or the number of sports teams the school has.

SUGGESTED LEARNING STRATEGIES: Create Representations

For the example double bar graph below, 100 people under 20, and 100 people over 60 were asked how they preferred to spend their free time. Notice that the data is categorical.

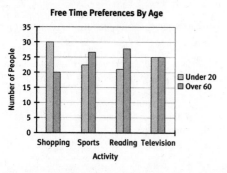

The bowling teams at the middle school are getting new bowling shirts. The coach asked the players what colors the jerseys should be. Here are the results of the voting.

	Red with Blue Numbers	Blue with White Numbers	White with Red Numbers
Boys	4	6	10
Girls	3	9	5

19. Make a *double bar graph* for the boys and the girls on the grid below.

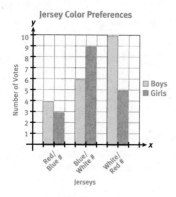

---

19 Create Representations, Students are asked to create a double bar graph.

20 Think/Pair/Share Students interpret which jersey choice is preferred by the boys, the girls, and the whole group.

21 Debrief, Group Presentation Students explain how the bowling coach can make a fair decision about the color of the new jerseys.

Suggested Assignment

CHECK YOUR UNDERSTANDING p. 280, #7–10

UNIT 5 PRACTICE p. 296, #17–19

CHECK YOUR UNDERSTANDING

1. Answers may vary.

2. A line graph as a sample answer:

Football Team Point Results

3. Sample answer: This is a picture of how well the team did in each game throughout the season.

4. Sample answer: Scatterplot

5.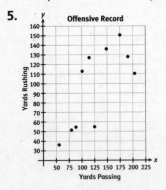

Offensive Record

6. Sample answer: There is a weak positive association between the number of yards passing and the number of yards rushing in a football game.

SUGGESTED LEARNING STRATEGIES: Debrief, Group Presentation, Think/Pair/Share

20. Analyze the information about jersey selection.

   a. What is the jersey choice among boys?

   White with red numbers won among boys.

   b. What is the jersey choice among girls?

   Blue with white numbers won among girls.

   c. Which jersey choice is preferred by the whole group if both the boys' and the girls' preferences are combined?

   There is a tie between white with red numbers and blue with white numbers.

21. Explain how the coach can make a fair decision regarding the color of the new jerseys.

   Answers may vary. Look for a logical thought process.

CHECK YOUR UNDERSTANDING

Write your answers on notebook paper. Show your work.

The CBMS football team manager provided the following data for the coach.

Week of Season	1	2	3	4	5	6	7	8	9	10
Points Scored	24	15	3	21	28	35	17	12	38	32

1. What type of graph would be best for visualizing this data set?

2. Create and label the type of graph you selected to display the data.

3. What does this graph tell you about the data set?

The manager also provided the coach with this data about the team's offensive record.

Yards Passing: {115, 85, 55, 125, 148, 175, 101, 77, 206, 185}

Yards Rushing: {127, 55, 37, 56, 137, 151, 112, 52, 111, 127}

4. What type of graph would be best for visualizing this data set?

5. Create and label the type of graph you selected to display this data for the coach.

6. What does this graph tell you about the data set?

The manager shared the results of a team survey for where to have dinner after the game with the coach.

	Offense	Defense
Pizza Palace	23	35
Burger Bungalow	21	9

7. What type of display would be best for visualizing this data set?

8. Create and label the graph you selected.

9. What does this graph tell you about the data set?

10. **MATHEMATICAL REFLECTION** Compare and contrast displays for univariate and bivariate data.

---

7. Sample answer: double bar graph

8.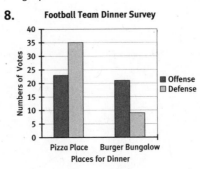

Football Team Dinner Survey

9. Pizza Palace was chosen by more students than Burger Bungalow.

10. Sample answer: Univariate data only accounts for one variable, while bivariate data accounts for two variables. Examples of univariate displays include stem plots and box-and-whisker plots. Examples of bivariate displays include scatter plots, back-to-back stem plots, and double bar graphs. Both can be categorical or numerical.

Sampling
Field Day Events

SUGGESTED LEARNING STRATEGIES: Activating Prior
Knowledge, Marking the Text, Summarize/Paraphrase/Retell,
Debrief, Discussion Group, Think/Pair/Share

Before field day at Desoto Middle School, Mr. Morrow, the physical
education teacher, wants to test some potential events. By sampling
students from the school, he hopes to collect information to answer
the question, "Which events should be included during field day?"

To select a representative group for testing the first trial event,
Mr. Morrow selects students using a **simple random sample**
(SRS). In a simple random sample, subjects are assigned digits
and then chosen according to a fair method that involves chance,
like flipping a coin, pulling names from a hat, or using a random
number table.

Of the 300 students at the middle school, the teacher wants to
choose 12 to be in the SRS.

1. How can number labels be assigned to the students?
Sample answer: 001 to 300

2. Use the random number table below, and the number labels from
Question 1, to choose 12 random students. Insert the numbers
for the students selected in the table below.

11164 36318 75061 37674 26320 75100 10431 20418 19228 91792
21215 91791 76831 58678 87054 31687 93205 43685 19732 08468
10438 44482 66558 37649 08882 90870 12462 41810 01806 02977
36792 26236 33266 66583 60881 97395 20461 36742 02852 50564
73944 04773 12032 51414 82384 38370 00249 80709 72605 67497

Sample answer:

111	061	075	100	104	041
228	121	054	197	088	087

Mr. Morrow chooses a **stratified sample** for the second field day
event. He divides students into grades six through eight and then
selects a random sample from each grade.

3. Each grade level at the schools contains 100 students. Eight
students are selected from each class.

a. Describe how number labels can be assigned to students
in the sixth grade.
00–99

> **My Notes**
>
> ### MATH TIP
> A *question of interest*
> identifies the topic for
> which information is to be
> collected using a survey or
> a study.
>
> **ACADEMIC VOCABULARY**
> simple random sample (SRS)
>
> ### MATH TERMS
> A **stratified sample** is taken
> by dividing a population into
> groups of individuals who share
> a particular characteristic so
> that each group can be
> sampled.

MINI-LESSON: Using Random Number Tables

Most students will not have experience using a random number table to
find a SRS. Show them the following example using the random number
table from the activity.

Example: If the labels assigned to 55 members of a population are the
two-digit numbers 01–55, then random numbers will need to be selected
from the table two at a time. Two are chosen at a time to ensure that the
numbers can divide evenly into multiple two-digit numbers. Consider the
first two numbers in the random number table: 11164 36318. Separating
those ten digits into five two-digit numbers gives: 11 – 16 – 43 – 63 – 18.
This would indicate that the population members with labels 11, 16, 43,
and 18 have been selected. 63 is an unassigned label so it is noted, but
skipped. Continuing down the lines of the table, additional selections
are made until the desired number of population members have been
identified to create the desired sample size.

ACTIVITY 5.4 Investigative

Sampling

Activity Focus
- Question of interest
- Population
- Census, stratified sample,
  SRS-simple random sample
- Data displays: dot plot,
  histogram, scatter plot
- Misleading presentations

Materials
- Number cubes
- Coins
- Random number generator

Chunking the Activity

Intro	#6	#11
#1	#7	#12
#2	#8	#13
#3–4	#9	#14–15
#5	#10	#16

TEACHER TO TEACHER In this field day context,
Mr. Morrow is gathering
information about a question of
interest – "Which events should
be included during the field day?"
The beginning of the activity
guides students through the three
types of samples that can be used
to gather information about the
school's population of students.

1 Debrief, Think/Pair/Share
It is important that students come
up with a three-digit number
labeling system in order to answer
the next question.

2-3 Debrief, Discussion Group,
Think/Pair/Share It will most
likely be necessary to cover the
mini-lesson before students can
answer these questions. Students
should not choose the same
number from the table twice, and
the numbers can be picked in
any pre-specified order from the
number table, as long as they are
picked in groups of 3.

4 Debrief, Discussion Group, Quickwrite During the debriefing following this question, distinctions between the strengths and weaknesses in each type of sample should be confirmed.

5 Debrief, Think/Pair/Share Students are asked to conjecture about why it is advantageous to run a simulation in some specific situations rather than collect actual data. If the class seems to be struggling, work the first one out as a class or in groups.

Suggested Assignment

CHECK YOUR UNDERSTANDING
p. 290, #1

UNIT 5 PRACTICE
p. 296–297, #20, 24

My Notes

b. Using the random numbers provided below, select eight sixth grade students according to the number labeling scheme from part a. Write the numbers of the eight students selected in the table below.

21215 91791 76831 58678 87054 31687 93205 43685 19732 08468

Sample answer:

21	59	17	91	76	83	15	86

For the third potential event, Mr. Morrow wants to survey every student in the school. When every single individual in a population is part of the sample, it is called a *census*.

4. When gathering information representative of the school, what are the advantages and disadvantages of each type of sample (SRS, stratified sample, census)?

Answers may vary. Sample answer:

- In an SRS every single person has the same chance of being chosen, regardless of grade or gender. An SRS contacts fewer people, so it is easier to collect data. A disadvantage is that it does not ask every single person.
- Stratified samples may have unequal samples from various strata. For example, it may be desired to have each stratum represented proportionally. Over-representation of small strata may also be desirable.
- A census asks everyone and thus gets all of the data, but in a larger population it may be impossible or too expensive to contact every person.

MATH TERMS

A **simulation** uses a device of random chance to model an event that can be represented numerically so that experimental trials can be performed to imitate reality and generate probabilities.

If events have numeric conditions that are countable, it may be easier and cheaper to gather data by running a **simulation** than by collecting actual data. Common methods used to perform a *simulation* are: flipping a coin, rolling a number cube, or using a random number generator.

5. For each situation below, explain why it may be advantageous to run a simulation rather than collect actual data using a sampling method.

a. Predicting the gender proportion for 1000 babies born at a local hospital in the coming year

Sample answer: To wait for 1000 babies to be born to get the data does not help planners be prepared for the babies' arrival. It would take too much time and be very inconvenient.

SUGGESTED LEARNING STRATEGIES: Marking the Text, Summarize/Paraphrase/Retell, Debrief, Discussion Group, Think/Pair/Share

My Notes

b. Determining how many people will catch the flu this winter if this year's vaccine is 85% effective.

Sample answer: Hospitals and health care officials can be prepared to treat the sick with the appropriate materials. They can count on a minimum of 15% of the population contracting the flu.

c. Studying how many flawed parts will be manufactured and shipped if the computer software for detecting flaws has an accuracy rate of 92%.

Sample answer: Waiting for all the parts to be made, and then hand inspecting each and every one would be extremely expensive, so running a simulation based on the accuracy of the checking machine should give an idea of how many flawed parts the manufacturer can reasonably expect to be shipping so that plans can be made to handle angry customers and to make amends.

Mr. Morrow wants to use simulation methods to create teams for the upcoming kickball tournament. He will use a standard number cube to simulate choosing sixth, seventh, and eighth graders, with ten students per team.

6. How can the numbers one through six on the faces of the number cube be assigned to represent a sixth, seventh, or eighth grade student who is selected for a team?

Answers may vary. Sample answer: Assign the numbers 1 and 2 to 6th graders, 3 and 4 to 7th graders, and 5 and 6 to 8th graders.

7. Use a number cube to perform the team selection simulation. Answer the following questions.

Answers will vary. Sample data given:

a. Roll the number cube ten times. How many students from each grade are selected with ten rolls of the number cube?

6th Grade __5__   7th Grade __3__   8th Grade __2__

b. Roll the number cube ten more times. How many students from each grade are selected using these ten rolls of the number cube?

6th Grade __3__   7th Grade __2__   8th Grade __5__

6-7 Think/Pair/Share, Debrief, Discussion Group Students are asked to identify how a number cube can be used to perform a simulation. They then perform the simulation and represent the results using a line plot.

ACTIVITY 5.4 Continued

8 Quickwrite, Create Representations, Debrief
Students should have experience creating histograms from previous courses, but they may need a refresher. It could be helpful to remind them that the key difference between histograms and bar graphs, is that histograms are drawn based on numeric intervals. Also there are no spaces between the bars of a histogram.

SUGGESTED LEARNING STRATEGIES: Debrief, Create Representations, Quickwrite

My Notes

c. Make a *dot plot* of the total number of students from each grade that were chosen by the twenty rolls of the number cube in parts a and b.

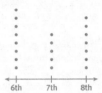

d. Are the results what you expected? Explain.

Sample answer: Yes, each grade was selected in about $\frac{1}{3}$ of the rolls.

8. Student Council members were at the event selling cold water and sports drinks. At the end of the day, the following amounts were turned in by the beverage sellers:

$11.75 $20.75 $27.50 $42.00 $9.25 $8.50 $14.00 $25.75 $29.00
$16.50 $19.25 $13.00 $30.25 $8.00 $27.50 $22.00 $28.25 $11.50

a. Give the minimum and maximum values for this data set.

Minimum ___$8.00___   Maximum ___$42.00___

MATH TERMS
In a histogram, a **class interval** is one of a number of non-overlapping intervals that the range has been divided into.

b. Create a histogram for this data using **class intervals** of $5 on the horizontal axis.

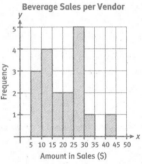

Beverage Sales per Vendor

c. Does the graph appear to have any outliers? Explain.

Answers may vary. Answers should be considered correct as long as they have a logical explanation.

SUGGESTED LEARNING STRATEGIES: Self/Peer Revision, Quickwrite, Create Representations, Group Presentation, Debrief

9. Compare and contrast the dot plot and histogram displays.

Sample answer. The dot plot shows univariate, categorical data: the numbers of students that are selected from each of three grades. The histogram shows bivariate, numerical data: the number of vendors whose sales totals fall into given intervals.

In addition to kickball, Mr. Morrow has a new field day event that involves the students' heights and arm spans. Rather than using a simulation to create a data set, collect actual data from your classmates.

10. Fill out the following table using data from your class.

Sample data:

My Notes

> **MATH TIP**
>
> Arm span is measured from the tip of one middle finger to the tip of the other middle finger with your arms outstretched.

Student's Name	Height (cm)	Arm Span (cm)
	135	127
	142	130
	144	131
	134	126
	140	128
	136	126
	142	131
	136	127
	136	128
	140	129
	142	133
	143	133
	137	127
	138	128
	138	129
	138	130

Student's Name	Height (cm)	Arm Span (cm)
	143	132
	135	128
	142	132
	142	130
	140	130
	135	129

ACTIVITY 5.4 *Continued*

9 Group Presentation, Debrief, Quickwrite, Self/Peer Revision Students recall the strengths and weaknesses of displaying data using a dot plot and a histogram.

10 Create Representations Students are asked to collect measurement data on height and arm span from members of the class, and to record them in the table provided.

11 Create Representations
Students are given a grid to create a scatter plot using the measurement data collected from the class.

> TEACHER TO TEACHER Encourage students to share methods for creating an appropriate scale for each axis. Many students may use a method similar to (maximum value – minimum value) divided by 10 and then selecting the closest benchmark number to that to create the scale increment. Giving students a forum to discuss their methods provides an opportunity to deepen their understanding of scales.

12 Work Backward, Look for a Pattern, Create Representations, Think/Pair/Share Students are asked to consider patterns revealed in the scatter plot and to make predictions based on the trend. Students are also asked to identify the population and conjecture what question could be answered using this information.

Suggested Assignment

CHECK YOUR UNDERSTANDING
p. 290, #2

UNIT 5 PRACTICE
p. 296, #21

My Notes

11. Plot the points for the ordered pairs (height, arm span) on the graph below. Label the axes, as well as use the maximum and minimum to determine and label the scale for the axes.

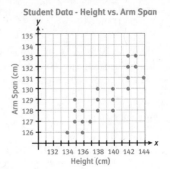

Student Data - Height vs. Arm Span

The data for height versus arm span is an example of *bivariate data* because two different variables, in this case height and arm span, are measured for each individual. Each individual is represented by one data point on the graph.

12. When analyzing this data, several questions need to be considered.

a. What is the population that this data set represents?
The students in the class make up the population.

b. How do the height and arm span appear to be related? Explain.
Sample answer: There appears to be a positive association because as height increases arm span increases.

c. What question might this data be used to answer?
Sample answer: You could use this data to predict the height of a student, given an arm span, or vice versa.

d. Based on the trend of the data, predict the arm span of a student 134 cm tall. Explain the method you used to make the prediction. Answers may vary. Sample answer: An arm span of 125 cm would be predicted for a height of 134 cm, which I found by extending the graph and using a line of good fit.

e. Based on the trend data, predict the height of a student with a 134 cm arm span. Explain.
Answers may vary. Sample answer: A height of 146 cm would be predicted for an arm span of 134 cm, which I found by extending the graph and using a line of good fit.

SUGGESTED LEARNING STRATEGIES: Create Representations,
Discussion Group, Debrief, Quickwrite

My Notes

13. Consider a student's backpack and its contents.

   a. What attributes can be measured using information about the student's backpack?
   Answers may vary. Sample answers: weights of items, colors of items, types of items (books, pencils, etc), prices of items.

   b. Select two attributes from the list in part a and tell whether the data will be categorical or numerical. Give the units or categories you will use to measure or classify the data for each attribute chosen.
   Answers may vary. Sample answers: Color of items will be categorical, and will be classified according to color. Prices of items will be numerical, and will be measured in dollars.

   c. What population does this data represent?
   The population consists of the objects in the backpack.

   d. What question can be answered using the data that you collected on the two attributes?
   Answers may vary. Sample answer: What is the average cost of an item in a backpack?

   e. What type of graph can be used to display the data for each attribute?
   Answers may vary. Sample answer: A bar graph can be used for each color; a histogram should be used for price.

14. Collect data on ten backpacks using the two attributes you identified in Question 13b.

   a. Enter the results in a table.
   Answers may vary.

   b. Use the data to create two different types of displays, one for each set of data.
   Answers may vary.

15. Based on the results of the data collection and displays you created, what conclusions can be made?
   Answers may vary.

ACTIVITY 5.4 Continued

13 Debrief, Discussion Group
Using backpacks as the focus, students are asked to identify attributes that can be measured so that data can be collected and displayed to answer a question of interest.

TEACHER TO TEACHER Some schools do not allow backpacks in class. If this is true for your school, then the data gathering activity in Item 14 will need to be assigned for homework or modified as appropriate.

14 Create Representations
Students are asked to collect data on ten backpacks. They must focus on the attributes they identified and make a chart and data display for the information.

15 Quickwrite Students are asked to make conclusions based on the data collected and displayed.

TEACHER TO TEACHER ⟩ An article with data displays is provided to allow students an opportunity to be critical statistical readers.

Since the article is lengthy, facilitate student understanding by having students participate in Shared Reading. Encourage students to use the reading strategies of Marking the Text, Summarizing the Information, and Taking Notes to work with the text so that students can better understand what they are reading. After finishing the article, allow students to discuss the answers to Item 16 in groups before writing a rough draft to share with fellow students. The final version of the paragraph should benefit from this preliminary work.

Connect to ⟩AP

An essential part of the AP Statistics curriculum is written communication. Many of the activities in Unit 5, including this one, encourage students to analyze statistical data and situations, make predictions, and summarize their conclusions in writing with appropriate mathematical justification. Free response scores on the AP Statistics Examination are obtained by using a rubric that assigns scores for both statistical knowledge *and* communication. A high scoring response has the following communication qualities:

- Provides a clear, organized, and complete explanation, using correct terminology, of what was done and why
- States appropriate assumptions and caveats
- Uses diagrams or plots when appropriate to aid in describing the solution
- States an appropriate and complete conclusion

My Notes

CONNECT TO AP

Written communication is an essential part of the AP Statistics course of study.

SUGGESTED LEARNING STRATEGIES: Marking the Text, Shared Reading, Summarize/Paraphrase/Retell

Matthew wrote the following article for the school newspaper about the field day activities.

Desoto Field Day a Huge Success!!

This year's field day was the best it has ever been. Both students and faculty agree that the new events brought to our school by our own Mr. Morrow added a new flavor to the day that we have not had before. While the boys enjoyed the tug-of-war and the potato sack race, most of the girls named "Hula Hoop Cha-Cha" as their favorite event.

The math department graphed the noise level on the field periodically. Their data shows that the noise level grew steadily throughout the day until everyone got tired.

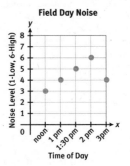

Field Day Noise

Kickball proved to be the highlight of the day when a special eighth grade team beat the faculty team in the last inning. The host of the event, Mr. Morrow, helped score three of the four runs for the faculty team. But his strong play was to no avail with the student team muscling their way to victory. It must be the youthfulness of the students that outweighed the teachers' maturity and skill.

One of the eighth grade boys said, "The eighth grade really is the best team, hands down!" while an eighth grade girl said, "Our team is clearly the best!" A seventh grader, who happened to be standing with the eighth graders, concurred with, "I cannot imagine that any of the other teams will be able to beat the eighth grade." Clearly, from our "straw poll," the eighth grade was the best team.

SUGGESTED LEARNING STRATEGIES: Self/Peer Revision, RAFT, Prewriting, Discussion Group

My Notes

When looking at the results in terms of medals won, you can see that, despite the student quotes, the seventh grade was clearly able to beat the other two teams.

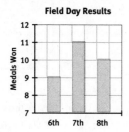

Field Day Results

All in all, this year's field day was a huge success.

16. Consider what might be faulty or misleading about this article. Write a paragraph that brings out any suspect information that you notice. Be sure to comment on the following aspects of the article.
    - Noise graph
    - Results graph
    - Student quotes
    - Conclusions by the author

    Answers may vary but should include points like:
    - Because the time skips on the *x*-axis, the data representation is misleading of what actually happened over time.
    - Because the quotes were only taken from eighth graders and eighth grade supporters, they were not a good representation of the entire middle school.
    - Because the *y*-axis is only counting from 7 through 12, it makes the difference in the medals won appear to be more distinct than they are.

ACTIVITY 5.4 *Continued*

16 Discussion Group, Prewriting, RAFT, Self/Peer Revision Students write a paragraph guided by the points listed. The graphs are drawn to be misleading, and student discussion should identify the flaws in the displays as well as the over-generalizations and prejudicial quotes included in the article.

Suggested Assignment

CHECK YOUR UNDERSTANDING
p. 290, #3–5

UNIT 5 PRACTICE
p. 297, #22–23

CHECK YOUR UNDERSTANDING

1a. Sample answer: 001–250

b. Sample answer: 246, 006, 051, 004, 127, 123, 046, 119

c. SRS; Sample answer: Because the subjects are assigned digits and chosen according to a fair method that involves chance.

2a.

4	5566
5	245679
6	367778
7	888
8	
9	5

b. Sample answer:

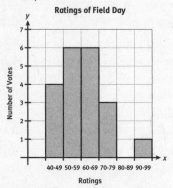

Ratings of Field Day

c. Sample answer: Most gave field day between 45 and 78, with one person giving Field Day a 95.

d. Sample answer: Both the stem plot and the histogram divide the data into intervals, and show how many pieces of data fall into each. The stem plot shows the individual data entries, and the histogram does not.

3a. Sample answer: The vertical scale starts at 2, which exaggerates the margin of victory.

b. Sample answer: Someone wanted to make the difference in the performance of the teams look greater than it is.

Answers may vary. Sample answers:

4a. How high must energy demand be to cause a failure in the region's energy grid?

CHECK YOUR UNDERSTANDING

Write your answers on notebook paper. Show your work.

1. A random sample from a school population of 250 students is to be selected to participate in the planning of next year's field day.

  a. How would you assign digits to the 250 students?

  b. Using the random digits provided, select 8 of the students.

  38448 48789 18338 24697 39364 42006
  76688 08708 81486 69487 60513 09297
  00412 71238 27649 39950 59636 88804
  04634 71197 19352 73089 84898 45785

  c. What type of sample is this? How do you know?

2. The field day committee selected in Item 1 decided to take a survey of the teachers. Teachers were asked to rate the field day on a scale of 1–100. Here are the ratings:

  54, 63, 78, 52, 66, 95, 45, 67, 57, 46, 45, 55, 56, 68, 78, 59, 46, 78, 67, 67

  a. Make a stem plot of the data.

  b. Make a histogram of the data.

  c. What do these displays tell you about the faculty's opinion of field day? Explain which display is more appropriate in this situation.

  d. Compare and contrast the stem plot and the histogram.

3. Consider the following display.

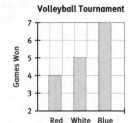

Volleyball Tournament

  a. What aspect of this display is misleading?

  b. What could be the motivation for creating a graph of the data that looks like this?

4. Consider a question of interest that can be addressed through simulation.

  a. Write out the question of interest.

  b. What population will be studied through the simulation?

  c. What type of data will need to be simulated (numerical, categorical, bivariate)? Explain.

  d. What kind of conclusions will be possible after the simulation is completed?

  e. What type of display would assist in the presentation of the data so that readers can visualize the results? Explain your choice.

5. **MATHEMATICAL REFLECTION** Compare and contrast an SRS, a stratified sample, and a census. Give examples for when it would advantageous to use each type of sample.

---

b. The "population" is the power system in a region.

c. The data is numeric because it involves two quantities that are measured: levels of energy usage, and the percent of the time that the power grid would fail at that level of usage. The data is also bivariate, because it relates these two variable amounts.

d–e. A scatter plot could show the data. The plot would enable you to see how the failure rate changes as energy usage grows.

5. An SRS and a stratified sample both contact only part of the population, while a census contacts the entire population. An SRS gives every person the same chance of being selected, while a stratified sample first divides the population into groups based on a particular variable (gender, grade level, etc.) and then chooses SRSs from each group and combines them all to make the actual sample.

Data Displays and Random Samples

FIELD DAY RESULTS

Write your answers on notebook paper. Show your work.

1. At the annual College Board Middle School Field Day, the 50-yard sack race had the following top 12 finishing times in seconds:

```
5 | 6 8
6 | 4
7 | 3 9
8 | 1 6 7
9 | 1 5 6 9
```

   a. Make a histogram of the 12 finishing times.

   b. What class interval did you choose for your histogram? Why?

   c. Write three statements about the sack race related to the histogram.

2. For a representative faculty tug-of-war team on Field Day, the administration runs a simulation to select a sample of 10 from the 80 teachers at the middle school.

   a. What numbers could you assign to the teachers so that team members can be selected using a random digit table?

   b. Which 10 teachers are chosen with the digits provided below based on your assignments in part a?

   96155 95009 27429 72918 08457 78134 48407 26061 58754 05326

   c. What is the population of this sample?

   d. For the team of 10 teachers, the administration wanted to make sure that about the same number of teachers from each grade level were chosen. What kind of sample should be taken to accomplish this?

Embedded Assessment 2

Assessment Focus
- Histogram
- Population of a sample
- Assign labels to population
- SRS from random number table
- Scatter plot
- Line of good fit
- Predictions using a model
- Outlier

Materials
- None

1 Students are asked to interpret a stem-and-leaf plot and to create a histogram for the same set of data.

2 Students are given an opportunity to explain the assigning of labels to the eighty subjects in the population. They go on to simulate, using a random number table, in which ten teachers will be selected.

Answer Key

1a. See below left.

  b. an interval of 10 seconds

  c. Answers may vary. Sample answers:
   - More students finished in a time greater than or equal to 70 seconds than finished in a time less than 70 seconds.
   - Two students finished in less than 60 seconds while four students finished in more than 90 seconds.
   - As many students finished from 60 to 79 seconds as finished from 80 to 89 seconds.

2a. You could number all of the teachers from 01 to 80.

  b. 15, 59, 50, 09, 27, 42, 29, 18, 08, 45

  c. all 80 of the teachers at the middle school

  d. stratified sample

1a.

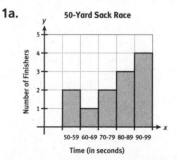

Embedded Assessment 2

 Students are provided with an opportunity to create a scatter plot of data and to find a good fit line to use for predictions. Since the data set contains an outlier that does not fit the pattern, students are asked to suggest a possible explanation for this extreme result.

3a.

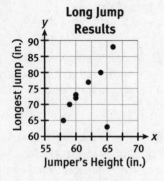

b.

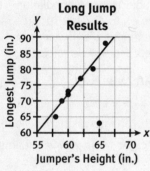

c. about 73 inches

Data Displays and Random Samples
FIELD DAY RESULTS

3. Another Field Day event is the long jump. Here is a table of eight students' heights with his or her long-jump distance.

Heights (in.)	58	59	60	60	62	64	65	66
Jump (in.)	65	70	72	73	77	80	62	88

a. Make a scatter plot of the data. Label the axes and use the maximums and minimums to determine the scale.

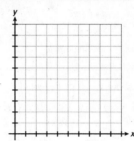

b. Place a line of good fit on the scatter plot.

c. Use your line to predict how far someone who is 60 inches tall will jump.

d. Use your line to predict how tall someone who jumped 70 inches will be.

e. Which point appears to be an outlier? How can this extreme value be explained?

	Exemplary	Proficient	Emerging
Math Knowledge 2b, c; 3e	• Correctly selects the teachers, based on the numbers selected (2b) • Gives the correct population for the sample (2c) • Correctly determines the outlier point (3e)	• Correctly selects some, but not all of the teachers	• Correctly selects none of the teachers • Gives an incorrect population for the sample • Determines an incorrect outlier point
Problem Solving 2a, d; 3c, d	• Correctly assigns label numbers so that a random digit table can be used to select team members (2a) • Names a correct kind of sample (2d) • Correctly predicts how far a 60-inch and a 70-inch person would jump (3c, d)	• Correctly assigns label numbers so that a random digit table can be used to select some, but not all, of the team members • Correctly predicts how far a 60-inch or a 70-inch person would jump.	• Does not assign label numbers correctly • Names an incorrect kind of sample • Predicts the jump distance for neither of the heights
Representations 1a, 3a, b	• Makes a histogram that correctly represents the finishing times (1a) • Makes a scatterplot that correctly represents the data, labels the axes, and determines a scale that is relevant to the maximums and minimums (3a) • Places a relevant line of good fit on the scatterplot (3b)	• Makes a histogram that correctly represents some, but not all, of the finishing times • Makes a scatterplot that correctly represents the data, labels the axes, but does not determine a relevant scale • Places a line on the plot that is a good fit for some, but not all, of the points	• Does not make a relevant histogram • Does not make a correct scatterplot • Places a line on the plot, but it is not a good fit
Communication 1b, c, 3e	• Gives an explanation for the chosen class interval (1b) • Writes three statements about the race relevant to the histogram (1c) • Gives an explanation for the extreme value (3e)	• Gives an incomplete explanation for the class interval chosen • Writes only two statements about the race • Gives an incomplete explanation for the extreme value	• Gives an incorrect explanation for the interval chosen • Writes fewer than two statements about the race • Gives an incorrect explanation for the extreme value

TEACHER TO TEACHER   You may wish to read through the rubric with students and discuss the differences in the expectation levels. Make sure students understand the meanings of any terms used.

Activity 5.1

1a. $\frac{8}{25}$

b. "the cone does not land on its base"; "the cone lands on its side"

2. Answers may vary. All logical answers are acceptable.

3. $\frac{8}{13}$

4. 48 yellow; 32 red

5a. Sample answer:

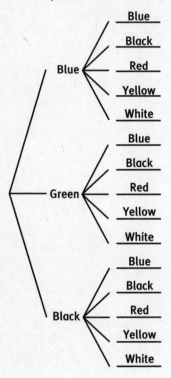

b. $\frac{2}{15}$

6a. $\frac{1}{19}$

b. $\frac{1}{20}$

c. Answers may vary.

Activity 5.2

7a. Mean = 13.75,
Median = 14.5,
Mode = 11, 15, and 17

b. The mean will be most affected; it will increase by 1.25.

ACTIVITY 5.1

1. Sam tossed a cone 25 times and recorded whether it landed on its base or on its side.

On its base	On its side
⊬⊦⊦ ⏐⏐⏐	⊬⊦⊦ ⊬⊦⊦ ⊬⊦⊦ ⏐⏐

a. What is the experimental probability of the cone landing on its base?

b. State the complement of the event "the cone lands on its base" in two ways.

2. Your friend, John, tosses a fair coin 50 times. The results are 21 heads and 29 tails. If you now pick up the coin and toss it 50 times, what results do you expect? Explain.

3. Andrea has just started collecting old coins. She has collected five quarters from 1940, six quarters from 1935, and two quarters from 1930. If she randomly chooses one quarter, what is the probability that it has a date from before 1936?

4. A bag contains 80 marbles. If the probability of drawing a yellow marble is $\frac{3}{5}$ and the probability of drawing a red marble is $\frac{2}{5}$, how many of each color are in the bag?

5. Marc owns 3 different pairs of pants (1 blue, 1 green, and 1 black) and 5 shirts (1 blue, 1 black, 1 red, 1 yellow, and 1 white). Every morning, he randomly chooses 1 pair of pants and 1 shirt to wear to school.

a. Draw a tree diagram to represent all of the possible outfits that Marc could choose.

b. What is the probability that Marc will choose a pair of pants and a shirt that are the same color?

6. Cards containing the numbers 1 through 20 are shuffled and placed number-side down before two cards are selected at random.

a. If the first card is not replaced before the second card is chosen, what is the probability that the second card will be 2? Assume that the first card was not 2.

b. If the first card is replaced before the second card is chosen, what is the probability that the card with the number 2 is chosen? Assume that the first card was not 2.

c. Compare and contrast the results from parts a and b.

ACTIVITY 5.2

7. The ages of participants in a race are:

9, 15, 17, 14, 15, 10, 11,
11, 12, 16, 17, 18

a. Determine the mean, median, and mode of the ages.

b. If one additional runner, whose age is 30, is added to the race, which measure of central tendency will be most affected by the outlier? Explain.

8. Money spent by students at the concession stand is shown in the table.

Student	Maddie	Matt	Devin	Tyler	Shelby	Derek
Money Spent	$4	$6	$5	$5	$6	$15

a. Identify the outlier.

b. Determine the mean of the data with and without the outlier.

c. Determine the median of the data with and without the outlier.

d. Determine the mode of the data with and without the outlier.

e. Which measure of central tendency is most affected by the outlier? Explain.

9. The table shows the countries that were the top 15 medal winners in the 2008 Olympics.

Country	Number of Medals
Australia	46
Belarus	19
Britain	47
China	100
Cuba	24
France	40
Germany	41
Italy	28
Japan	25
Korea	31
Spain	18
Canada	18
Russia	72
Ukraine	27
United States	110

a. Make a box-and-whisker plot of the data.

b. Give the five-number summary for this data.

c. Describe the distribution of the data.

d. Which measure of central tendency is most representative of this data set? Explain.

10. Give a data set that could be graphed using the box-and-whisker plot below.

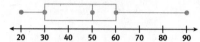

ACTIVITY 5.3

The CBMS basketball team manager provided the following data for the coach about the points scored each game by the team compared to the number of weeks into the basketball season.

Weeks	1	2	3	4	5	6	7	8	9	10
Points	48	25	33	57	17	44	58	77	35	44

11. What type of graph would be best for visualizing this data set?

12. Create and label the graph you selected.

13. What does this graph tell you about the data set?

8a. $15

b. Mean without outlier = $5.20, Mean with outlier = $6.83

c. Median without outlier = $5, Median with outlier = $5.50

d. Mode without outlier = $5 and $6, Mode with outlier = $5 and $6

e. The mean is most affected by the outlier. It increases by $1.63.

9a.

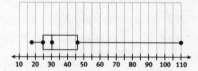

b. minimum = 18, lower quartile = 24, median = 31, upper quartile = 47, maximum = 110

c. Sample answer: 25% between 18 and 24, 25% between 24 and 31, 25% between 31 and 47 and 25% between 47 and 110

d. Sample answer: The mode is 18 which is the minimum value and not too near the center of the distribution. The mean is 43.067 and the median is 31. Because the data set contains two relatively extreme values of 100 and 110, the median is the better measure for a representative value for this data set.

10. Answers may vary. Sample answer: 20, 30, 35, 50, 55, 60, 90.

Activity 5.3

11. Sample answer: line graph

12.

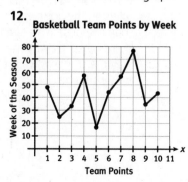

Basketball Team Points by Week

13. Sample answer: This is a picture of how well the team did in each game throughout the season.

14. Sample answer: scatter plot

15.

Basketball Rebounds and Points

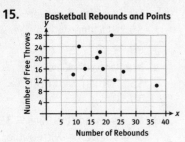

16. Sample answer: There is no association (or a very weak negative association) between the number of rebounds and the number of free throws in a basketball game.

17. double bar graph

18.

Basketball Team Breakfast Survey

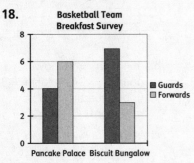

Guards
Forwards

Pancake Palace   Biscuit Bungalow

19. Sample answer: The same number of students chose Pancake Palace and Biscuit Bungalow, but more guards like Biscuit Bungalow and more forwards like Pancake Palace.

Activity 5.4

20a. Sample answer: 001–350

b. Sample answer: 034, 057, 125, 314, 254, 099, 019, 272, 253, 045, 095, 328

c. Sample answer: You could first divide the school into males and females, and then use the random number table to pick six from each group.

21a. Write the following data on the board.

Minutes Studied	75	63	54	27	33	65	15	41	99
Test Grade	88	75	66	54	95	75	45	80	85

The manager also provided the coach this data on the team's record.

Number of Rebounds	Number of Free Throws
9	14
22	28
19	16
17	20
11	24
37	10
18	22
26	15
13	16
23	12

14. What type of graph would be best suited for this data set?

15. Create and label the graph you selected to display this data.

16. What does this graph tell you about the data set?

The manager shared the results of a team survey for where to have breakfast the day of the game with the coach.

	Guards	Forwards
Pancake Palace	4	6
Biscuit Bungalow	7	3

17. What type of display would be best for visualizing this data set?

18. Create and label the type of graph you identified in Question 17.

19. What does this graph tell you about the data set?

ACTIVITY 5.4

20. A random sample from a student body of 350 students at a local middle school is to be selected.

   a. How will you assign digits to the students of the middle school?

   b. Using the random digits below, select 9 of the students.

   9223 95034 05756 28713 96409 12531
   42544 82853 73676 47150 99400 01927
   27754 42648 82425 36290 45467 71709
   77558 00095 32863

   c. What changes are necessary to make this a sample stratified based on gender?

21. The following data is collected from the twelve students in the sample about the number of minutes that each student studied for the test. Their grades are shown.

   a. Graph the data points. Label the axes and the scale.

   b. How are the two quantities in this graph related?

   c. Are there any outliers? Explain.

   d. If this data were collected through self-reporting by students, what are some reasons the data may not represent the actual relationship between the amount of time spent studying and the grade?

Student Study Time vs. Test Grade

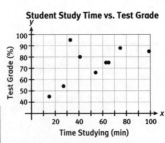

b. positive association; In general, the more studied, the higher the test score.

c. (33, 95) and (99, 85)

d. Sample answer: The data relies on the accuracy of their responses. The data could be skewed by the way the students want to present themselves.

22. Consider the following graph.

Weekly Punctuality Record

Day Number of the Week

The caption for this graph read, "Steady Decline in Student Tardies."

a. What is the misleading aspect of this graph?

b. Is the caption an accurate representation of the facts? Explain.

23. Consider the two cases below. Write an analysis of the conclusions made by each interviewer.

a. An interviewer asked ten people at the local mall how much money they spent per week eating out. Their responses are given in the histogram below. The interviewer concluded that families in town spend an average of $100 a week eating out.

Eating Out

$ per Week

b. A phone interviewer used a random number table to determine what page of the phone book and which person on the page to call. If the person called was home, and would talk, the interviewer asked the person's age and the number of times per week that they ate meals away from home. A scatter plot of the data follows. The interviewer concluded that young people eat out more than older people.

Eating Out

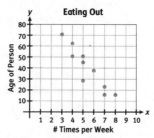

Times per Week

24. Select a question of interest or topic that can be investigated through a collection of data.

a. Write the question of interest.

b. What population will be studied through the data collection?

c. What type of data will need to be collected (numerical, categorical, bivariate)? Explain.

d. What type of sample would be most appropriate (SRS, stratified, census)? Explain.

e. What type of display would assist in the presentation of the data so that readers can visualize the results? Explain your choice.

22a. The x-axis is not in the correct numeric order.

b. No; Sample answer: Tardiness did not decrease steadily all week, it increased from day 3 to day 4.

23a. Sample answer: The histogram suggests this conclusion, but a histogram does not reveal the individual data points that make up the graph. The true answer could differ significantly from $100. In addition, taking a small sample of only mall shoppers is not a good representation of a whole town.

b. Sample answer: Again, this is a very small sampling to take as representative of a whole town. There are only ten people represented on the graph. Second, the interviewer used a convenience sample since some people who were selected refused to participate, and/or were absent. Perhaps a better statement would be "older persons who were at home and willing to talk to me ate out less than younger persons who were at home and were willing to talk to me."

Answers may vary:

24a. Do students prefer tomato soup or chicken noodle soup?

b. The students at your middle school.

c. Bivariate categorical data will be gathered through a survey with a scale of 1 to 5. One will stand for "does not like the taste" and 5 will stand for "one of my favorite foods." The survey will have two questions, "How much do you like tomato soup?" and "How much do you like chicken noodle soup?"

d. A sample stratified by grade and gender would work well to look at preferences of the different groups.

e. The data can be displayed in side-by-side bar graphs to indicate preferences according to sub-groups.

Reflection

Student Reflection

Discuss the essential questions with students. Have them share how their understanding of the questions has changed through studying the concepts in the unit.

Review the academic vocabulary. You may want students to revisit the graphic organizers they have completed for academic vocabulary terms and add other notes about their understanding of terms.

Encourage students to evaluate their own learning and to recognize the strategies that work best for them. Help them identify key concepts in the unit and to set goals for addressing their weaknesses and acquiring effective learning strategies.

Teacher Reflection

1. Of the key concepts in the unit, did any present special challenges for students?

2. How will you adjust your future instruction for students/ activities?

3. Which strategies were most effective for facilitating student learning?

4. When you teach this unit again, what will you do differently?

Reflection

An important aspect of growing as a learner is to take the time to reflect on your learning. It is important to think about where you started, what you have accomplished, what helped you learn, and how you will apply your new knowledge in the future. Use notebook paper to record your thinking on the following topics and to identify evidence of your learning.

Essential Questions

1. Review the mathematical concepts and your work in this unit before you write thoughtful responses to the questions below. Support your responses with specific examples from concepts and activities in the unit.

   1 How do different displays help you interpret data?

   2 Why is it important to know if events are dependent or independent when calculating probabilities?

Academic Vocabulary

2. Look at the following academic vocabulary words:

   - categorical variables
   - experimental probability
   - numerical data
   - outlier
   - range
   - simple random sample (SRS)
   - theoretical probability

   Choose three words and explain your understanding of each word and why each is important in your study of math.

Self-Evaluation

3. Look through the activities and Embedded Assessments in this unit. Use a table similar to the one below to list three major concepts in this unit and to rate your understanding of each.

Unit Concepts	Is Your Understanding Strong (S) or Weak (W)?
Concept 1	
Concept 2	
Concept 3	

   a. What will you do to address each weakness?

   b. What strategies or class activities were particularly helpful in learning the concepts you identified as strengths? Give examples to explain.

4. How do the concepts you learned in this unit relate to other math concepts and to the use of mathematics in the real world?

Additional Notes

UNIT 5 Math Standards Review

These two pages provide practice with four standardized test question formats that are used in many national and state high-stakes tests:

- Multiple choice
- Gridded response
- Short response
- Extended response

These items also provide practice with the mathematics content of this unit.

1 Multiple choice
- Interpret Data Displays

2 Gridded response
- Interpret Data Displays

3 Short Response
- Measure of Central Tendency

4 Extended response
- Create Scatterplots
- Interpret data using trend lines

---

1. From the box and whisker plot, what is the percentage of students scoring below 34 points on their math quiz?

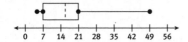

   0 5 10 15 20 25 30 35 40 45 50 55 60

   A. 100%   **B.** 75%

   C. 50%   **D.** 25%

1. Ⓐ Ⓑ Ⓒ Ⓓ

2. What is the interquartile range for the points scored in the state football championship games?

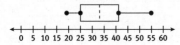

   0   7   14 21 28 35 42 49 56

2.

3. Deante earned the following scores on her tests in United States History:

   $$75, 95, 80, 60, 95$$

   Part A: Find the measures of central tendency for Deante's test scores (mean, median, mode).

   Solve and Explain

   Mean = 81

   Median = 80

   Mode = 95

   Part B: If Deante earns a 45 on her next test, explain which measure of central tendency will be affected the most.

   Solve and Explain

   The mode will not change. The median will go to 77.5.

   The mean will go to 75. The mean changes the most, it

   drops 6 points.

Unit 5 • Probability and Statistics   **299**

TEACHER TO TEACHER You might read through the extended-response item with students and discuss your expectation levels. Make sure students understand the meanings of any terms used.

Read
Solve
Explain

4. Tomas is working on his science fair thesis. He wants to show a relationship between the average monthly temperature and the amount of rainfall for the month.

Month	Jan	Feb	March	April	May	June	July	Aug	Sept	Oct	Nov
Avg. Temp (°F)	61	62	67	72	78	81	83	83	81	75	68
Rainfall (in.)	2.2	2.7	3.4	1.8	2.9	5.6	7.3	7.9	6.3	2.3	1.8

Part A: Create a scatter plot of the data.

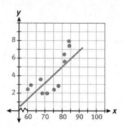

Part B: Explain whether Tomas' hypothesis—temperature is related to rainfall—is supported.

Solve and Explain

His hypothesis appears to be correct. As the temperature gets higher, the amount of rainfall increases, and when the temperature drops so does the amount of rainfall.

Part C: Draw a line of good fit.

Part D: If the average temperature for December is 65°, predict the amount of rainfall that should occur. Justify your prediction.

Solve and Explain

Predictions should be between about 2 and 3 inches.

Sample answer: Two inches. When I read my line of good fit at 65°, the *y*-value is approximately 2.

In prior units, students have learned characteristics of two dimensional figures, including right triangles, explored proportional relationships, and used unit conversions. In this unit, students will extend their knowledge of right triangles through the application of the Pythagorean theorem. In addition, students will use their knowledge of two-dimensional polygons to find the surface area and volume of three-dimensional figures and compare the dimensions of similar three-dimensional solids.

Academic Vocabulary

Blackline masters for use in developing students' vocabulary skills are located at the back of this Teacher's Edition. Encourage students to explore the meanings of the academic vocabulary words in this unit, using graphic organizers and class discussions to help students understand the key concepts related to the terms. Encourage students to place their vocabulary organizers in their Math notebooks and to revisit these pages to make notes as their understanding of concepts increases.

Embedded Assessments

The two Embedded Assessments for this unit follow Activities 6.2 and 6.5.

CollegeBoard
inspiring minds™

AP/College Readiness

Unit 6 extends student understanding of right triangles and continues to develop student understanding of the geometry of two and three dimensions by:

- Allowing students to communicate mathematics and explain solutions verbally and in written form.

- Modeling written descriptions of physical situations.

- Using technology to help solve problems and support conclusions.

- Encouraging students to determine the reasonableness of solutions including size, relative accuracy, and units of measure.

Embedded Assessment 1	Camp Euclid
● Pythagorean theorem	

Embedded Assessment 2	Air Dancing
● Lateral area	
● Volume	

Suggested Pacing

The following table provides suggestions for pacing either a 45-minute period or a block schedule class of 90 minutes. Space is left for you to write your own pacing guidelines based on your experiences in using the materials.

	45-Minute Period	90-Minute Period	Comments on Pacing
Unit Overview	$\frac{1}{2}$	$\frac{1}{4}$	
Activity 6.1	4	2	
Activity 6.2	2	1	
Embedded Assessment 1	1	$\frac{1}{2}$	
Activity 6.3	4	2	
Activity 6.4	5	$2\frac{1}{2}$	
Activity 6.5	3	$1\frac{1}{2}$	
Embedded Assessment 2	1	$\frac{1}{2}$	
Total	$20\frac{1}{2}$	$10\frac{1}{4}$	

Unit Practice

Practice Problems for each activity in the unit appear at the end of the unit.

Math Standards Review

To help accustom students to the formats and types of questions they may encounter on high stakes tests, additional problems are provided at the end of the unit. These problems are constructed for multiple choice, short response, extended response, and gridded responses.

Three-Dimensional Geometry

Unit Overview
In this unit you will investigate 2- and 3-dimensional figures, and apply formulas to determine areas and volumes of these figures. Your study will include right triangles and the Pythagorean Theorem, polygons, prisms, and cylinders. You will relate geometric concepts to real world situations.

Academic Vocabulary
Add this word to your vocabulary notebook.
- solid

Essential Questions

 How are two- and three-dimensional figures related?

 How do changes in dimensions of a geometric figure affect area, surface area, and volume?

EMBEDDED ASSESSMENTS

This unit has two Embedded Assessments. These embedded assessments allow you to demonstrate your understanding of the Pythagorean Theorem and its uses, and lateral area and volume.

301

UNIT 6 OVERVIEW

Unit Overview
Ask students to read the overview and to share what they already know about three-dimensional figures and the Pythagorean theorem.

Essential Questions
Read the essential questions with students and ask them to provide real-world situations where knowing about three-dimensional figures and their properties may be useful.

Materials
- Paper clips
- Gift boxes (optional)
- Construction paper (optional)

Academic Vocabulary
Ask students to provide informal, everyday definitions of the word. Discuss how the word can be defined using mathematical terms.

You may wish to assign some or all of these exercises to gauge students' readiness for Unit 6 topics.

Prerequisite Skills
• Finding powers and roots (Item 1)
• Ratios (Item 2)
• Area (Items 3, 7, 8)
• Describe/classify polygons (Items 4, 5)
• Perimeter and circumference (Item 6)

Answer Key

1a. 36

b. 1.44

c. $\frac{9}{25}$

d. 64

e. 125

f. 7

g. 15

2a. $\frac{3 \text{ inches}}{1 \text{ foot}}$ or $\frac{3 \text{ inches}}{12 \text{ inches}}$

b. $\frac{13}{40}$

3. The square is 4 by 4, and the rectangle is either 1 by 16 or 2 by 8.

4. Check students' drawings. Answers may vary:

a. Scalene: 3 sides and 3 angles of different lengths and measures

b. Isosceles: 2 sides and 2 angles have the same measure

c. Equilateral: 3 and 3 angles have the same measure

d. Right: has one angle that measures 90 degrees

5. trapezoid, hexagon, octagon, pentagon, triangle

6a. $P = 16$ units

b. $P = 42$ units

c. $C = 6\pi \approx 18.85$ units

d. $P = 28$ units

Write your answers on notebook paper. Show your work.

1. Simplify the following squares, cubes, and square roots.
  a. 6^2 **b.** $(1.2)^2$
  c. $\left(\frac{3}{5}\right)^2$ **d.** 4^3
  e. 5^3 **f.** $\sqrt{49}$
  g. $\sqrt{225}$

2. Write the ratio of the following:
  a. 3 inches to 1 foot
  b. 13 days to 40 days

3. A square and a rectangle both have an area of 16 square units and dimensions that are whole-number units. Find the dimensions of the square and the rectangle.

4. Draw a representation of each of the following triangles and describe the characteristics of each.
  a. Scalene   **b.** Isosceles
  c. Equilateral   **d.** Right

5. Name each figure.

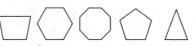

6. Find the perimeter or circumference of each of the figures below.

a.

b.

c.

d.

7. Find the area of each figure in Item 6.

8. Explain using specific formulas how you could find the area of the shaded area of the figure below.

7a. $A = 14.31$ square units

b. $A = 84$ square units

c. $A = 9\pi \approx 28.27$ square units

d. $A = 36$ square units

8. $A_{shaded} = \frac{1}{2}bh - \pi r^2$; Explanations may vary.

The Pythagorean Theorem
Diamond in the Rough

SUGGESTED LEARNING STRATEGIES: Shared Reading, Activating
Prior Knowledge, Visualization, Interactive Word Wall

My Notes

Cameron is a catcher trying out for the school baseball team. He
has played baseball in the community and is able to easily throw
the ball from home plate to second base to throw out a runner
trying to steal second base. However, the school baseball diamond
is a regulation size field and larger than the field he is accustomed
to. Will he be able to consistently throw out runners trying to steal
second if he is able to throw the baseball 130 feet?

The distance between each consecutive base on a regulation
baseball diamond is 90 feet and the baselines are perpendicular.
The imaginary line from home plate to second base divides the
baseball diamond into two right triangles. There is a relationship
between the lengths of the three sides of any right triangle that
might be helpful for determining if Cameron can throw across a
regulation baseball diamond.

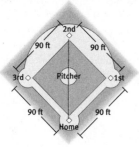

1. Use the terms **hypotenuse** and **leg** to identify and label the parts
   of the right triangle below.

   a.

   b. Explain the differences between the hypotenuse and the legs
   of a right triangle.

   Answers may vary. Sample answer: The hypotenuse is
   opposite the right angle. The legs form the sides of the
   right angle.

CONNECT TO AP

In AP Calculus, the Pythagorean
theorem is useful when solving
related rates problems.

ACTIVITY 6.1 Investigative

The Pythagorean Theorem

Activity Focus
• The Pythagorean Theorem

Materials
• No special materials required

Chunking the Activity

#1	#13
#2–5	#14–17
#6–8	#18
#9–12	

TEACHER TO TEACHER ↳ Some students may be
unfamiliar with baseball
and the regulations associated
with it. Reading this introduction
using learning strategies like
Shared Reading and Questioning
the Text will allow all students to
begin the activity with the
necessary information.

1 Activating Prior Knowledge,
Visualization, Interactive Word
Wall The terms *hypotenuse* and
leg have been covered in previous
math courses. This question
serves as formative assessment
for the teacher regarding previous
knowledge and as a review for
the students. The terms should
be placed on the Interactive Word
Wall.

Connect to **AP**

The Pythagorean Theorem is useful in AP Calculus when solving
related rates problems. For example, suppose a runner was moving
from 3rd base to home plate at a constant speed. You could use
calculus to determine how fast the distance between home plate
and the runner was changing at a particular instant in time. To
solve a problem like this, students will need to be able to set up
an equation using the Pythagorean Theorem where the distance
between the runner and third base and the distance between the
runner and home plate are variables and the distance between
third base and home plate is a constant.

TEACHER TO TEACHER | Students are often reluctant to write out the work involved when using formulas and solving problems with them. In order to find student errors, it is essential that students write the formula, show the replacement of variables with the actual values given in the problem, and then show the process of solving the problem.

Reviewing the Pythagorean Theorem through the reading of the Math Terms box is essential for the next part of the activity. The actual formula will be developed in Item 2.

2 Create Representations, Think/Pair/Share, Debrief Be sure to debrief the class after the students have had a chance to draw the triangle and create a formula.

3 Think/Pair/Share, Group Presentation Students will use the formula they wrote in Item 2 to find the hypotenuse of these right triangles. Sharing student work through group presentations will allow students to see how others solved the problems. Be sure that this formula goes on the Interactive Word Wall.

Students may need more practice using the Pythagorean Theorem to find the length of a hypotenuse. Additional examples to be used are included in the mini-lesson on this page.

4 Work Backwards, Think/Pair/Share, Group Presentation It is important for students to write out the formula and add the given information. This will help them to notice that they are not solving for the hypotenuse in this situation and that these problems will require them to solve for a different variable. If extra examples are needed, see the mini-lesson at the bottom of the next page.

My Notes

> **SUGGESTED LEARNING STRATEGIES:** Questioning the Text, Create Representations, Think/Pair/Share, Group Presentation, Work Backwards

> **MATH TERMS**
> The **Pythagorean theorem** states that: *The square of the length of the hypotenuse of a right triangle is equal to the sum of the squares of the lengths of the legs of the triangle.*

The **Pythagorean theorem** describes triangles containing a right angle.

2. In a right triangle, let c be the length of the hypotenuse and let a and b be the lengths of the legs of the triangle.

   a. Draw and label a right triangle using a, b, and c.

   b. Write an equation using a, b and c to represent the Pythagorean theorem. $c^2 = a^2 + b^2$

3. Use the Pythagorean theorem to find the length of the hypotenuse in each of the following triangles.

   a.

   $c = 5$

   b.

   $c = 17$

4. Use the Pythagorean theorem to find the length of the missing leg in each of the following triangles.

   a.

   $b = 24$

   b.

   $a = 8$

MINI-LESSON: Using the Pythagorean Theorem

Give students the two leg lengths from some of the Pythagorean Triples below with diagrams and others without diagrams. When they are not given a diagram, have the students create their own from the given information before solving for the hypotenuse.

5, 12, 13	12, 16, 20	30, 40, 50
9, 40, 41	15, 20, 25	10, 24, 26
11, 60, 61	12, 35, 37	28, 45, 53
9, 12, 15		

SUGGESTED LEARNING STRATEGIES: Create Representations, Think/Pair/Share, Group Presentation, Group Discussion

My Notes

5. Use the Pythagorean theorem to find p in terms of r and t.

$p = \sqrt{(t^2 - r^2)}$

6. Sketch a diagram of a regulation baseball diamond showing the baselines and the imaginary line from home plate to second base. Identify and label the hypotenuse and legs of any right triangles. What are the lengths of the legs of the triangles?

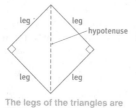

The legs of the triangles are 90 feet long.

7. Write an equation that can be used to find the distance from home plate to second base.

$c^2 = 90^2 + 90^2$

8. Can the distance from home plate to second base be found without a calculator? Why or why not?

Answers may vary. Sample answer: It can be done, but is much simpler to do with a calculator. $\sqrt{16,200}$ is a large number.

Because it may be difficult to find some distances without a calculator, estimation is often a useful problem solving tool.

9. Use the Pythagorean theorem to find the exact length of the hypotenuse for each of the right triangles described in the table below. Then estimate the value of the square root to find the estimated length of the hypotenuse.

> **TECHNOLOGY Tip**
>
> If you take the square root of a number that is not a perfect square, the result is a decimal number that does not terminate or repeat and is called an irrational number. The exact value of an irrational number must be written using a radical sign. Decimal approximations of irrational numbers are found using technology such as a calculator.

Triangle	Length of Leg 1	Length of Leg 2	Exact Length of Hypotenuse	Estimated Length of Hypotenuse
1	1 unit	2 units	$\sqrt{5}$	2.24
2	1 unit	3 units	$\sqrt{10}$	3.16
3	2 units	2 units	$\sqrt{8}$	2.83
4	2 units	3 units	$\sqrt{13}$	3.61
5	9 units	9 units	$\sqrt{162}$	12.73

MINI-LESSON: Using the Pythagorean Theorem to Solve for a Leg

The list of Pythagorean Triples below can be used to practice the skill of solving for a leg given the hypotenuse and other leg. Again, have students draw diagrams of the triangles given the information and work through the process needed to solve for the leg.

24, 32, 40	10, 24, 26	20, 21, 29
15, 36, 39	16, 63, 65	11, 60, 61
14, 48, 50	33, 44, 55	25, 60, 65

5 Create Representations, Think/Pair/Share, Group Presentation The students are being asked to develop the formula that they have been using for finding the length of a leg of a right triangle. Having students present their ideas to the group provides a vehicle for classroom discussion and serves as formative assessment regarding students' understanding of this process.

6-7 Create Representations, Debrief Students can compare their diagrams and equations for accuracy.

8 Group Discussion, Debrief Students may answer either yes or no. It is possible to find an approximate square root without a calculator but it is more difficult without technology. Students may compare methods that they are familiar with for estimating a square root.

9 Think/Pair/Share, Group Presentation This task can be split among groups and answers shared on a large copy of the table from Item 9.

Students may not understand that the exact length is written with a radical sign. They may assume that this answer needs to be simplified. The Math Tip on the side of the page mentions this idea and should be read and discussed before beginning work on this question. How many decimal places to take the estimation to also needs to be given to the students before beginning work. They may think that they have to extend their estimates beyond the hundredths place.

Suggested Assignment

CHECK YOUR UNDERSTANDING
p. 310, #1–3

UNIT 6 PRACTICE
p. 339, #1–4

Students estimated square roots in Unit 1, but some students may need to be reminded of the process. The mini-lesson on this page can be used if any students are struggling with Item 9.

10-12 Simplify the Problem, Think/Pair/Share, Group Presentation Students should note that triangle 5 is similar to the triangle they are trying to find the hypotenuse of and be able to describe the relationship. Debriefing the class on their thought process will help those students who did not see the connection.

13 Activating Prior Knowledge, Think/Pair/Share, Debrief This question is good formative assessment of the students' ability to apply the Pythagorean Theorem.

TEACHER TO TEACHER It will be interesting for students to compare the size of the softball diamond to the baseball diamond. There could be many opinions about why softball diamonds are smaller. Students might consider the size and weight of the ball involved as well.

Suggested Assignment

CHECK YOUR UNDERSTANDING
p. 310, #5

UNIT 6 PRACTICE
p. 339, #5–9

ACTIVITY 6.1 continued The Pythagorean Theorem
Diamond in the Rough

My Notes

SUGGESTED LEARNING STRATEGIES: Simplify the Problem, Think/Pair/Share, Group Presentation, Activating Prior Knowledge

10. Which of the triangles in the table in Item 9 could be used to help Cameron estimate the distance from home plate to second base? Justify your choice.

Explanations may vary. Sample answer: Triangle 5. That is the only isosceles triangle in the table. Also, the actual baseline lengths are multiples of the legs of that triangle.

11. Use the Pythagorean theorem and the information in the table in Item 9 to find the distance from home plate to second base. Show all your work.

Actual distance: ≈ 127 feet. In Triangle 5, $a = 9$, $b = 9$, and $c \approx 12.7$. So, when $a = 90$ and $b = 90$, $c \approx 10 \cdot 12.7$, or 127.

12. If Cameron can throw the baseball 130 feet, will he be able to consistently throw out a runner trying to steal second base? Explain your reasoning.

Explanations may vary. Sample answer: Yes. Since Cameron can throw the ball 130 feet, and the throw he has to make is less than that, he will be able to consistently throw out a runner trying to steal second.

13. On a regulation softball diamond, the distance between consecutive bases is 60 feet and the baselines are perpendicular.

a. Sketch and label a scale drawing of a softball diamond.
Sample answer sketched.

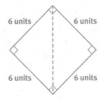

6 units   6 units

6 units   6 units

b. Use the Pythagorean theorem and your sketch to estimate the distance from home plate to second base on a softball field. Show all your work.

Actual softball field: $c \approx 85$ feet. From part (a) $6^2 + 6^2 = c^2$; $c \approx 8.5$ units; since $6^2 + 6^2 \approx (8.5)^2$, $60^2 + 60^2 \approx 85^2$.

306 SpringBoard® Mathematics with Meaning™ **Level 3**

MINI-LESSON: Estimating Square Roots

To practice estimating square roots, have the students use a number line.

- First, graph the two perfect squares on either side of the number they are estimating the square root of. (Example: To find the square root of 18, graph 16 and 25.)

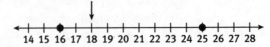

14 15 16 17 18 19 20 21 22 23 24 25 26 27 28

- The estimated square root will be between 4 and 5 because these are the square roots of 16 and 25.
- Next, decide if the square root is closer to the lower or higher perfect square to estimate what the digit in the tenths place should be. (Example: 18 is much closer to 16 than 25 so the estimated square root will be well below 4.5. This is not a linear relationship, but the estimates are close.)
- The estimated square root is 4.2.

Have the students do several of these with numbers that are at different points between the perfect squares.

The Pythagorean Theorem
Diamond in the Rough

During summer vacation, Cameron's parents take him to see his favorite baseball team, the Anglers, play. On their last day of vacation, he discovers that he will not be able to carry the autographed bat he won home on the plane. His dad suggests that he speak to the concierge at the hotel about options for shipping the bat home. The concierge only has one box that he thinks might be long enough. After measuring the dimensions of the box to be 16″ × 16″ × 27″, the concierge apologizes for not having a box long enough for the 34″ bat. Cameron thinks he might still be able to use the box. His idea is to put the bat in the box at an angle as shown in the diagram below. He wonders if the bat will fit in the box.

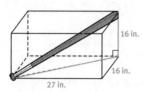

16 in.

16 in.

27 in.

My Notes

CONNECT TO TRAVEL

In a hotel, a concierge is a person who helps guests with various tasks ranging from restaurant reservations to travel plans.

14. The diagonal of the box is the hypotenuse of a right triangle. Outline this triangle in the diagram above.

15. What are the lengths of the legs of this right triangle? Show any work needed to find these lengths.

The legs of this triangle are 16 inches and 31.4 inches.
$c^2 = 16^2 + 27^2$, $c \approx 31.4$.

16. Find the length of the diagonal of the box. Show any necessary calculations.

≈ 35.2 inches; $c^2 \approx (31.4)^2 + 16^2$

TEACHER TO TEACHER Students need to read and discuss the problem situation so that all students are clear on how the bat is sitting in the box.

14 Visualization, Create Representations, Debrief Have students compare the diagonals that they drew so that they all have the same information before beginning work on the problem.

15-16 Create Representations, Think/Pair/Share, Group Presentation Students may struggle with understanding that these questions require the Pythagorean Theorem to be used twice. It is first used in Item 15 to find the hypotenuse of the triangle on the bottom of the box with legs of 27 and 16 inches. It is used a second time in Item 16 to find the hypotenuse of the triangle that they drew that has leg lengths of 16 and the length that they found in Item 15. This may require physical modeling with a box so that students can visualize the process.

17 Think/Pair/Share

18 Group Presentation, Create Representations, Debrief Be sure to have students draw their right triangles for this question on the graph paper, leaving room for the squares to be drawn on the outside edges of the legs.

This question can be done in groups to save time and materials. Groups can be assigned different size triangles to work with. The table in Part c can be drawn on large paper, or the board, and groups can fill in their information to share with the class.

My Notes

17. Will Cameron be able to use the box to ship his bat? Justify your response.

Yes. The bat is 34 inches long. Since the diagonal of the box is 35.2 inches, it will fit if he places it diagonally in the box.

18. When Cameron returns to school, he tells his math teacher how he applied the Pythagorean Theorem while on vacation. She is excited and tells him they will do some investigation into why the Pythagorean Theorem works.

a. On centimeter grid paper or graph paper, draw right triangles having legs with each of the following lengths. Use one piece of paper for each triangle.
Check students' work.
Triangle 1:   3 units and 4 units
Triangle 2:   5 units and 12 units
Triangle 3:   8 units and 15 units

b. Use the Pythagorean Theorem to find the length of the hypotenuse in each of the triangles.

Hypotenuse of Triangle 1: 5 units
Hypotenuse of Triangle 2: 13 units
Hypotenuse of Triangle 3: 17 units

c. On each leg of each of the right triangles, draw a square with sides the same length as the leg of the triangle. Find the area of each of these squares and complete the table below.

Triangle	Length of Leg 1	Area of Square on Leg 1	Length of Leg 2	Area of Square on Leg 2
1	3	9	4	16
2	5	25	12	144
3	8	64	15	225

d. How does the area of each square relate to the length of a leg of the triangle?
Area = (length of leg)^2

SUGGESTED LEARNING STRATEGIES: Group Presentation, Create Representations

e. Cut out each of the triangles and the squares drawn on each of the legs.
Check students' work.

f. Use the small squares drawn on the legs of each right triangle to build a large square on the hypotenuse of that triangle. You may cut and rearrange the small squares any way necessary to create one larger square having side length equal to the length of the hypotenuse of the triangle.
Check students' work.

g. Find the area of the square created on the hypotenuse of each triangle.

Area of square on the hypotenuse of Triangle 1: 25
Area of square on the hypotenuse of Triangle 2: 169
Area of square on the hypotenuse of Triangle 3: 289

h. What is the relationship between the areas of the squares drawn on each of the legs of the triangle and the large square built on the hypotenuse? Explain your reasoning.
The sum of the areas of the squares on leg 1 and leg 2 is equal to the area of the square on the hypotenuse.

i. How does this relationship illustrate the Pythagorean Theorem in the form $c^2 = a^2 + b^2$?
Answers may vary. Sample answer:

$c^2 = $ (length of hypotenuse)$^2 = $ area of the square on the hypotenuse

$a^2 = $ (length of leg 1)$^2 = $ area of the square on leg 1

$b^2 = $ (length of leg 2)$^2 = $ area of the square on leg 2

Since the area of the square on the hypotenuse = (area of the square on leg 1) + (area of the square on leg 2), then $c^2 = a^2 + b^2$.

My Notes

18 *continued* Group Presentation, Create Representations, Debrief If this question is done in groups, groups should lay their work for parts e and f on their desk so that members of other groups can see their work.

The class will need to discuss their findings so that they can answer Parts g, h, and i, keeping in mind examples other than the one that they personally developed.

Suggested Assignment

CHECK YOUR UNDERSTANDING
p. 310, #4, 6, 7

UNIT 6 PRACTICE
p. 339, #10–12

ACTIVITY 6.1 *Continued*

CHECK YOUR UNDERSTANDING

1. $x \approx 17.2$

2. $x \approx 3.5$

3. $x = 26$

4. 25 feet

Sample answers:

5a. 3.5

b. 4.1

c. 6.3

d. 9.9

6. 6.7 units

7. $c^2 > a^2 + b^2$ in an obtuse triangle. $c^2 < a^2 + b^2$ in an acute triangle.

ACTIVITY 6.1 *continued*
The Pythagorean Theorem
Diamond in the Rough

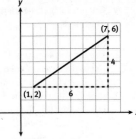

You can also use the Pythagorean theorem to find the distance between two points on a coordinate plane. Just think of the two points as the endpoints of the hypotenuse of a right triangle. Then draw the legs and use their lengths in the formula.

19. Find the distance from point (1, 2) to point (7, 6) to the nearest tenth of a unit. 7.2

20. Find the distance from point (3, 1) to point (5, 5) to the nearest tenth of a unit. 4.5 units

CHECK YOUR UNDERSTANDING

Write your answers on notebook paper. Show your work.

Find *x* in each of the following.

1.
14, *x*, 10

2.
4, 2, *x*

3.
24, 10, *x*

4. A painter uses a ladder to reach a second-story window on the house she is painting. The bottom of the window is 20 feet above the ground. The foot of the ladder is 15 feet from the house. How long is the ladder?

5. Estimate the square roots of each of the following:

a. 12

b. 17

c. 40

d. 99

6. Find the distance from point (2, 6) to point (8, 3) to the nearest tenth of a unit.

7. **MATHEMATICAL REFLECTION** In what type of triangle is $c^2 > a^2 + b^2$? In what type of triangle is $c^2 < a^2 + b^2$? Explain your answers.

310 SpringBoard® Mathematics with Meaning™ **Level 3**

310 SpringBoard® Mathematics with Meaning™ **Level 3**

© 2010 College Board. All rights reserved.

Verifying Right Triangles
Paper Clip Chains

SUGGESTED LEARNING STRATEGIES: Shared Reading, Create Representations, Activating Prior Knowledge, Think/Pair/Share

It is believed that the Pythagorean Theorem was applied in the building of the pyramids and the establishment of land boundaries in ancient Egypt. Egyptian surveyors, known as rope stretchers, applied the theorem to reestablish property lines after the annual flooding of the Nile. They created right angles by forming right triangles using long ropes with 13 equally spaced knots tied in them to create 12 equal sections of rope.

To understand how the Egyptian rope stretchers made their right triangles, complete the following problems.

1. Use 12 paper clips to create a chain. Use your paper clip chain to create a right triangle like the ones the Egyptians made from rope. Draw a sketch of the triangle you create. Label the number of paper clips on each side and the location of what you believe is the right angle.

   Students should create a 3, 4, 5 right triangle. The hypotenuse should be 5 paper clips long.

2. Give reasons to support your belief that your triangle is a right triangle.

   Answers may vary. Sample answers include choosing to justify an answer using the Pythagorean Theorem to show that $5^2 = 3^2 + 4^2$; or justifying an answer by measuring the angle with the corner of a sheet of paper or a note card.

3. Form another triangle, with side lengths different from your original triangle, using a chain of 12 paper clips. What are the lengths of the sides? What is the best name for the triangle you made?

   Answers may vary. Sample answers: A 4, 4, 4 equilateral triangle and a 5, 5, 2 isosceles triangle.

Verifying Right Triangles

Activity Focus
• Verifying Right Triangles

Materials
• Paper clips (40 per group)

Chunking the Activity

#1–3	#7	#11
#4–5	#8–10	#12
#6		

TEACHER TO TEACHER Seeing a map of Egypt may help students to visualize the Nile River and its boundaries.

1 Create Representations, Debrief Students should hook the 12 paper clips together to create a chain. Where the paper clips meet represents the knots on the rope and the paper clips themselves represent the space between the knots on the rope.

2 Activating Prior Knowledge, Think/Pair/Share, Debrief Students will have varying levels of experience with this concept. It is acceptable for students to use the corner of a note card or piece of paper to show that the corner of the triangle is a right angle. It is also acceptable for students to use the Pythagorean Theorem to prove that the angle is a right angle if they are able to. Have students debrief their methods. This question serves as formative assessment of student knowledge regarding use of the Pythagorean Theorem.

3 Activating Prior Knowledge, Create Representations, Debrief Students should be able to show that this triangle is not a right triangle and tell what type of triangle it is. Debriefing the triangles made and the type that they are is good review of geometry concepts for students. Students may classify the triangles made by side or by angle or both. This information can be posted in the classroom as review.

4 Create Representations, Think/Pair/Share, Debrief Students will need to create chains with the specified number of paper clips and make triangles with the correct number of paper clips in each side. At this point, they are using a note card to determine if the triangles are right or not. They will confirm their choices using the Pythagorean Theorem in the next question.

5 Look for a Pattern, Think/Pair/Share, Debrief Students now use the Pythagorean Theorem to check their work from Item 4. Have students debrief their answers to check for accuracy. This is an opportune time to review the $\neq$ sign. Students may not recall that this sign can be used in the equations where c^2 does not equal $a^2 + b^2$.

My Notes

4. Use paper clip chains to create triangles having the given side lengths. Use a corner of a notecard to test the largest angle of each triangle for a right angle and predict whether or not the given triangles are right triangles. Draw and label a sketch of each triangle formed.

Triangle side lengths	Right Triangle?	Pictorial Representation	Triangle side lengths	Right Triangle?	Pictorial Representation
6, 8, 10	Yes		4, 12, 14	No	
5, 9, 10	No		9, 15, 16	No	
5, 12, 13	Yes		8, 15, 17	Yes	

5. Using $c^2 = a^2 + b^2$, verify your predictions for each triangle in Item 4.

Students should show work to indicate each of the following:
$$10^2 = 6^2 + 8^2$$
$$10^2 \neq 5^2 + 9^2$$
$$13^2 = 5^2 + 12^2$$
$$14^2 \neq 12^2 + 4^2$$
$$16^2 \neq 15^2 + 9^2$$
$$17^2 = 15^2 + 8^2$$

Verifying Right Triangles
Paper Clip Chains

SUGGESTED LEARNING STRATEGIES: Look for a Pattern,
Quickwrite, Create Representations, Think/Pair/Share,
Interactive Word Wall

My Notes

6. If the sides of a triangle satisfy the equation $c^2 = a^2 + b^2$, what
can be said about the triangle? What must be true about c?

It is a right triangle, and c must be the hypotenuse.

7. Do the following sets of side lengths form right triangles? Justify
your response.

a. 7, 24, 25   Yes; $25^2 = 24^2 + 7^2$

b. 6, 12, 13   No; $13^2 \neq 12^2 + 6^2$

c. 9, 12, 15   Yes; $15^2 = 12^2 + 9^2$

8. A Pythagorean Triple is a group of three whole numbers that
satisfies the equation $c^2 = a^2 + b^2$. List 3 Pythagorean triples
from Items 1 through 7 in the first column of the table below.
Multiply each Pythagorean Triple by 2. Is the new set of
numbers a Pythagorean Triple? Repeat by multiplying
each original set of numbers by 3.

Answers may vary. Sample answer:

Pythagorean Triple	Multiply by 2	Pythagorean Triple?	Multiply by 3	Pythagorean Triple?
3, 4, 5	6, 8, 10	Yes	9, 12, 15	Yes
5, 12, 13	10, 24, 26	Yes	15, 36, 39	Yes
8, 15, 17	16, 30, 34	Yes	24, 45, 51	Yes

9. Predict how many Pythagorean triples can be created by
multiplying the side lengths in a known triple by a constant.

An infinite number of Pythagorean Triples can be created by
multiplying the side lengths in a known triple by a constant.

6 Look for a Pattern,
Quickwrite, Debrief Students
are generalizing what is true
about a triangle that satisfies
the Pythagorean Theorem. Have
students debrief their answers so
that a variety of explanations can
be heard by the group.

Suggested Assignment

CHECK YOUR UNDERSTANDING
p. 314, #1–2

UNIT 6 PRACTICE
p. 339, #13–17

7 Create Representations,
Think/Pair/Share, Debrief Have
students compare their work for
accuracy.

8 Create Representations,
Debrief, Interactive Word
Wall This question can be done
using groups or Think/Pair/Share
to save time if needed. Students
should discuss solutions to this
item so that they see that each
of the Pythagorean Triples from
Items 1–7 is still a Pythagorean
Triple when multiplied by 2 or 3.
The term Pythagorean Triple can
be added to the Interactive Word
Wall.

9 Quickwrite, Debrief

10 Think/Pair/Share, Group Presentation A classroom list can be generated on chart paper for this question. It could be left open-ended for further investigation, with students adding more Pythagorean Triples as they discover them.

11 Quickwrite, Debrief Sharing the responses to this question can serve as formative assessment of student understanding that any triangle that has side lengths that form a Pythagorean Triple is a right triangle. Listen carefully to what reasoning students use to justify their responses.

12 Think/Pair/Share, Group Presentation Students may not see the two groupings at first. Employ questioning strategies that guide the class to notice that that some of these triples are primitive triples and others are multiples of these. The vocabulary term "primitive triples" can be introduced here if you wish.

Suggested Assignment

CHECK YOUR UNDERSTANDING
p. 314, #3–5

UNIT 6 PRACTICE
p. 339, #18–20

CHECK YOUR UNDERSTANDING

1. No, $13^2 \neq 10^2 + 11^2$

2. Yes, $1^2 = \left(\frac{4}{5}\right)^2 + \left(\frac{3}{5}\right)^2$

3. Yes, the numbers are all whole numbers, and $41^2 = 40^2 + 9^2$.

4. Answers may vary. Sample responses are: 6, 8, 10; 9, 12, 15; 12, 16, 20; 15, 20, 25

5. Yes. They will be fractions, and therefore not Pythagorean Triples, but they will satisfy $c^2 = a^2 + b^2$.

SUGGESTED LEARNING STRATEGIES: Think/Pair/Share, Group Presentation, Quickwrite

My Notes

10. List as many Pythagorean triples as you can that include the number 24. Answers may vary. Sample answers:

7, 24, 25	10, 24, 26	24, 45, 51
18, 24, 30	24, 32, 40	

11. The three numbers in a Pythagorean triple are the side lengths of what kind of triangle? Justify your response.

A right triangle. Any Pythagorean Triple satisfies the equation $c^2 = a^2 + b^2$.

12. Below are sets of triangle side lengths. Sort the sets of lengths into two groups. Explain how you grouped the sets.

3, 4, 5	6, 8, 10	5, 12, 13	14, 48, 50
10, 24, 26	8, 15, 17	9, 12, 15	16, 30, 34
7, 24, 25	20, 48, 52	24, 45, 51	12, 16, 20

Answers may vary. Sample answer:

Primitive Triples	Multiples
3, 4, 5	6, 8, 10
	12, 16, 20
7, 24, 25	14, 48, 50
8, 15, 17	10, 24, 26
5, 12, 13	9, 12, 15
	16, 30, 34
	20, 48, 52
	24, 45, 51

CHECK YOUR UNDERSTANDING

Write your answers on notebook paper. Show your work.

1. Determine whether 10, 11 and 13 can be the sides of a right triangle. Justify your answer.

2. Determine whether $\frac{4}{5}$, $\frac{3}{5}$ and 1 can be the sides of a right triangle. Justify your answer.

3. Is 9, 40, 41 a Pythagorean triple? Explain your reasoning.

4. 3, 4, 5 is a Pythagorean triple. Give 4 other Pythagorean triples that can be generated from this one.

5. **MATHEMATICAL REFLECTION** If you multiply a Pythagorean triple by a number between 0 and 1, will the resulting numbers be the sides of a right triangle?

Right Triangles
CAMP EUCLID

Sam is spending part of his summer vacation at Camp Euclid with some of his friends. On the first day of camp, they must pass an open water swimming test to be allowed to use the canoes, kayaks, and personal watercraft. Sam and his friends must be able to swim across the river that they will be boating on. The river is 30 meters wide. On the day of the test, Sam begins on one bank and tries to swim directly across the river to the point on the opposite bank where his counselor is waiting. Because the river has a slight current, Sam ends up 35 meters downstream from his counselor.

1. Label the diagram for the problem situation.

2. How far did Sam actually swim? Justify your answer.

3. Sam's friend Alex started at the same spot but swam 50 meters. How far downstream was he from their counselor when he arrived at the opposite bank? Justify your answer.

In a lake fed by the river, a triangular area marked with buoys is roped off for swimming during free time at camp. The distances between each pair of buoys are 40 meters, 50 meters, and 60 meters.

4. Draw and label a diagram for the problem situation.

5. Is the swimming area a right triangle? Justify your answer.

6. Find the missing side length in each of the following triangles. Show all your work.

a.

b.

c.

Assessment Focus
• The Pythagorean theorem

Materials
• No additional materials are required.

1 Students need to analyze the material given in the introductory paragraph by labeling the diagram of the problem situation. They should notice the right triangle from the diagram by its symbol.

2 Students solve for the distance Sam swims, the hypotenuse, using the Pythagorean theorem.

3 This question requires that students notice they are solving for a leg of the right triangle instead of the hypotenuse.

4 Students are asked to create a diagram from given information.

5 In this question, students use the Pythagorean theorem to prove that this triangle is not a right triangle. Be sure to look for student reasoning on this question.

6 Students need to show their work for finding the lengths of the missing measures for each of these triangles.

Answer Key

2. He swam 46.1 meters.

3. He was 40 meters from the counselor.

4.
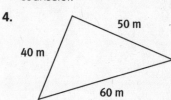

5. No. $60^2 \neq 40^2 + 50^2$

6a. $b = 15$

b. $a = 7$

c. $4\sqrt{2} \approx 5.66$

Embedded Assessment 1

7 Students need to show their work for determining which of the sets of side lengths shown are Pythagorean triples and which are not.

Answer Key

7a. Yes, 9, 40, 41 is a Pythagorean triple.

b. No, $31^2 \neq 20^2 + 21^2$

c. Yes, $\left(\frac{10}{7}\right)^2 = \left(\frac{8}{7}\right)^2 + \left(\frac{6}{7}\right)^2$

TEACHER TO TEACHER — You may wish to read through the rubric with students and discuss the differences in the expectation levels. Make sure students understand the meanings of any terms used.

Right Triangles
CAMP EUCLID

7. Determine which of the following sets of triangle side lengths form right triangles. Justify each response.

   a. 9, 40, 41

   b. 20, 21, 31

   c. $\frac{6}{7}, \frac{8}{7}, \frac{10}{7}$

	Exemplary	Proficient	Emerging
Math Knowledge 6a–c	The student finds the three correct missing lengths. (6a–c)	The student finds only two correct lengths.	The student finds fewer than two correct lengths.
Problem Solving 2, 3, 5, 7a–c	The student: • Finds the distance that Sam actually swam. (2) • Finds the distance that Alex was from the counselor. (3) • Correctly determines whether the swimming area is a right triangle. (5) • Correctly determines whether the three sets of side lengths form right triangles. (7a–c)	The student: • Uses a correct method to find the distance but makes a computational error. • Uses a correct method to find the distance but makes a computational error. • Correctly determines whether only two sets form right triangles.	The student: • Does not find the correct distance. • Does not find the correct distance. • Incorrectly determines whether the area is a right triangle. • Correctly determines whether fewer than two sets form right triangles.
Representations 1, 4	The student: • Labels the diagram to correctly reflect the situation. (1) • Draws and labels the diagram to correctly reflect the situation. (4)	The student: • Puts some, but not all, correct labels on the diagram. • Draws the diagram correctly but some of the labels are incorrect.	The student: • Puts no correct labels on the diagram. • Does not draw a correct diagram.
Communication 2, 3, 5, 6a–c	The student: • Correctly justifies the distance Sam swam. (2) • Correctly justifies the distance Alex was from the counselor. (3) • Justifies the decision as to whether the swimming area is a right triangle. (5) • Shows correct work to find the missing lengths. (6a–c)	The student: • Gives an incomplete justification. (2) • Gives an incomplete justification. (3) • Gives an incomplete justification. (5) • Shows some, but not all, correct work. (6a–c)	The student: • Gives an incorrect justification. (2) • Gives an incorrect justification. (3) • Gives an incorrect justification. (5) • Shows no correct work. (6a–c)

Surface Area of Solids
The Gift Box

SUGGESTED LEARNING STRATEGIES: Activating Prior Knowledge

J.T. is the creative director for a paper products company. The company is introducing a new line of gift boxes, called *No Wrapping Required*, for hard-to-wrap gifts. The boxes come in a variety of shapes, sizes, colors, and themes for birthdays, anniversaries, and holidays.

1. Match each of the following gift boxes with the net used to create it. Give the most appropriate geometric name for each gift box.

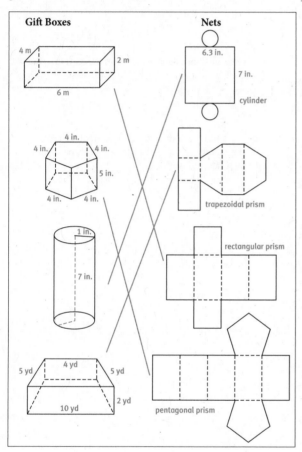

Gift Boxes — Nets

trapezoidal prism
rectangular prism
pentagonal prism
cylinder

My Notes

ACADEMIC VOCABULARY

A **solid** is a three-dimensional figure having length, width, and height.

Surface Area of Solids

Activity Focus
• Surface Area of Solids

Materials
• 8 by 11 inch paper to create prisms
• Gift boxes (optional)

Chunking the Activity

#1	#4–5	#10–14	#20–21
#2	#6	#15–18	#22–24
#3	#7–9	#19	#25

TEACHER TO TEACHER Ask students to bring in gift boxes that they may have at home. If it is possible, unfold the gift boxes so that students can see what two-dimensional shapes were used in the creation of the three-dimensional gift box.

1 Activating Prior Knowledge, Debrief Students will have varying levels of familiarity with nets. This question allows students to discuss how nets and the figures formed by them are related. Students should be able to explain how the different shapes in the net are represented in the sketches.

The term *solid* from the Academic Vocabulary box on this page should be included on the Interactive Word Wall.

You may need to review the meaning of prism (a three-dimensional figure with two congruent parallel bases that are both polygons) and have students add this word to the interactive word wall.

ACTIVITY 6.3 Continued

2 Interactive Word Wall, Identify a Subtask, Debrief After the students read the introduction to this question, have them add the term *lateral face* to the Interactive Word Wall. After they read Part b, have them add the term *lateral area* to the Interactive Word Wall, too. Student work on this question should be debriefed so that students recognize that all of the faces on this prism are congruent. Students also should recognize that lateral area does not include the bases. This may be a new concept for them as they may be accustomed to finding surface area.

My Notes

MATH TERMS

The **lateral face** of a prism is any face that is not the base of the prism. The word lateral means "related to the side."

A **lateral face** of a solid is a face that is not a base. A right prism is a prism in which the lateral faces are rectangles and are perpendicular to the bases.

2. Examine the right hexagonal prism below.

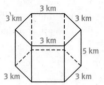

a. Give the dimensions of each lateral face in the solid, and then find the area of each lateral face. Show your work.

Dimensions: 3 km by 5 km

Area of each lateral face: 15 km; $3 \cdot 5 = 15$

b. The **lateral area** of a solid is the sum of the areas of the lateral faces. Find the lateral area of the solid. Show all your work.

$L = 90$ km^2; $15 \cdot 6 = 90$

SUGGESTED LEARNING STRATEGIES: Create Representations, Think/Pair/Share, Group Presentation

3. Use the right triangular prism below to complete parts (a)–(f).

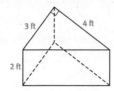

a. Sketch each base and label its dimensions.

b. Sketch each lateral face and label its dimensions.

c. Find the lateral area, L, of the prism. Show all calculations.
$L = 24 \text{ ft}^2$

d. Find the perimeter of the base, P.
$L = 12 \text{ ft}$

e. Multiply the perimeter of the base, P, times the height of the prism, h.
24 ft^2

f. Compare your responses to parts (c) and (e). What do you notice?
They are both 24 ft^2

My Notes

MATH TIP

Area of a Triangle:

$A = \frac{1}{2}bh$ where b represents the length of the base of the triangle and h represents the height of the triangle.

3 Create Representations, Think/Pair/Share, Group Presentation Students may ask about the dimension for the third side of the triangular base. Since students have worked with the Pythagorean Theorem in the two previous activities, they can use it to solve for the hypotenuse, or they may simply recognize 3, 4, 5 as a Pythagorean Triple.

Students should recognize that the lateral faces on this prism are not congruent. Their sketches should reflect this. Presenting their sketches to the class will allow students to see the sketches of others and edit their own.

Students may not be aware of the relationship between lateral area and perimeter. Part f needs to be discussed thoroughly so that all students note that Parts c and e give the same answer, just using two different methods. This relationship will be further explored in the following questions.

4 Create Representations, Look for Patterns, Debrief, Group Presentation This question can be done in groups in order to save time. Each group can work with one of the prisms. The groups will need to share out the data for their prisms on a large classroom chart. If groups are not used, be sure that students review their answers for accuracy. The students should discuss the completed table and look for patterns in it. Specifically, they should notice the relationship between perimeter, height, and lateral area.

5 Quickwrite, Debrief Students should have noticed from the table that there is a relationship between lateral area and perimeter and height in the previous question. Now they are being asked to formalize the relationship. Make sure that students know what the variables in this question mean prior to having students write the formula.

My Notes

SUGGESTED LEARNING STRATEGIES: Create Representations, Look for a Pattern, Group Presentation, Quickwrite

4. Complete the table below using what you know about prisms.

Prism	Lateral Area	Labeled Sketch of Base	Perimeter of Base	Height of Prism
4 m, 2 m, 6 m	40 m²	6 m, 4 m, 4 m, 6 m	20 m	2 m
4 in., 4 in., 4 in., 5 in., 4 in., 4 in.	100 in.²	4 in., 4 in., 4 in., 4 in., 4 in.	20 in	5 in
5 yd, 4 yd, 5 yd, 2 yd, 10 yd	48 yd²	4 yd, 5 yd, 5 yd, 10 yd	24 yd	2 yd

> **MATH TIP**
>
> **Area of a Trapezoid:**
> $A = \frac{1}{2}h(b_1 + b_2)$, where b_1 and b_2 are the lengths of the bases of a trapezoid and h is the height of the trapezoid.

5. Use variables P, h, and L to explain how to find the lateral area, L, of a prism.

$L = Ph$

Surface Area of Solids
The Gift Box

SUGGESTED LEARNING STRATEGIES: Identify a Subtask, Visualization, Quickwrite

My Notes

6. Find the lateral area, L, for each of the following solids.

a.

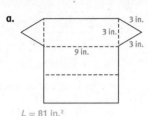

$L = 81$ in.²

b.

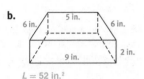

$L = 52$ in.²

c. a rectangular prism with height 10 mm and a square base with side length 4 mm

160 mm²

7. The **surface area** of a prism is the sum of the areas of the lateral faces and the areas of the bases. Describe the relationship between the lateral area and the surface area of a prism.

Answers may vary. Sample answer: Since surface area is found by adding the lateral area and the areas of the bases of the prism, the surface area is larger than the lateral area.

WRITING MATH
Surface area is represented by *SA* or by *T* in an expression.

6 Identify a Subtask, Debrief This question provides formative assessment regarding the students' ability to find lateral area. Note whether students use the formula that they wrote in Item 5 or use the method of finding the area of each side and then adding to find the total. If students are still using the latter, have groups present their work so that both methods are shown and students can see that the formula is actually less work for them. If students struggle on Part c, encourage them to sketch the prism.

TEACHER TO TEACHER If students need more practice finding lateral area, use a variety of everyday objects in the shape of prisms. Students can measure the objects using a ruler and find the lateral area based on their measures. Have more than one group do the same object so that measures and lateral areas can be compared.

7 Visualization, Quickwrite, Debrief Students have familiarity with surface area from previous courses. Students may need to discuss this term to review it before answering the question. While the phrasing of the question does guide the answer, the important thing all students should take away from this item is that surface area is distinct from lateral area. Surface area will always be greater.

ACTIVITY 6.3
continued

8-9 Identify a Subtask, Think/Pair/Share, Group Presentation Have groups present their work on these questions to compare methods for solving and to check for accuracy. Encourage students to use the formula they found in Item 5 when finding the lateral area. Students may need to sketch the prism in Item 9b.

Differentiating Instruction

Students may practice finding surface area with the same objects they used for further practice in finding lateral area. This can prove helpful to students as they already know the lateral area and can make the connection that they need to only find the areas of the bases and add this total to their previous work.

Suggested Assignment

CHECK YOUR UNDERSTANDING
p. 328, #1–3

UNIT 6 PRACTICE
p. 340, #21, 23, 24, 27, 28

Connect to **AP**

Many applications of surface area and volume exist in the calculus curriculum. At the most basic level, a definite integral can be thought of as a product of a fixed *x* and variable *y*, similar to areas of plane figures being a product of two dimensions. Surface area and volume computations for various solid figures can also be computed using a definite integral. Students in middle school need a firm grounding in the concepts of area, surface area, and volume. They only need to memorize the most basic area formulas and the general formula for volume ($V = Bh$, where B is the area of the base). Other formulas are provided on the Advanced Placement Exam.

This activity will help students to understand that surface area is dependent on the sums of the

---

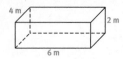

ACTIVITY 6.3 Surface Area of Solids
continued The Gift Box

SUGGESTED LEARNING STRATEGIES: Identify a Subtask, Think/Pair/Share, Group Presentation

My Notes

MATH TIP

$1 m^2 = 10,000 cm^2$

$1 yd^2 = 9 ft^2$

$1 ft^2 = 144 in.^2$

8. Consider these gift boxes from the first page of this activity.

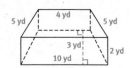

a. Find the surface area of each box. Show all your calculations.
rectangular prism: 88 m²; $L = Ph$, $L = 20 \cdot 2 = 40$ m²;
A(Bases) $= 6 \cdot 4 \cdot 2 = 48$ m²; $L + A$(Bases) $= 88$ m²
trapezoidal prism: 90 yd²; $L = 24 \cdot 2 = 48$ yd²; A(Bases) $=$
$2 \cdot \frac{1}{2} \cdot 3(10 + 4) = 42$ yd²; $L + A$(Bases) $= 90$ yd²

b. Sometimes, you may need to express a measurement in different units from the ones given. Express the surface area of the above-left box in square centimeters.
880,000 cm²

c. What is the surface area of the above-right box in square feet?
810 ft²

9. Find the surface area for each of the following solids.

a.
$T = 150.08$ cm²

CONNECT TO **AP**

There are many applications of surface area and volume in calculus.

b. A right triangular prism has a height 6 cm. The base of the triangular base is 3 cm and the height of the triangular base is 4 cm.
$T = 84$ cm²

c. Express the surface area you found in 9b in square meters.
0.0084 m²

---

areas of each side of a figure. To take the work in this activity a bit further, work with students on solving the formulas in this activity and the following activity for different variables. For example, solve the following equation for the total surface area of a cylinder for *h*.

Given:

$SA = 2\pi r^2 + 2\pi rh$

Solution:

$SA = 2\pi r^2 + 2\pi rh$

$SA - 2\pi r^2 = 2\pi rh$

$\dfrac{SA - 2\pi r^2}{2\pi r} = \dfrac{2\pi rh}{2\pi r}$

$h = \dfrac{SA - 2\pi r^2}{2\pi r}$

Surface Area of Solids
The Gift Box

SUGGESTED LEARNING STRATEGIES: Use Manipulatives, Debrief, Activating Prior Knowledge, Quickwrite, Look for a Pattern

My Notes

10. Fold a piece of 8.5 by 11 in paper into the prism that your teacher has assigned you.

Check students' work.

11. As the number of sides increases, what shape is the base getting closer to?

a circle

12. As the number of sides increases what is happening to the perimeter of the base?

Answers may vary. Sample answer: As the number of sides increases, the perimeter of the base is approaching the circumference of a circle.

13. Using your answers to Items 11 and 12, describe how you would determine the lateral area of the cylinder in Item 1.

Sample answer: To find the lateral area of a cylinder, find the circumference of the base and then multiply it by the height of the cylinder.

14. Using your answers to Items 11 and 12, describe how you would find the surface area of the cylinder.

Sample answer: To find the surface area of a cylinder, add the areas of the two circular bases to the lateral area of the cylinder.

15. Find the lateral area and the surface area of the cylinder from Item 1. Show all calculations.

$L = 2\pi(1) \cdot 7 = 14\pi$ in.²; $A(\text{bases}) = 2\pi(1)^2 = 2\pi$ in.²;
$T = 14\pi + 2\pi = 16\pi$ in.² ≈ 50.3 in.²

16. How does the way you find the surface area of a prism compare with the way you find the surface area of a cylinder?

Sample answer: The methods for finding the surface area of a prism and the surface area of a cylinder are very similar. In a prism, you use the perimeter of the base while in a cylinder you use the circumference of the base. Both are multiplied by the height and both include the areas of the two bases.

15 Look for a Pattern, Debrief Students should use the ideas they wrote about in Items 13 and 14 to find the lateral and surface area of the cylinder. Debrief to compare work and check for accuracy.

16 Quickwrite, Debrief

ACTIVITY 6.3 Continued

10-12 Use Manipulatives, Debrief This question allows students to discover, via visualization, that as the number of sides in a regular prism increases, the prism approaches the shape of a cylinder. Students will fold 8.5" by 11" sheets of paper into different regular prisms. The paper needs to be folded in such a way that the 11" edge will become the perimeter of the base when the prism is formed. As shown in the image below.

The following fractional parts can be used as the number of folds for each group or student:

$$\frac{1}{2}, \frac{1}{3}, \frac{1}{4}, \frac{1}{6}, \frac{1}{8}, \frac{1}{12}, \frac{1}{16} \cdots$$

Example:

Triangular Prism, 3 folds

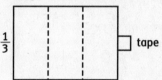

The students should tape the short edges together, and line their shapes up in a series so that they can answer Items 11 and 12. It is necessary that all folds be in the same direction so that the paper makes a tube.

Each group in the classroom can be assigned a certain number of folds, or one student in each group can be responsible for a certain number.

13-14 Activating Prior Knowledge, Quickwrite, Debrief Debrief the class after these questions so that it can come out that the formula they wrote in Item 5 still applies when finding the lateral area of a cylinder. The difference is that instead of referring to perimeter, the formula would refer to circumference. Students should also note that the method they used earlier for finding surface area of a prism still applies when working with cylinders.

17-18 Create Representations, Think/Pair/Share, Debrief This question serves as practice and formative assessment regarding students' ability to find the lateral and surface areas of a cylinder. Be sure to debrief to compare student work and check for accuracy.

TEACHER TO TEACHER If students need additional practice in finding the lateral and surface areas of a cylinder, everyday examples of cylinders can be used. Students can measure these using a ruler, and then calculate the lateral and surface areas.

Suggested Assignment

CHECK YOUR UNDERSTANDING
p. 328, #4

UNIT 6 PRACTICE
p. 340, #22, 26

19 Activating Prior Knowledge, Quickwrite, Think/Pair/Share, Debrief You want students to notice that the formula for lateral area that they've been using will not work for pyramids. Instead, they may have to revert to finding the area of each piece and adding them as they did prior to discovering the formula in Item 5. In Part c, students are given dimensions and asked to find the lateral and surface areas of this prism. Debrief to compare methods and check for accuracy.

My Notes

17. Draw a 3-dimensional sketch of a cylinder and a net for the same cylinder with height 6 inches and base radius 4 inches.

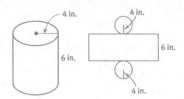

18. Find the lateral area and surface area of the cylinder in Item 17.

$L = 48\pi \approx 150.8$ in^2
$T = 80\pi \approx 251.3$ in

19. Use the net below to respond to parts (a)–(c).

a. Describe the solid that can be created from the net.

square pyramid

b. Describe what you would do to find the lateral area and the surface area of the solid created from the net.

Answers may vary. Sample answer: To find the lateral area, find the area of the four triangles. To find the surface area, find the area of the four triangles and add the area of the square base.

SUGGESTED LEARNING STRATEGIES: Interactive Word Wall,
Create Representations, Quickwrite

c. Assume the perimeter of the square base is 24 cm and the height of each of the triangular faces is 5 cm. Label the dimensions and find the lateral area and the surface area of the solid. Show all your work.

$L = \frac{1}{2}(5 \cdot 6) \cdot 4 = 60$ cm²; A(base) $= 6^2 = 36$ cm²;
$T = L + A$(base) $= 96$ cm²

20. In a pyramid, the height of each of the triangular lateral faces is called the **slant height** of the pyramid. The slant height is represented by the letter, l.

a. On the net, draw the segment that represents the slant height.

b. Describe the difference between the slant height, l, and the height, h, of the pyramid.

Answers may vary. Sample answer: The slant height, l, is the height of the triangular face and a measure of the distance from the base of a pyramid to the vertex along a lateral face. The height, h, is the perpendicular distance from the base to the vertex measured in the center of the pyramid.

My Notes

MATH TERMS

The **slant height** is the distance measured from the base of the figure along a lateral face to the top of the figure.

MATH TERMS

The **lateral faces** in a pyramid are triangles that intersect at the vertex of the pyramid.

ACTIVITY 6.3 *Continued*

20 Interactive Word Wall, Create Representations, Quickwrite, Debrief After reading Item 20, add the term *slant height* to the Interactive Word Wall. Have students review this question to be sure that they have drawn in the slant heights at the correct place on the net of the pyramid. Students should understand that the height of the pyramid will be less than the slant height due to the inclination of the lateral faces of the pyramid. This can be illustrated using a cut out net of a pyramid.

21 Create Representations, Think/Pair/Share, Debrief, Interactive Word Wall This question takes students through the steps necessary to show that the formula for the lateral area of a pyramid is similar to the formula the lateral area of a prism that they developed in Item 5. Students will discover that the lateral area of the pyramid is $\frac{1}{2}$ of the total area found by multiplying the perimeter by the slant height. This may make sense to some students as the formula for the area of a triangle is $\frac{1}{2}bh$. If this point is discussed, others may note the same relationship. Part e asks students to write the formula for finding the lateral area of a pyramid. Be sure to discuss this and add it to the Interactive Word Wall.

My Notes

SUGGESTED LEARNING STRATEGIES: Create Representations, Think/Pair/Share, Interactive Word Wall

21. Consider a square pyramid with base edges 12 cm and slant height 10 cm.

   a. Draw a net and label the dimensions of the base edges and the slant height.

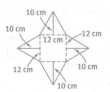

   b. Find the lateral area of the pyramid.
   $L = 240$ cm²

   c. Find the perimeter of the base of the pyramid.
   $P = 48$ cm

   d. Multiply the perimeter of the base by the slant height.
   $Pl = 480$ cm²

   e. What is the relationship between the lateral area of the pyramid and the product of the perimeter of the base and the slant height?
   Answers may vary. Sample answer: The lateral area is $\frac{1}{2}$ the product of the perimeter of the base and the slant height.

   f. Explain how P and l can be used to find the lateral area, L, of a pyramid.
   $L = \frac{1}{2}Pl$

SUGGESTED LEARNING STRATEGIES: Activating Prior Knowledge, Quickwrite, Create Representations, Identify a Subtask, Think/Pair/Share, RAFT

My Notes

22. Describe the relationship between the lateral area and the surface area of a pyramid.

Answers may vary. Sample answer: The surface area is larger than the lateral area. The surface area includes the area of the base.

23. Find the surface area, T, of the pyramid in Item 21.

$T = 384$ cm²

24. Find the lateral area and surface area of a square pyramid with base perimeter 64 in. and slant height 12 inches. Show all your work.

$L = \frac{1}{2}(64)(12) = 384$ in.²; $A(\text{base}) = 16^2 = 256$ in.²;
$T = L + A(\text{base}) = 640$ in.²

25. J.T. needs to expand the inventory of gift boxes *No Wrapping Required* keeps in stock.

   a. He knows he wants to include a triangular pyramid. The base will be an equilateral triangle base with 2 inch sides. The slant height of the pyramid needs to be 3 inches. Draw a net for the new box, find the lateral and surface area, and build the box.

$L = 9$ in.²
$T \approx 10.7$ in.²

   b. Write a proposal for J.T. explaining what other sizes of boxes shaped as prisms, cylinders, or pyramids he should include in his inventory expansion. Provide him with the dimensions and amount of materials needed to build three new boxes. Be sure to include a prism, a cylinder, and a pyramid.

Answers may vary. Students should include a prism, a cylinder and a pyramid. Student responses should include the linear dimensions of each box as well as the surface area of each.

---

22 Activating Prior Knowledge, Quickwrite, Debrief Students should note that the ideas they have stated previously regarding lateral area and surface area still hold true. Pyramids are not an exception to this.

23-25 Create Representations, Identify a Subtask, Think/Pair/Share, Activating Prior Knowledge, RAFT, Debrief Students will practice finding the lateral and surface areas of pyramids. In Item 23, students are adding the base on to the lateral area that they have already found. Item 24 may be easier for some students if they draw a sketch of the figure, since the dimensions are given but no sketch is included. Item 25a takes students back to the context of the activity, asking them to draw a net and find lateral and surface area of a gift box with the given dimensions. This is preparation for Item 25b, which allows students to explore other sizes of gift boxes. Also in 25a, students will have to use the Pythagorean Theorem to find the height of the base.

In 25b, students are writing as if they are employees at the paper products company. The directions ask for a prism, a cylinder and a pyramid. The teacher may ask for a certain number of each type. Students may work in groups on this, or work individually. In addition, the teacher may choose to set parameters for the style and content of this RAFT so that the proposal is similar to one used in business.

Suggested Assignment

CHECK YOUR UNDERSTANDING
p. 328, #5–6

UNIT 6 PRACTICE
p. 340, #25

CHECK YOUR UNDERSTANDING

1. $L = 45$ in.^{2}

2. $L = 88$ in.^{2}
   $T = 148$ in.^{2}

3. $L = 48$ in.^{2}
   $T = 60$ in.^{2}

4. $L = 36\pi$ in.$^2 \approx 113.1$ in.^{2}
   $T = 54\pi$ in.$^2 \approx 169.6$ in.^{2}

5. $T = 340$ cm^2

6. 0.034 m^2

7. Answers may vary. Sample answer: In both the prism and the pyramid, you find the perimeter of the base, P. However, in the prism you multiply P by the height of the figure, and in a pyramid you use $\frac{1}{2}P$ and then multiply by the slant height.

CHECK YOUR UNDERSTANDING

Write your answers on notebook paper. Show your work.

1. Find the lateral area of the pentagonal prism created from the net shown below.

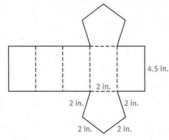

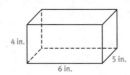
4.5 in.
2 in.
2 in.   2 in.
2 in.   2 in.

2. Find the lateral area and surface area of the rectangular prism shown below.

4 in.
5 in.
6 in.

3. Find the lateral and surface area of the right triangular prism shown below.

5 in.
4 in.
3 in.
4 in.

4. Find the lateral and surface area of the cylinder below.

6 in.
3 in.

5. Find the surface area of the square pyramid shown below.

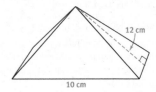
12 cm
10 cm

6. What is the surface area of the pyramid above in square meters?

7. **MATHEMATICAL REFLECTION** Describe the similarities and differences in how you would find the lateral areas of a prism and a pyramid that have congruent bases.

Volume of Solids
Castles in the Sand

SUGGESTED LEARNING STRATEGIES: Shared Reading, Activating Prior Knowledge

The eighth grade class at LWH middle school in Montana hosted a spring festival to raise money for their end-of-year trip to the beach. They decided to sponsor a sand castle building contest as a part of the festivities. Because the sand for the sand castles had to be trucked in to the school, students who wanted to participate in the castle building contest were required to submit a proposal to Archie Medes, the geometry teacher. The proposals had to contain a sketch of the castle the student or group of students wanted to build, a list of the solids used and their dimensions, and the volume of sand required to build it.

Shayla wanted to enter the contest. She decided to research castles to help brainstorm ideas for her proposal. One of the castles she looked at was Fantasy Castle in a nearby theme park.

1. What solids would Shayla need to use to build a sand replica of the Fantasy Castle? Answers may vary. Sample answers: prism, cylinder, pyramid, cone

Shayla's friend Shelly built last year's winning castle out of prisms, pyramids, cylinders, cones, and spheres. To help Shayla prepare for the contest, Shelly showed Shayla her plans from last year and explained how she determined the amount of sand she would need to build her winning castle.

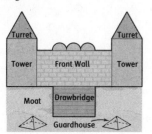

My Notes

Volume of Solids

Activity Focus
• Volume of Solids

Materials
• Construction paper or poster board for Question 10 (optional)

Chunking the Activity

#1	#4–5	#8
#2	#6	#9
#3	#7	#10

TEACHER TO TEACHER Students may not be overly familiar with castles and the common parts of a castle that are going to be used to find volume in this activity. Having pictures of different castles in the classroom, and talking about the various parts of a castle may prove helpful.

1 Shared Reading, Activating Prior Knowledge, Debrief Students should share reading the introduction to this question and discuss various castles that they may have seen. Students may see a variety of solids when looking at the picture of this castle for Item 1. Discussing the solids that the students see will help all students to identify the variety of solids that exist in this castle and recall their properties.

TEACHER TO TEACHER Items 2–7 ask students to sketch a solid and find its volume. If students struggle with any of the solids, time can be taken out of the activity to practice finding the volume of that type of solid using several examples. Making a classroom poster of these formulas, or putting them on the Interactive Word Wall can be helpful as well.

2 Create Representations, Think/Pair/Share, Group Presentation Students should share their sketches, work, and answers with the group. As the activity develops, continue to work with students on labeling their sketches accurately by placing the dimensions where they belong in the sketch. Group presentations will help with this process, allowing students to view the work of others, and edit their own.

3 Create Representations, Think/Pair/Share, Group Presentation Be sure that students do not confuse the height, 9 inches, with the slant height of the pyramid. Since both types of heights were discussed in the previous activity, this offers a good opportunity for the students to review the concepts.

4 Create Representations, Think/Pair/Share, Group Presentation Have the students share their sketches, work, and answers for both parts of this problem. Students may need to discuss the term *diameter* in their groups before labeling it. A common mistake is to confuse the terms radius, diameter, and circumference.

My Notes

MATH TiP

The variables commonly used in volume formulas to represent quantities are:

$V \rightarrow$ volume
$B \rightarrow$ area of the base of the solid
$h \rightarrow$ height of the solid
$P \rightarrow$ perimeter of the base of the solid

MATH TiP

In the volume formula for a cylinder, $V = \pi r^2 h$, πr^2 represents the area of the base of the solid.

2. For the front wall:

a. Draw and label a sketch of the prism used for the front wall of the castle if the wall was 36 inches long, 24 inches high, and 4 inches wide.

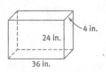

24 in.   4 in.
36 in.

b. Use the volume formula for a prism, $V = Bh$, to find the number of cubic inches of sand needed to build the front wall. $V = 3456$ in.³

3. For the guardhouses:

a. Draw and label a sketch of one of the pyramids used for the guardhouses at the entrance to the drawbridge if the base of each pyramid is a square with side length of 6 inches and a height of 9 inches.

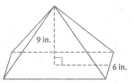

9 in.   6 in.

b. Use the volume formula for a pyramid, $V = \frac{1}{3}Bh$, to find the number of cubic inches of sand needed to build both guardhouses. $V_{both} = 216$ in.³

4. For the towers:

a. Draw and label a sketch of one of the cylinders used to create the base of the two towers if the diameter of each cylinder is 10 inches and the height of each cylinder is 28 inches.

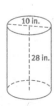

10 in.   28 in.

Differentiating Instruction

Students may have a difficult time with the sketching involved in this activity. Encourage them to think about the shapes involved in creating each sketch and consider what would be a good starting place. It can be helpful to have some diagrams of the various shapes in the classroom so that students have a reference for their sketches.

SUGGESTED LEARNING STRATEGIES: Quickwrite, Create Representations, Think/Pair/Share, Group Presentation, Visualization, Identify a Subtask

My Notes

b. Use the volume formula for a cylinder to find the number of cubic inches of sand needed to build the two congruent cylindrical bases for the towers. $V_{both} \approx 4398.2$ in.^{3}

5. Shelly tells Shayla that she uses the formula $V = Bh$ to find the volume of both cylinders and prisms. Why does this work?

Answers may vary. Sample answer: In a cylinder, the area of the base, B, can be found using the expression πr^2.

6. For the turrets:

a. Draw and label a sketch of one of the cones used to create the turrets if the diameter of the base of each cone is 10 inches and the height of each cone is 16 inches.

16 in.

10 in.

b. Use the volume formula for a cone, $V = \frac{1}{3}\pi r^2 h$, to find how many cubic inches of sand are needed to build the two congruent conical turrets. How many cubic feet are needed?

$V_{both} \approx 837.8$ in.^{3}; $V \approx 0.5$ ft^3

7. Use the volume formula for a sphere, $V = \frac{4}{3}\pi r^3$, to find how many cubic inches of sand are needed to build the three congruent decorative hemispheres on top of the wall if the radius of each hemisphere is 2 inches.

$V_{three} \approx 50.3$ in.^{3}; $V \approx 5.2$ ft^3

8. How many total cubic inches of sand did the entire front of Shelly's sand castle require? How many cubic feet were required?

$V_{front} \approx 8958.3$ in.^{3}

> **MATH TIP**
> 1 ft^3 = 1728 in.^{3}

MINI-LESSON: Prisms and Pyramids/Cylinders and Cones

In previous courses, students may have worked with a rectangular prism and a pyramid with congruent bases and heights, and also a cylinder and cone with congruent bases and heights. In both cases, students fill the smaller solid with rice or a similar substance and then see how many of these it takes to fill the larger solid. Students see it takes three of the smaller to fill the larger, allowing them to recognize why the volume formulas for the cone and pyramid are $\frac{1}{3}$ the amount for the prism and cylinder. If most students have not performed this exercise, it is still a grade appropriate activity, and an enlightening one for the class to explore.

ACTIVITY 6.4 *Continued*

5 Quickwrite, Debrief Students discussed the connection between the surface area formulas for cylinders and prisms in Activity 6.3. This question serves as review and formative assessment on this concept. Look for the students to recall that as the sides of a regular polygon base increase, the prism approaches the shape of a cylinder. Guide them to this connection if they are overlooking it.

6 Create Representations, Think/Pair/Share, Group Presentation During this group presentation, question the students regarding the relationship between the volume of cones and cylinders. Students may have previous experience with this relationship (see mini-lesson).

Suggested Assignment

CHECK YOUR UNDERSTANDING
p. 332, #1–4, 6

UNIT 6 PRACTICE
p. 340, #29

7 Visualization, Group Presentation Students should consider that there are three hemispheres on the castle, so 1.5 spheres are what is being solved for in this question.

8 Identify a Subtask, Debrief Students will need to organize their information in order to be sure and include all the necessary volumes of the parts of the castle. While debriefing the class, discuss the organizational schemes students used. This will allow some students to benefit from the work of others and add to their knowledge of organizational systems.

9 Create Representations, Think/Pair/Share, Debrief It may be helpful to discuss these complex solids before students begin their work. Students can share with the class the formulas they plan to use based on the shapes of the solids.

TEACHER TO TEACHER For more practice on complex solids, have students create their own complex solid from everyday objects, and then find the volume. Examples may include an overturned bowl on top of an oatmeal box, a can on top of a shoebox, a baseball on top of a gift box, etc. Students may also make their solid, and then trade with another student to find the volume.

10 Role Play, Group Presentation This question can be minimized or maximized depending on the time available. The question states that the rectangular prism creating the wall of the castle is already made. This rectangular prism can be created using poster board, construction paper, or another appropriate medium. It may be of any size. A pre-made rectangular prism such as a cereal box or other container may be used.

Students use the pre-made wall and then create and label the other parts of the castle. Students can use any appropriate medium for their creations. You may give the dimensions for these parts or may leave this open-ended, having the students decide on what size to make their assigned parts so that it is a reasonable size in relation to the prism that you created or gave them.

This activity can be further extended by having groups find the volume of the part they designed or the volume of the entire castle.

Suggested Assignment

CHECK YOUR UNDERSTANDING
p. 332, #5

UNIT 6 PRACTICE
p. 340–341, #30–33

My Notes

SUGGESTED LEARNING STRATEGIES: Create Representations, Think/Pair/Share, Use Manipulatives, Group Presentation

9. Use the appropriate formula to find the volume of each of the following solids. Draw a sketch if needed. Show all calculations.

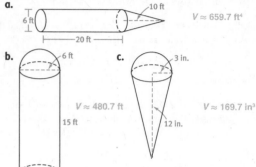

a. $V \approx 659.7$ ft³

b. $V \approx 480.7$ ft³ c. $V \approx 169.7$ in³

MATH TIP
The volume formula for a sphere is $V = \frac{4}{3}\pi r^3$.

10. Sandy has created the rectangular prism for the front wall and the decorative accents for her castle. She wants to add guardhouses, towers with turrets, and a drawbridge. Design and build the portion of Sandy's castle assigned to you by your teacher. Create a label for your creation that gives the dimensions of your solid.

Student responses will vary according to the portion of the castle assigned to them by the teacher. Dimensions will also vary.

CHECK YOUR UNDERSTANDING

Write your answers on notebook paper. Show your work.

Find the volume of each of the following solids.

1.
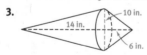

2. a square pyramid having a base perimeter of 25 cm and a height of 6 cm

3.
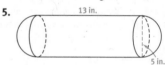

4. a cone having a base circumference of 36π meters and height of 12 meters

5.
13 in.

5 in.

6. MATHEMATICAL REFLECTION Shelly believes that if she builds a sand castle with dimensions twice as large as the dimensions of Shelly's winning castle she will need twice as much sand for her castle as Shelly did for hers. Is Shayla correct? Justify your response.

CHECK YOUR UNDERSTANDING

1. $V = 148.8$ in.³

2. $V \approx 78.1$ cm³

3. $V \approx 523.6$ in.

4. $V \approx 4071.5$ m³

5. $V \approx 320.7$ in.³

6. No; Sample answer: She will need 8 times as much sand. For example, in a rectangular prism $V = l \cdot w \cdot h$. If she doubles each dimension, then $V = 2l \cdot 2w \cdot 2h = 8 \cdot l \cdot w \cdot h$.

Changing Dimensions
Twice as Big

SUGGESTED LEARNING STRATEGIES: Work Backwards,
Think/Pair/Share, Group Presentation, Quickwrite

In 1997, in an effort to build enthusiasm for recycling, the citizens
of Rome, Italy, built a model of St. Peter's Basilica from aluminum
beverage cans. When the model was finished, it was one-fifth the
size of the actual Basilica. The model was 26 meters high, 49 meters
wide, 93 meters long and made it into the *Guinness Book of World
Records* for the number of cans used.

1. Use the information provided about the model of St. Peter's
   Basilica to find the following:

   a. the dimensions of the actual cathedral.
   130 m high, 465 m long, and 245 m wide

   b. the ratio of the dimensions of the model to the dimensions
   of the actual cathedral.
   1:5

2. The model of St Peter's Basilica used over 10 million cans.
   Why do you think it took so many cans? Thinking of concepts
   covered so far in this unit, brainstorm characteristics builders
   had to consider when planning the can-model Basilica.
   Answers may vary. Sample answer: The surface area was
   probably very important for modeling purposes.

My Notes

> **CONNECT TO HISTORY**
>
> St. Peter's Basilica is located
> within Vatican City in Rome, Italy.
> It is considered one of the most
> beautiful and famous of Rome's
> many cathedrals.

ACTIVITY 6.5 Investigative

Changing Dimensions

Activity Focus
• Scale Factors

Materials
• No additional materials are
  needed

Chunking the Activity
#1–2   #3–4   #5–7   #8

1 Work Backwards, Think/Pair/
Share, Group Presentation
Students will use the information
given in the introductory
paragraph to find the dimensions
of St. Peter's Basilica. Student
groups should share their work
with the class. The introduction
tells students that the model is
one-fifth the size of the church,
but in Part b students need to
write this in the form of a ratio.

2 Quickwrite, Debrief Students
may overlook the enormity of
the surface area of the basilica.
Having a class discussion will help
to bring this point out. By the end
of the discussion, students should
understand that the surface area
of the model and the actual
church are related by a scale
factor.

3-4 Interactive Word Wall, Think/Pair/Share, Debrief After reading the introductory paragraph, the terms *similar solids* and *scale factor* should be added to the Interactive Word Wall.

Students may not recall that scale factors need to be simplified to their lowest terms. They may give the answer to Part a as 2:8 or 8:32. This point needs to be addressed while debriefing.

The table on scale factors will be expanded on through the next few questions. At this point, students should read through and discuss it, initially looking for patterns. This should activate prior knowledge regarding exponents and their relationship to length, area, and volume.

5 Activating Prior Knowledge, Think/Pair/Share, Debrief Part a of this question provides review and formative assessment opportunities for surface area and volume.

In Part b, students will notice that the ratio of the surface areas is very close to $\frac{1}{16}$, and in Part c the ratio of the volumes is very close to $\frac{1}{64}$. Students may be concerned that these are not exact ratios. Remind them that they are using an approximation for *Pi* when finding the surface area and volume. If the measures are left in terms of *Pi*, the ratios will be exact.

In Part d, students need to use the values that they found to confirm the relationships in the table on the previous page. Students should note that $\frac{1}{16}$ can be rewritten as $\frac{1}{4^2}$ and $\frac{1}{64}$ can be rewritten as $\frac{1}{4^3}$, which is the relationship the table shows.

My Notes

Similar solids have the same shape but not necessarily the same size. They have congruent corresponding angles and corresponding sides must be in proportion. The ratio of the lengths of the corresponding sides of similar solids is called the **scale factor**.

3. Give the scale factor for the two similar cylinders below.

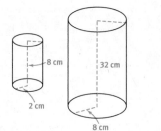

$\frac{1}{4}$

4. Give the scale factor for the two similar rectangular prisms below.

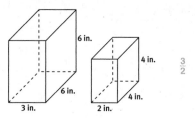

$\frac{3}{2}$

The relationships between surface areas and volumes of similar solids can be stated as ratios. Examine the table below.

Scale Factors in Similar Solids	
Ratio of lengths	$a:b$
Ratio of surface areas	$a^2:b^2$
Ratio of volumes	$a^3:b^3$

5. Use the solids from Item 3 to answer the following.

a. Find the surface area and volume of the cylinders.
small cylinder: $T = 40\pi \approx 125.7$ cm³; $V = 32\pi \approx 100.5$ cm³
large cylinder: $T = 640\pi \approx 2010.6$ cm³; $V = 2048\pi \approx 6434$ cm³

b. Write the ratio of their surface areas. $\frac{1}{16}$

SUGGESTED LEARNING STRATEGIES: Create Representations

c. Write the ratio of their volumes.

$\frac{1}{64}$

d. Use the ratios of the surface areas and volumes to confirm the scale factors in similar solids relationships.

$\frac{40\pi}{640\pi} = \frac{1}{16} = \frac{1^2}{4^2}, \frac{32\pi}{2048\pi} = \frac{1}{64} = \frac{1^3}{4^3}$

6. The triangular prism below is similar to another smaller triangular prism. The scale factor is 2:1.

a. Sketch the smaller prism and label the dimensions.

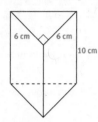
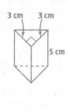

6 cm   6 cm
10 cm

3 cm   3 cm
5 cm

b. Find the surface area and volume of the larger prism.

$T \approx 240.9 \text{ cm}^2$, $V = 180 \text{ cm}^3$

c. What is the ratio of the surface areas of the two prisms? Use the ratio to find the surface area of the smaller prism.

ratio: $\frac{4}{1}$, $T \approx 60.2 \text{ cm}^2$

d. What is the ratio of the volumes of the two prisms? Use the ratio to find the volume of the smaller prism.

ratio: $\frac{8}{1}$, $V = 22.5 \text{ cm}^3$

ACTIVITY 6.5 *Continued*

6 **Create Representations, Debrief** Students may look back to Item 3 for help in creating this diagram if they are having difficulty with Part a. In addition, they will need to use the Pythagorean Theorem to find the missing side length in the triangle.

In Part b, students are practicing the skills of finding surface area and volume. These skills are review from activities 6.3 and 6.4.

In Part c, students will need to use the information from the table on scale factors (p. 334). They were given the ratio of the lengths as 2:1, so the ratio of the surface areas is 2^2:1 or 4:1. They can then divide the surface area of the larger figure by 4 to find the surface area of the smaller figure. A similar procedure will be used for finding the volume of the smaller prism in Part d. The only difference is the ratio will be 8:1.

7 Think/Pair/Share, Debrief This question asks students to sketch solids and find the ratio of the surface areas and volumes as they have in previous questions. This question provides practice and formative assessment for these concepts.

Differentiating Instruction

Being able to visualize the sizes being discussed may be helpful for students. They may benefit from either drawing a diagram of this situation on their paper or creating a representation that is true to life on the white board or wall.

8 Think/Pair/Share, Debrief Students will need to remember to change 6 feet 4 inches into inches before writing their ratios. Parts a and b confirm the students' ability to write and interpret ratios. Part c confirms the students' ability to apply the relationships that exist between length and surface area that they have learned about during the activity.

Suggested Assignment

CHECK YOUR UNDERSTANDING
p. 336, #1–5

UNIT 6 PRACTICE
p. 341, #34–39

CHECK YOUR UNDERSTANDING

1a. $\frac{3}{5}$

b. $\frac{9}{25}$

c. $\frac{27}{125}$

2. $\frac{27}{1}$

3. $\frac{4}{5}$

4. 9,953,280 in.³

5. 12 in. ball; Sample answer: It contains 8 times the amount of yarn at only 6.5 times the cost.

My Notes

SUGGESTED LEARNING STRATEGIES: Think/Pair/Share

7. Sketch two similar solids with a scale factor 4:5. Give the ratio of their surface areas and volumes.

Answers may vary. Sample answer:

Ratio of Surface Areas: $\frac{16}{25}$

Ratio of Volumes: $\frac{64}{125}$

 8 cm, 4 cm

 10 cm, 5 cm

8. In preparation for his exhibit on Abraham Lincoln at the 1964 New York World's Fair, Walt Disney and his Imagineers built models of President Lincoln. The models were in proportion to the life-size, moving, speaking figure they wanted to create. One of the models they built was 8 inches tall. Mr. Lincoln was actually 6 feet 4 inches tall.

a. What was the ratio of the height of the model to the actual height of President Lincoln? $\frac{2}{19}$

b. How many times taller was President Lincoln than the model Walt Disney built? 9.5 times larger

c. How much larger would the surface area of the life-size display be than the surface area of the small model?
90.25 times larger

CHECK YOUR UNDERSTANDING

Write your answers on notebook paper. Show your work.

1. Two similar cylinders have radii 3 cm and 5 cm. Find the ratios of each of the following:

   a. the heights of the cylinders

   b. the surface areas of the cylinders

   c. the volumes of the cylinders

2. All spheres are similar. Find the ratio of the volumes of two spheres if the radius of one sphere is three times the radius of the other sphere.

3. Two similar prisms have lateral areas of 16 mm² and 25 mm². Find the ratio of their heights.

4. Richard built a scale model of a coal powered steam train. The scale for the model was 1:48. If the model coal car could hold 90 cubic inches of coal, how many cubic inches of coal could the coal car on the actual train hold?

5. **MATHEMATICAL REFLECTION** A craft store sells skeins of yarn in 6 in. or 12 in. diameters. The 6 in. skeins cost $2.00 and the 12 in. skeins cost $13.00. Which size of yarn is the better buy? Justify your answer.

Area and Volume

AIR DANCING

A group of students who will be attending the new Plato Middle School want to find a way to welcome the entire student body on the first day of school. After some investigation, the students decide an air dancer is a good idea and begin brainstorming ideas. The design they finally agree on has two cylindrical legs, a right triangular prism for a body, two rectangular prisms for arms with square pyramids for hands, a cylindrical neck, a hemispherical head, and a conical shaped hat.

Note: The drawing at the right does not necessarily represent the design that the students chose. To complete the items below, make your own drawing, showing the correct solid shape for each body part.

1. The students have been given $1000 to spend. The price of the air dancer depends on the amount of vinyl needed to create it. In order to decide if they can use their design they must find the amount of vinyl their dancer would require.

   a. Since the legs must be open on each end in order for air to pass through, find the lateral areas of the cylindrical legs if each one is 10 feet tall and 2 feet in diameter.

   b. Find the lateral area of the right triangular prism to be used for the body. A diagram is shown to the right.

   c. Find the lateral area of the rectangular prism used for one of the 5-foot long arms if the base of each is a square with side length 1 foot.

   d. Find the lateral area of one of the hands if the pyramid has square bases with side length 1 foot, and slant height 4 feet.

   e. Find the lateral area of the cylindrical neck if it is 2 feet tall and has a diameter of 1.5 feet.

   f. Find the surface area of the hemispherical head if it has a radius of 1 foot, and an open base.

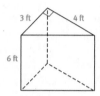

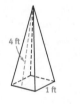

2. The students know the lateral area of the conical hat is 12.95 ft².

   a. Find the amount of vinyl needed to create the custom air dancer.

   b. If the company charges $3.00 per square foot, and $100.00 for shipping, will the $1000 the students have be enough? Justify your response.

Embedded Assessment 2

Assessment Focus
- Lateral area
- Volume

Materials
- No additional materials are required.

1 Students need to show the work that they do to find the lateral area of each of the body sections of the air dancer. It may be helpful to most students to draw diagrams and label them for each of the shapes.

To find the surface area of a hemisphere (half of a sphere), have students use the formula for the surface area of a sphere: $SA = 4\pi r^2$.

2 After finding the total lateral area of all of the pieces comprising the air dancer, the students will find the price of the vinyl using the given charge of $3 per square foot plus $100 for shipping. Again, students need to show their work.

3 The last part of this assessment requires the students to find the volume of air required to keep the air dancer inflated. Students should show their work for this problem.

Answer Key

1a. $L \approx 125.66$ ft²

   b. $L = 72$ ft²

   c. $L = 20$ ft²

   d. $L = 8$ ft²

   e. $L \approx 9.42$ ft²

   f. $L \approx 6.28$ ft²

2a. 282.31 ft²

   b. $946.93; the students will have enough money.

3. $V_{legs} \approx 62.8$ ft³, $V_{body} = 36$ ft³;
   $V_{arms} = 10$ ft³, $V_{hands} = 2.6$ ft³;
   $V_{neck} \approx 3.53$ ft³,
   $V_{head} \approx 2.09$ ft³;
   $V_{hat} \approx 4.19$ ft³

   121.21 ft³ of air must be maintained.

Embedded Assessment 2

Area and Volume
AIR DANCING

TEACHER TO TEACHER Students may not understand why only lateral areas are needed for this problem. This is especially true for students who are unfamiliar with the concept of an "air dancer." It may be necessary to review the picture in the problem or to have the students draw and label the air dancer.

You may wish to read through the rubric with students and discuss the differences in the expectation levels. Make sure students understand the meanings of any terms used.

3. The students must also consider fans to keep a certain amount of air moving in the dancer. How much air must they maintain in their dancer to keep it inflated? Use the fact that the conical hat has a base radius of 1 foot and a height of 4 feet. The height of each of the pyramids used for the hands is 3.9 feet. Show all your work.

	Exemplary	Proficient	Emerging
Math Knowledge 1a–f; 2a	The student: • Finds the correct lateral areas for the legs, body, one arm, hands, and neck of the dancer. (1a–e) • Finds the correct surface area of the head of the dancer. (1f) • Finds the correct amount of vinyl needed to create the dancer. (2a)	The student: • Finds the correct measures for three or four of the body parts. • Uses a correct method to find the surface area, but makes a computational error. • Uses a correct method to find the amount, but makes a computational error.	The student: • Finds the correct measures for fewer than three of the parts. • Does not find the correct surface area. • Does not find the correct amount.
Problem Solving 2b, 3	The student: • Correctly determines whether or not $1,000 will be enough for the project. (2b) • Correctly determines the correct amount of air needed to keep the dancer inflated. (3)	The student: • Uses a correct method to find the amount of air, but makes a computational error.	The student: • Makes an incorrect determination about the adequacy of the $1,000. • Does not find the correct amount of air.
Communication 2b, 3	The student: • Writes a complete and mathematically correct justification for the adequacy of $1,000 for the project. (2b) • Shows correct work for the amount of air needed. (3)	The student: • Writes an incomplete justification that contains no mathematical errors. • Shows incomplete work that contains no mathematical errors.	The student: • Writes a justification that contains mathematical errors. • Shows work that contains mathematical errors.

ACTIVITY 6.1

Find x in each of the following.

1.

2.

3.

4.

For Items 5–9, estimate the square root to the nearest tenth.

5. 14

6. 24

7. 104

8. 60

9. 2

Draw a diagram to represent each of the following problem situations. Find the requested information. Show all calculations.

10. At a certain time of day, a 12 foot tree casts a 15 foot long shadow. How far is it from the top of the tree to the tip of the shadow?

11. A 19-inch television screen measures 19 inches on the diagonal. If a 19-inch screen is 15.1 inches wide, how tall is the screen?

12. A 17 foot ladder leans against a wall. The foot of the ladder is 8 feet from the wall.

   a. How high does the ladder reach up the wall?

   b. If the foot of the ladder slips out 2 feet, how far up the wall will the ladder reach?

ACTIVITY 6.2

Determine whether each of the following sets of numbers could be the sides of a right triangle. Justify your answers.

13. 8, 10, 12

14. 2, 8, 12

15. 10, 24, 26

16. $\frac{1}{3}, \frac{2}{3}, 1$

17. 0.25, 0.75, 1.25

Each of the following is a Pythagorean triple. Give 2 other Pythagorean triples that can be generated from the original set.

18. 9, 40, 41

19. 7, 24, 25

20. 600, 800, 1000

UNIT 6 PRACTICE

Activity 6.1

1. $x \approx 8.5$

2. $x \approx 4.0$

3. $x \approx 5.3$

4. $x \approx 5.7$

Items 5–9, sample answers:

5. 3.7

6. 4.9

7. 10.2

8. 7.7

9. 1.4

10. ≈ 19.2 feet

11. ≈ 11.5 inches

12a. 15 feet

   b. ≈ 13.7 feet

Activity 6.2

Items 13–17, sample answers:

13. No, $12^2 \neq 10^2 + 8^2$

14. No, not a triangle because $2 + 8 < 12$

15. Yes, $26^2 = 10^2 + 24^2$

16. No, $1^2 \neq \left(\frac{1}{3}\right)^2 + \left(\frac{2}{3}\right)^2$

17. No, not a triangle because $0.25 + 0.75 < 1.25$

18. Answers may vary. Sample answers: 18, 80, 82 and 27, 120, 123

19. Answers may vary. Sample answers: 14, 48, 50 and 21, 72, 75

20. Answers may vary. Sample answers: 300, 400, 500 and 1200, 1600, 2000

Activity 6.3

21. $L = 288$ cm²
    $T = 360$ cm²

22. $L \approx 47.1$ in.²

23. $L = 192$ yds²

24. $L = 200$ ft²

25. $L = 480$ m²
    $T = 736$ m²

26. $T \approx 100.5$ in.²

27. $L = 60$ in.²

28. $L = 90$ in.²
    $T = 150$ in.²

Activity 6.4

29. $V = 224$ in.³

30. $V \approx 617.2$ in.³

31. $V = 312$ km³

32. $V \approx 1231.5$ in.³

ACTIVITY 6.3

21. Find the lateral area and surface area of a rectangular prism with a height of 12 cm and a square base with a 6-cm edge.

22. Find the area of the label covering a soup can that has a diameter of 3 inches and a height of 5 inches.

23. Find the lateral area of a right hexagonal prism with height 8 yards if the perimeter of the base is 24 yards.

24. Find the lateral area of the pentagonal prism shown below.

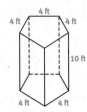

25. Find the lateral area and the surface area of a square pyramid whose slant height is 15 meters and whose base is a square with an area of 256 square meters.

26. Find the surface area of a special promotional soda can with base radius 2 inches and height 6 inches.

27. Find the lateral area of the trapezoidal prism shown below.

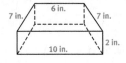

28. Find the lateral and surface area of the right triangular prism shown below.

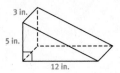

ACTIVITY 6.4

For Items 29–33, find the volume of the solid.

29.

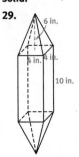

30. the volume of the rectangular prism that surrounds the cylinder

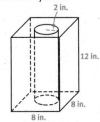

31. a right triangular prism with base having legs 24 km and 13 km and height 2 km

32.

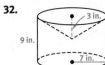

33. a cylinder with base diameter 7 decimeters and height 4 decimeters

ACTIVITY 6.5

34. Two similar cones have heights 10 cm and 15 cm. Find the ratios of each of the following:

a. the radii of the cones
b. the surface area of the cones
c. the volume of the cones

35. Two similar pyramids have volumes 3 in.³ and 375 in.³. Find the ratios of each of the following:

a. the heights of the pyramids
b. the lateral areas of the pyramids
c. the surface areas of the pyramids

36. Assume the Earth and the moon are perfect spheres. The radius of the Earth is approximately 6400 km and the radius of the moon is approximately 1600 km. Find the Earth to moon ratio of each of the following:

a. their diameters
b. their equators
c. their surface areas
d. their volumes

37. Find the ratio of the diameters of two spheres if the surface area of one is four times the surface area of the other.

38. A square pyramid has a height of 18 ft and a surface area of 648 ft². A smaller, similar pyramid has a height of 6 ft.

a. How much smaller is the surface area of the smaller pyramid than that of the larger? State your answer as a ratio.

b. What is the surface area of the smaller pyramid?

39. At Legoland in California, there is a replica of the Statue of Liberty built entirely of Legos. It stands 4 feet tall.

a. If the Statue of Liberty itself is 111 feet tall, what is the ratio of the height of the model to the height of the actual statue?

b. How many times taller is the Statue of Liberty than the model in Legoland?

c. How many times greater would the surface area of the actual statue be than that of the Legoland model?

d. How many times greater would the volume of the Statue of Liberty be than that of the Legoland model?

33. $V \approx 153.9$ dm³

Activity 6.5

34a. $\frac{2}{3}$

b. $\frac{4}{9}$

c. $\frac{8}{27}$

35a. $\frac{1}{5}$

b. $\frac{1}{25}$

c. $\frac{1}{25}$

36a. $\frac{4}{1}$

b. $\frac{4}{1}$

c. $\frac{16}{1}$

d. $\frac{64}{1}$

37. $\frac{2}{1}$

38a. one-ninth the size

b. 72 ft²

39a. $\frac{4}{111}$

b. 27.75 times larger

c. approx. 770.06 times larger

d. approx. 21,369.2 times larger

Reflection

Student Reflection

Discuss the essential questions with students. Have them share how their understanding of the questions has changed through studying the concepts in the unit.

Review the academic vocabulary. You may want students to revisit the graphic organizers they have completed for academic vocabulary terms and add other notes about their understanding of terms.

Encourage students to evaluate their own learning and to recognize the strategies that work best for them. Help them identify key concepts in the unit and to set goals for addressing their weaknesses and acquiring effective learning strategies.

Teacher Reflection

1. Of the key concepts in the unit, did any present special challenges for students?

2. How will you adjust your future instruction for students/activities?

3. Which strategies were most effective for facilitating student learning?

4. When you teach this unit again, what will you do differently?

An important aspect of growing as a learner is to take the time to reflect on your learning. It is important to think about where you started, what you have accomplished, what helped you learn, and how you will apply your new knowledge in the future. Use notebook paper to record your thinking on the following topics and to identify evidence of your learning.

Essential Questions

1. Review the mathematical concepts and your work in this unit before you write thoughtful responses to the questions below. Support your responses with specific examples from concepts and activities in the unit.

   - How are two- and three-dimensional figures related?
   - How do changes in dimensions of a geometric figure affect area, surface area, and volume?

Academic Vocabulary

2. Look at the following academic vocabulary word:

   - solid

   Explain your understanding of this word and why it is important in your study of math.

Self-Evaluation

3. Look through the activities and Embedded Assessments in this unit. Use a table similar to the one below to list three major concepts in this unit and to rate your understanding of each.

Unit Concepts	Is Your Understanding Strong (S) or Weak (W)?
Concept 1	
Concept 2	
Concept 3	

   a. What will you do to address each weakness?

   b. What strategies or class activities were particularly helpful in learning the concepts you identified as strengths? Give examples to explain.

4. How do the concepts you learned in this unit relate to other math concepts and to the use of mathematics in the real world?

1. Which side lengths do **not** create a right triangle?

   F. 6 cm, 12 cm, 15 cm

   G. 15 cm, 20 cm, 25 cm

   H. 5 cm, 12 cm, 13 cm

   J. 3 cm, 4 cm, 5 cm

1. Ⓕ Ⓖ Ⓗ Ⓙ

2. A rectangle has side lengths 6 ft and 8 ft. What is the length of one of the rectangle's diagonals?

2.

**Read
Solve
Explain**

3. Samuel is parachuting from a plane for his 14th birthday. The plane will be flying at an altitude of 1200 feet when Samuel makes the jump. The target will not be directly below the plane when he jumps. Measured on the ground, the target will be 500 feet from the point where Samuel jumps. How far must he parachute to land on the target?

Solve and Explain

$500^2 + 1200^2 = c^2$

$250,000 + 1,440,000 = c^2$

$1,690,000 = c^2$

$c = 1300$; I know the answer is positive and not negative

because I'm looking for how far Samuel jumps.

UNIT 6 Math Standards Review

These two pages provide practice with four standardized test question formats that are used in many national and state high-stakes tests:

- Multiple choice
- Gridded response
- Short response
- Extended response

These items also provide practice with the mathematics content of this unit.

1 Multiple choice
- Apply properties of triangles

2 Gridded response
- Use Pythagorean Theorem

3 Short Response
- Solve problems using the Pythagorean Theorem

4 Extended response
- Solve problems using the Pythagorean Theorem
- Use the distance formula

Math Standards Review
Unit 6 (continued)

TEACHER TO TEACHER You might read through the extended-response item with students and discuss your expectation levels. Make sure students understand the meanings of any terms used.

Read
Solve
Explain

4. The Ericksons sail their boat to an island 50 miles due west of Naples. The island is due south of the mouth of Tampa Bay. The coastline from the mouth of Tampa Bay to Naples is approximately 120 miles.

Part A: Find the distance the Ericksons must sail from the mouth of Tampa Bay to reach the island. Round to the nearest mile.

Solve and Explain

$50^2 + b^2 = 120^2$

$2500 + b^2 = 14400$

$b^2 = 11900$

$b \approx 109$ miles

Part B: If they sail at 15 miles per hour, how long will it take the Ericksons to reach the island?

Solve and Explain

$109 \div 15 \approx 7.3$ hours

Part C: After spending several nights on the island, the Ericksons learn that a storm is approaching from the south. Due to the increased winds, they can only travel at 12 miles per hour. If the storm is traveling 30 miles per hour and is still 290 miles from the mouth of Tampa Bay when the Ericksons set sail, will they make it to Tampa Bay before the storm hits? Justify your answer.

Solve and Explain

Ericksons: $109 \div 12 \approx 9.08$ hours

Storm: $290 \div 30 \approx 9.7$ hours

The Ericksons can beat the storm to the mouth of Tampa

Bay by a little more than half an hour.

Symbols

$<$	is less than
$>$	is greater than
$\leq$	is less than or equal to
$\geq$	is greater than or equal to
$=$	is equal to
$\neq$	is not equal to
$\approx$	is approximately equal to
$\lvert a \rvert$	absolute value: $\lvert 3 \rvert = 3$; $\lvert -3 \rvert = 3$
$\sqrt{}$	square root
$\%$	percent
$\perp$	perpendicular
$\parallel$	parallel
(x, y)	ordered pair
$\overset{\frown}{AB}$	arc
$\overleftrightarrow{AB}$	line AB
$\overrightarrow{AB}$	ray AB
$\overline{AB}$	line segment AB
$\angle A$	angle A
$m\angle A$	measure of angle A
$\triangle ABC$	triangle ABC
π	pi; $\pi \approx 3.14$; $\pi \approx \dfrac{22}{7}$

Formulas

Perimeter	
P	= sum of the lengths of the sides
Rectangle	$P = 2l + 2w$
Square	$P = 4s$
Circumference	$C = 2\pi r$

Area	
Circle	$A = \pi r^2$
Parallelogram	$A = bh$
Rectangle	$A = lw$
Square	$A = s^2$
Triangle	$A = \frac{1}{2}bh$
Trapezoid	$A = \frac{1}{2}h(b_1 + b_2)$

Volume	
Cylinder	$V = Bh, B = \pi r^2$
Rectangular Prism	$V = lwh$
Triangular Prism	$V = Bh, B = \frac{1}{2}bh$
Pyramid	$V = \frac{1}{3}Bh$
Cone	$V = \frac{1}{3}\pi r^2 h$
Sphere	$V = \frac{4}{3}\pi r^3$

Formulas (*continued*)

Surface Area	
Cube	$SA = 6e^2$
Rectangular Prism	$SA = 2lw + 2lh + 2wh$
Cylinder	$SA = 2\pi r^2 + 2\pi rh$
Cone	$SA = \pi r^2 + \pi rl$
Regular Pyramid	$SA = B + \frac{1}{2}pl$
Sphere	$SA = 4\pi r^2$

Linear function	
Slope	$m = \dfrac{y_2 - y_1}{x_2 - x_1}$
Slope-intercept form	$y = mx + b$
Point-slope form	$y - y_1 = m(x - x_1)$
Standard form	$Ax + By = C$

Quadratic Equations	
Standard Form	$ax^2 + bx + c = 0$
Quadratic Formula	$x = \dfrac{-b \pm \sqrt{b^2 - 4ac}}{2a}$

Other Formulas	
Pythagorean Theorem	$a^2 + b^2 = c^2$, where c is the hypotenuse of a right triangle
Distance	$d = \sqrt{(x_2 - x_1)^2 + (y_2 - y_1)^2}$
Direct variation	$y = kx$
Inverse variation	$y = \dfrac{k}{x}$

Temperature	
Celsius	$C = \dfrac{5}{9}(F - 32)$
Fahrenheit	$F = \dfrac{9}{5}C + 32$

Properties of Real Numbers

Reflexive Property of Equality	For all real numbers a, $a = a$.
Symmetric Property of Equality	For all real numbers a and b, if $a = b$, then $b = a$.
Transitive Property of Equality	For all real numbers a, b, and c, if $a = b$ and $b = c$, then $a = c$.
Substitution Property of Equality	For all real numbers a and b, if $a = b$, then a may be replaced by b.
Additive Identity	For all real numbers a, $a + 0 = 0 + a = a$.
Multiplicative Identity	For all real numbers a, $a \cdot 1 = 1 \cdot a = a$.
Commutative Property of Addition	For all real numbers a and b, $a + b = b + a$.
Commutative Property of Multiplication	For all real numbers a and b, $a \cdot b = b \cdot a$.
Associative Property of Addition	For all real numbers a, b, and c, $(a + b) + c = a + (b + c)$.
Associative Property of Multiplication	For all real numbers a, b, and c, $(a \cdot b) \cdot c = a \cdot (b \cdot c)$.
Distributive Property of Multiplication over Addition	For all real numbers a, b, and c, $a(b + c) = a \cdot b + a \cdot c$.
Additive Inverse	For all real numbers a, there is exactly one real number $-a$ such that $a + (-a) = 0$ and $(-a) + a = 0$.
Multiplicative Inverse	For all real numbers a and b where $a \neq 0$, $b \neq 0$, there is exactly one number $\frac{b}{a}$ such that $\frac{b}{a} \cdot \frac{a}{b} = 1$ and $\frac{a}{b} \cdot \frac{b}{a} = 1$.
Multiplication Property of Zero	For all real numbers a, $a \cdot 0 = 0$ and $0 \cdot a = 0$.
Addition Property of Equality	For all real numbers a, b, and c, if $a = b$, then $a + c = b + c$.
Subtraction Property of Equality	For all real numbers a, b, and c, if $a = b$, then $a - c = b - c$.
Multiplication Property of Equality	For all real numbers a, b, and c, if $a = b$, then $a \cdot c = b \cdot c$.
Division Property of Equality	For all real numbers a, b, and c, $c \neq 0$ if $a = b$, then $\frac{a}{c} = \frac{b}{c}$.
Zero Product Property of Equality	For all real numbers a and b, if $a \cdot b = 0$ then $a = 0$ or $b = 0$ or both a and b equal 0.
Addition Property of Inequality*	For all real numbers a, b, and c, if $a > b$, then $a + c > b + c$.
Subtraction Property of Inequality*	For all real numbers a, b, and c, if $a > b$, then $a - c > b - c$.
Multiplication Property of Inequality *	For all real numbers a, b, and c, $c > 0$, if $a > b$, then $a \cdot c > b \cdot c$. For all real numbers a, b, and c, $c < 0$, if $a > b$, then $a \cdot c < b \cdot c$.
Division Property of Inequality*	For all real numbers a, b, and c, $c > 0$, if $a > b$, then $\frac{a}{c} > \frac{b}{c}$. For all real numbers a, b, and c, $c < 0$, if $a > b$, then $\frac{a}{c} < \frac{b}{c}$.

*These properties are also true for $<, \leq, \geq$.

Table of Measures

Customary	Metric
Distance/Length	
1 foot (ft) = 12 inches (in.)	1 centimeter (cm) = 10 millimeters (mm)
1 yard (yd) = 3 feet (ft) = 36 inches (in.)	1 meter (m) = 100 centimeters (cm)
1 mile (mi) = 5280 feet (ft)	1 kilometer (km) = 1000 meters (m)
Volume	
1 cup (c) = 8 fluid ounces (fl oz)	1 liter (L) = 1000 milliliters (mL)
1 pint (pt) = 2 cups (c)	
1 quart (qt) = 2 pints (pt)	
1 gallon (gal) = 4 quarts (qt)	
Weight/Mass	
1 pound (lb) = 16 ounces (oz)	1 gram (g) = 1000 milligrams (mg)
	1 kilogram (kg) = 1000 grams (g)
Time	
1 minute (min) = 60 seconds (sec)	1 year (yr) = 365 days (d)
1 hour (hr) = 60 minutes (min)	1 year (yr) = 52 weeks (wk)
1 day (d) = 24 hours (hr)	1 year (yr) = 12 months (mo)
1 week (wk) = 7 days (d)	

SpringBoard Learning Strategies

READING STRATEGIES

STRATEGY	DEFINITION	PURPOSE
Activating Prior Knowledge	Recalling what is known about a concept and using that information to make a connection to current studies	Helps establish content connections
Chunking the Activity	Grouping a set of items/questions for specific purposes	Provides an opportunity to relate concepts, assess understanding and maintain focus
Close Reading	Reading, rereading and analyzing small chunks of text word-for-word, sentence-by-sentence, and line-by-line	Assists in developing a comprehensive understanding of the text
Graphic Organizer	Arranging information into maps and charts	Builds comprehension and facilitates discussion by representing information in visual form
Interactive Word Wall	Creating an interactive visual display of vocabulary words to serve as a constant reminder of words and groups of words as they are introduced, used, and mastered over the course of a year	Provides a visual reference for reading and writing, and an ever-present tool for building word knowledge and awareness
KWL Chart (Know, Want, Learn)	Activating prior knowledge by identifying what the student **K**nows, **W**ants to know, and then reflects on was **L**earned	Assists in organizing information and reflecting on learning to increase comprehension and interest
Marking the Text	Highlighting, underlining, and /or annotating parts of the text to focus on key elements to help solve the problem or understand the text	Helps identify, examine and interact with important information from the text
Predict and Confirm	Making conjectures about what results will develop in an activity; confirming or modifying the conjectures based on outcomes	Stimulates thinking by making, checking, and correcting predictions based on evidence in the material
Questioning the Text	Developing questions about the text as it is being read.	Focuses reading, to allow the reader to form questions, seek out answers, and lead discussions
Role Play	Assuming the role of a character in the material	Helps interpret and visualize information in a problem
Shared Reading	Reading the text aloud by the teacher or a student, with other students following along silently	Helps auditory learners to decode, interpret, and analyze challenging text
Summarize/ Paraphrase/Retell	Restating, in your own words, essential information expressed in the text	Assists with comprehension, recall of text, and problem solving
Think Aloud	Describing the thinking process used to make sense of the text in order to solve a problem	Assists in processing the text, understanding the components of the problem, and thinking about possible paths to a solution
Visualization	Picturing (mentally and/or literally) what is read in the text	Increases reading comprehension and promotes active engagement with the text
Vocabulary Organizer	Using a designated format to maintain an ongoing record of vocabulary words with definitions, pictures, notation, and connections	Facilitates and sustains a systemic process of vocabulary development

SpringBoard Learning Strategies

COLLABORATIVE STRATEGIES

STRATEGY	DEFINITION	PURPOSE
Debriefing	Facilitating a discussion that leads to consensus understanding	Helps solidify and deepen understanding of content
Discussion Group	Engaging in an interactive, small group discussion	Gain information and understanding about a concept, idea, or problem
Group Presentation	Working collaboratively, students present information in a variety of formats	Allows opportunities to present collaborative solutions and share responsibility for delivering information to an audience
Think-Pair-Share	**Thinking** a problem through alone, **Pairing** with a partner to share ideas, and concluding by **Sharing** with the class	Enables construction of responses to a problem, then tests and revises ideas, and finally considers and interprets the ideas of others

PROBLEM-SOLVING STRATEGIES

STRATEGY	DEFINITION	PURPOSE
Create Representations	Creating pictures, tables, graphs, lists, equations, models, and/or verbal expressions to interpret text or data	Helps organize information using multiple representations to solve a problem or answer a question
Guess and Check	Guessing the solution to a problem, checking for accuracy, and using the information obtained to make a more reasonable guess	Allows exploration of a problem and determines a pathway to a more formal solution.
Identify a Subtask	Breaking a problem into smaller pieces whose outcomes lead to a solution	Enables organization of the work of solving a complex problem
Look for a Pattern	Observing trends by organizing data or creating representations	Helps generalize patterns and make predictions
Simplify the Problem	Using "friendlier" numbers to solve a problem	Provides insight into the problem or strategies needed to solve the problem
Work Backward	Tracing a possible answer back through the solution process to the starting point	Provides another way to check possible answers for correctness
Use Manipulatives	Using objects to examine relationships between, and among, the information given	Enables visualization information and relationships

SpringBoard Learning Strategies

WRITING STRATEGIES

STRATEGY	DEFINITION	PURPOSE
Note Taking	Creating a record of information while listening to a speaker	Facilitates active listening to record and organize ideas that assist in processing information
Prewriting	Brainstorming and refining your thoughts, reflecting and organizing your ideas prior to writing	Provides a system for beginning the writing process
Quickwrite	Writing for a short, specific amount of time about a designated topic	Enables generation of multiple ideas in a quick fashion
RAFT (Role of Writer, Audience, Format, and Topic)	Writing formally with a clearly identified Role of writer, Audience, Format, and Topic	Provides a framework for formal writing
Self Revision/ Peer Revision	Working alone or with a partner to examine a piece of writing for accuracy and clarity	Provides an opportunity to edit a written text to ensure correctness of identified components

Glossary

Glosario

A

absolute value (p. 10)   The distance of a number from zero on a number line. Distance or absolute value is always positive. For example, the absolute value of both −6 and 6 is 6.

valor absoluto (pág. 10)   Distancia entre un número y el cero en una recta numérica. La distancia o valor absoluto es siempre positivo. Por ejemplo, el valor absoluto tanto de −6 como de 6 es 6.

alternate exterior angles (p. 192)   A pair of angles that are formed by two lines and a transversal and that are outside the two lines and on opposite sides of the transversal. When the two lines crossed by a transversal are parallel, the alternate exterior angles are congruent.

ángulos alternos externos (pág. 192)   Par de ángulos formados por dos rectas y una transversal y que están fuera de las dos rectas y en lados opuestos de la transversal. Cuando las dos rectas cruzadas por una transversal son paralelas, los ángulos alternos externos son congruentes.

alternate interior angles (p. 192)   A pair of angles that are formed by two lines and a transversal and that are inside the two lines and on opposite sides of the transversal. When the two lines crossed by a transversal are parallel, the alternate interior angles are congruent.

ángulos alternos internos (pág. 192)   Par de ángulos formados por dos rectas y una transversal y que están dentro de las dos rectas y en lados opuestos de la transversal. Cuando las dos rectas cruzadas por una transversal son paralelas, los ángulos alternos internos son congruentes.

angle (p. 188)   The union of two rays with a common endpoint.

ángulo (pág. 188)   Unión de dos rayos con un extremo en común.

association (p. 165)   A collection of data points has a *positive association* if it has the property that *y* tends to increase as *x* increases. It has a *negative association* if *y* tends to decrease as *x* increases. An association is also known as a **correlation**.

asociación (pág. 165)   Una colección de datos tiene una *asociación positiva* si tiene la propiedad de que *y* tiende a aumentar a medida que *x* aumenta *y* tiene una *asociación negativa* si *y* tiende a disminuir a medida que *x* aumenta. Una asociación también se conoce como **correlación**.

B

bivariate data (p. 164)   Data that can be written as ordered pairs, where each numerical quantity represents measurement information recorded about a particular subject.

datos bivariados (pág. 164)   Datos que pueden escribirse como pares ordenados, donde cada cantidad numérica representa información de las medidas registradas acerca de un tema en particular.

box-and-whisker plot (p. 267)   A data display organized into four sections, each representing 25% of the data. Also known as a **box plot.**

gráfica de frecuencias acumuladas (pág. 267)   Representación de datos organizados en cuatro secciones, en que cada una representa un 25% de los datos. También se le conoce como **gráfica de cuadrículas.**

C

categorical variable (p. 266)   A variable that describes an attribute; gender and eye color are examples of categorical data.

variable categórica (pág. 266)   Variable que describe un atributo; el género y el color de los ojos son ejemplos de datos categóricos.

census (p. 282)   A study that gains information about every member of a population.

censo (pág. 282)   Estudio que obtiene información acerca de cada miembro de una población.

central angle (p. 224)   An angle whose vertex is the center of a circle.

ángulo central (pág. 224)   Ángulo cuyo vértice es el centro de un círculo.

complementary angles (p. 188)   Two angles whose measures have a sum of 90°.

ángulos complementarios (pág. 188)   Dos ángulos cuyas medidas suman 90°.

complementary events (p. 258)   Two events with no outcomes in common and that together contain all of the possible outcomes of the experiment.

sucesos complementarios (pág. 258)   Dos sucesos que no tienen resultados en común y que conjuntamente contienen todos los resultados posibles del experimento.

compound inequality (p. 105)   An inequality that combines two inequalities. For example, $2 < x < 8$ is a compound inequality for the inequalities $x > 2$ and $x < 8$.

desigualdad compuesta (pág. 105)   Una desigualdad compuesta combina dos desigualdades. Por ejemplo, $2 < x < 8$ es una desigualdad compuesta para las desigualdades $x > 2$ y $x < 8$.

congruent triangles (p. 204)   Triangles in which all the corresponding sides are congruent and all the corresponding angles are congruent.

triángulos congruentes (pág. 204)   Triángulos en que todos los lados correspondientes son congruentes y todos los ángulos correspondientes son congruentes.

consecutive terms (p. 60)   Terms that follow one after the other in a sequence.

términos consecutivos (pág. 60)   Términos que van uno a continuación el otro en una secuencia.

continuous data (p. 131)   A set of data with no breaks in its domain or range; the graph of a continuous data has no holes or gaps.

datos continuos (pág. 131)   Conjunto de datos sin interrupciones en su dominio o rango; la gráfica de los datos continuos no tiene espacios vacíos ni brechas.

corresponding angles (p. 193)   A pair of nonadjacent angles that are formed by two lines and a transversal such that the angles are on the same side of the transversal and one of the angles is outside the two lines while the other angle is between the two lines. When the two lines crossed by a transversal are parallel, the corresponding angles are congruent.

ángulos correspondientes (pág. 193)   Par de ángulos no adyacentes formados por dos rectas y una transversal y que están al mismo lado de la transversal, con uno de los ángulos fuera de las dos rectas y el otro ángulo entre las dos rectas. Cuando las dos rectas cruzadas por una transversal son paralelas, los ángulos correspondientes son congruentes.

counterexample (p. 101)   An example that shows that a statement is not true.

contraejemplo (pág. 101)   Ejemplo que demuestra que un enunciado no es verdadero.

D

dependent events (p. 261)   Events for which knowing that one of them has occurred affects the probability that the other event occurs.

sucesos dependientes (pág. 261)   Sucesos para los cuales el saber que uno de ellos ha ocurrido afecta la probabilidad de que el otro suceso ocurra.

dilation (p. 233)   A transformation in which the image is similar (but not congruent) to the pre-image.

dilatación (pág. 233)   Transformación en la que la imagen es semejante (pero no congruente) a la preimagen.

discrete data (p. 131)   A set of data with a finite number of data values; the graph of discrete data shows as a individual points on a number line or coordinate plane.

datos discretos (pág. 131)   Conjunto de datos con un número finito de valores; la gráfica de datos discretos muestra puntos individuales sobre una recta numérica o plano de coordenadas.

domain (p. 127)   The set of all input values for a relation or function.

dominio (pág. 127)   Conjunto de todos los valores de entrada de una relación o función.

E

equation (p. 68)   A mathematical statement that shows that two expressions are equal.

ecuación (pág. 68)   Enunciado matemático que muestra que dos expresiones son iguales.

evaluate (p. 58)   To substitute a given value or values for a variable and simplify.

evaluar (pág. 58)   Reemplazar una variable por un valor o valores dados, y luego simplificar.

event (p. 254)   Any outcome or group of outcomes from a probability experiment.

suceso (pág. 254)   Cualquier resultado o grupo de resultados de un experimento de probabilidad.

experimental probability (p. 254)   The ratio of the number of times an event occurs to the total number of trials in the experiment.

probabilidad experimental (pág. 254)   Razón del número de veces que ocurre un suceso al número total de pruebas realizadas en el experimento.

exponent (p. 14)   A number that indicates how many times another number, called the base, is used as a factor.

exponente (pág. 14)   Número que indica las veces que otro número, llamado base, se utiliza como factor.

expression (p. 58)   A mathematical phrase that uses numbers, or variables, or both, such as $4 + 3$ or $6n$.

expresión (pág. 58)   Frase matemática que usa números o variables, o ambos, como $4 + 3$ ó $6n$.

F

formula (p. 84)   A rule or equation that shows a relationship between two or more quantities.

fórmula (pág. 84)   Regla que muestra una relación entre dos o más cantidades.

function (p. 128)   A relation that pairs each element of the domain with exactly one element of the range.

función (pág. 128)   Relación que empareja cada elemento del dominio con un solo elemento del rango.

H

horizontal reflection (p. 197)   If a pre-image is reflected over a vertical line, the transformation is a horizontal reflection.

reflexión horizontal (pág. 197)   Si una preimagen se refleja sobre una recta vertical, la transformación es una reflexión horizontal.

hypotenuse (p. 303)   The side of a right triangle that is opposite the right angle.

hipotenusa (pág. 303)   Lado de un triángulo rectángulo que es opuesto al ángulo recto.

hypothesis (p. 26)   An assumption that is based on the observation of an event or series of events.

hipótesis (pág. 26)   Supuesto que se basa en la observación de un suceso o serie de sucesos.

I

independent events (p. 255)   Two events are independent if the outcome of the first event does not affect the probability of the second event.

sucesos independientes (pág. 255)   Dos sucesos son independientes si el resultado del primer suceso no afecta la probabilidad del segundo suceso.

inequality (p. 99)   A mathematical statement showing that one quantity is greater than or less than another. Inequalities use these symbols; $>$ (is greater than); $<$ (is less than); $\geq$ (is greater than or equal to); and $\leq$ (is less than or equal to).

desigualdad (pág. 99)   Enunciado matemático que muestra que una cantidad es mayor o menor que otra. Las desigualdades usan estos símbolos: $>$ (mayor que); $<$ (menor que); $\geq$ (mayor o igual a) y $\leq$ (menor o igual a).

interquartile range (IQR) (p. 268)   The difference between the lower and upper quartiles of a set of ordered data.

rango intercuartil (RI) (pág. 268)   Diferencia entre el cuartil inferior y el cuartil superior de un conjunto de datos ordenados.

inverse operations (p. 71)   Operations that "undo" each other. Adding and subtracting are inverse operations. Multiplying and dividing are inverse operations.

operaciones inversas (pág. 71)   Operaciones que se "anulan" una a la otra. Sumar y restar son operaciones inversas. Multiplicar y dividir son operaciones inversas.

irrational number (p. 44)   A number that cannot be written as the ratio of two integers.

número irracional (pág. 44)   Número que no puede escribirse como razón de dos enteros.

isosceles triangle (p. 204)   A triangle with two congruent sides, called the legs. The angles opposite the legs, called base angles, are also congruent.

triángulo isósceles (pág. 204)   Triángulo que tiene dos lados congruentes. Los ángulos opuestos a los lados congruentes, llamados ángulos de la base, también son congruentes.

L

lateral area (p. 318)   The sum of the areas of the lateral faces of a solid.

área lateral (pág. 318)   Suma de las áreas de las caras laterales de un cuerpo geométrico.

lateral face (p. 318)   A face of a solid that is not one of the bases.

cara lateral (pág. 318)   Cara de un cuerpo geométrico que no es una de las bases.

line graph (p. 278)   A graph that uses ordered pairs to represent data that change over time. The ordered pairs are connected to show a trend over time.

gráfica lineal (pág. 278)   Gráfica que usa pares ordenados para representar datos que cambian en el tiempo. Los pares ordenados se conectan para mostrar una tendencia en el tiempo.

line of good fit (p. 276)   A line drawn on a scatterplot to show the general direction of the association between two sets of data.

recta de ajuste (pág. 276)   Recta que se traza en un diagrama de dispersión para mostrar la dirección general de la asociación entre dos conjuntos de datos.

linear data (p. 122)   Data are linear if the points representing the data on a coordinate plane lie on a (straight) line; that is, if the rate of change is constant.

datos lineales (pág. 122)   Los datos son lineales si los puntos que representan los datos en un plano de coordenadas yacen sobre una recta; es decir, si la tasa de cambio es constante.

literal equation (p. 83)   An equation containing several variables. To solve a literal equation, use the properties of equality to isolate one of the variables on one side of the equal sign.

ecuación literal (pág. 83)   Ecuación que contiene varias variables. Para resolver una ecuación literal, se usan las propiedades de la igualdad para aislar una de las variables a un lado del signo de igualdad.

lower quartile (p. 267)   The median of the lower half of an ordered data set.

cuartil inferior (pág. 267)   Mediana de la mitad inferior de un conjunto de datos ordenados.

M

mapping (p. 128)   A visual representation of a relation in which an arrow associates each input with its output.

mapeo (pág. 128)   Representación visual de una relación en la que una flecha asocia cada entrada con su salida.

mean (p. 265)   The arithmetic average of a set of data, found by taking the sum of the data and then dividing by the total number of data items

media (pág. 265)   Promedio aritmético de un conjunto de datos, que se calcula dividiendo la suma de los datos entre el número total de datos.

measures of central tendency (p. 265)   The mean, median, and mode of a numerical data set are called measures of central tendency. Since these measures are usually located in the middle of the data, they are chosen as representatives of the entire data set. Also called **measures of center.**

medidas de tendencia central (pág. 265)   La media, la mediana y la moda de un conjunto de datos numéricos se llaman medidas de tendencia central. Como estas medidas normalmente se ubican en el centro de los datos, se escogen como representativas de todo el conjunto de datos. También se llaman **medidas de centro.**

median (p. 265)   The middle number of a set of ordered data.

mediana (pág. 265)   Número que está en el medio de un conjunto de datos ordenados.

mode (p. 265)   The value or values that occur most often in a set of data.

moda (pág. 265)   Valor o valores que ocurren con mayor frecuencia en un conjunto de datos.

mutually exclusive events (p. 261)   If events A and B are in the sample space and have no outcomes in common, then A and B are mutually exclusive events.

sucesos mutuamente excluyentes (pág. 261) Si los sucesos A y B están en el espacio muestral y no tienen resultados en común, entonces A y B son sucesos mutuamente excluyentes.

N

n^{th} figure (p. 64)   Figure number n in a sequence.

enésima figura (pág. 64)   Figura número n en una secuencia.

numerical data (p. 266)   Data gathered through measurement. Examples of numerical data include age, height, and weight.

datos numéricos (pág. 266)   Datos reunidos por medio de mediciones. Ejemplos de datos numéricos incluyen la edad, la altura y el peso.

O

ordered pair (p. 126)   Two numbers written in a certain order. Most often, ordered pair refers to the x- and y-coordinates of a point on the coordinate plane, which are written (x, y). Ordered pair may also refer to any values paired together according to a specific order.

par ordenado (pág. 126)   Dos números que se escriben en cierto orden. Más frecuentemente, el par ordenado se refiere a las coordenadas x e y de un punto sobre el plano de coordenadas, que se escriben (x, y). El par ordenado puede también referirse a valores cualesquiera emparejados según un orden específico.

outcome (p. 254)   A possible result in a probability experiment.

resultado (pág. 254)   Alternativa posible en un experimento de probabilidad.

outlier (p.277)   A value in a data set that does not fit the overall pattern of data values in the set.

valor atípico (pág. 277)   Valor de un conjunto de datos que no calza dentro el patrón general de los datos del conjunto.

P

power (p. 16)   A mathematical expression with two parts, a base and an exponent. For example, in the power 5^3, 5 is the base and 3 is the exponent.

potencia (pág. 16)   Expresión matemática con dos partes, una base y un exponente. Por ejemplo, en la potencia 5^3, 5 es la base y 3 es el exponente.

pre-image (p. 196)   The original image in a transformation.

preimagen (pág. 196)   Imagen original en una transformación.

prism (p. 317)   A solid with parallel congruent bases that are both polygons. The sides (faces) of a prism are all parallelograms or rectangles. A prism is named according to the shape of its bases.

prisma (pág. 317)   Cuerpo geométrico que tiene como bases dos polígonos paralelos y congruentes. Los lados (caras) de un prisma son todos paralelogramos o rectángulos. Un prisma recibe su nombre según la forma de sus bases.

property (p. 79)   In mathematics, a property is a rule or statement that is always true.

propiedad (pág. 79)   En matemáticas, una propiedad es una regla o enunciado que es siempre verdadero.

Pythagorean theorem (p. 304)   This theorem states that the sum of the squares of the lengths of the legs of a right triangle equals the square of the length of the hypotenuse.

Teorema de Pitágoras (pág. 304)   Este teorema establece que la suma de los cuadrados de las longitudes de los catetos de un triángulo rectángulo es igual al cuadrado de la longitud de la hipotenusa.

Q

question of interest (p. 281)   The topic about which information is collected using a survey or study.

pregunta de interés (pág. 281)   Asunto acerca del cual se reúne información por medio de una encuesta o estudio.

R

range of data (p. 269)   The difference between the minimum and maximum values of a set of data.

rango de datos (pág. 269)   Diferencia entre el valor máximo y el valor mínimo de un conjunto de datos.

range of a function (p. 127)   The set of all output values of a function.

rango de una función (pág. 127)   Conjunto de todos los valores de salida de una función.

rate of change (p. 119)   In a relationship, the ratio of vertical change in the output to the horizontal change in the input. The output is often represented by the variable y, and the input is often represented by the variable x.

tasa de cambio (pág. 119)   En una relación, razón del cambio vertical en la salida al cambio horizontal en la entrada. La salida se representa habitualmente con la variable y, y la entrada se representa

ratio (p. 139)   A comparison of two quantities. Ratios can be written as fractions (indicating a quotient), with the word "to," or with a colon. habitualmente con la variable x.

razón (pág. 139)   Comparación entre dos cantidades. Las razones pueden escribirse como fracciones (que indican un cociente) o usando la palabra "a" o usando dos puntos (:).

rational number (p. 44)   Any number that can be written as the ratio of two integers where the divisor is not zero; for example, 8, 1.5, $\frac{2}{5}$, and −3.

número racional (pág. 44)   Cualquier número que pueda escribirse como la razón entre dos enteros, donde el divisor no es cero; por ejemplo, 8, 1.5, $\frac{2}{5}$ y −3.

real numbers (p. 44)   The set of numbers consisting of all rational numbers and all irrational numbers.

números reales (pág. 44)   Conjunto de números que consta de todos los números racionales y todos los números irracionales.

reciprocal (p. 38)   Two numbers are reciprocals if their product is 1. Another name for reciprocal is multiplicative inverse.

recíproco (pág. 38)   Dos números son recíprocos si su producto es 1. Otro nombre para recíprocos es inversos multiplicativos.

reflection (p. 196)   A transformation in which a figure is flipped over a line of reflection. Each point of the image is the same distance from the line of reflection as its corresponding point in the pre-image.

reflexión (pág. 196)   Transformación en la que una figura se invierte sobre un eje de reflexión. Cada punto de la imagen está a la misma distancia del eje de reflexión que el correspondiente punto de la preimagen.

regular polygon (p. 203)   A polygon with all sides congruent and all angles congruent.

polígono regular (pág. 203)   Polígono que tiene todos los lados congruentes y todos los ángulos congruentes.

relation (p. 127)   Any set of ordered pairs.

relación (pág. 127)   Cualquier conjunto de pares ordenados.

rotation (p. 196)   A transformation in which each point of the pre-image travels clockwise or counterclockwise around a fixed point a certain number of degrees.

rotación (pág. 196)   Transformación en la que cada punto de la preimagen se mueve un determinado número de grados alrededor de un punto fijo en el sentido de las manecillas del reloj o en el sentido contrario al de las manecillas del reloj.

S

scale drawing (p. 218)   A figure that is similar to the figure it represents. The lengths of the corresponding sides are in proportion, and the corresponding angles are congruent.

dibujo a escala (pág. 218)   Figura que es semejante a la figura que representa. La longitud de los lados correspondientes está en proporción y los ángulos correspondientes son congruentes.

scale factor (p. 231)   In similar figures and similar solids, the ratio of the lengths of any pair of corresponding sides or edges.

factor de escala (pág. 231)   En figuras semejantes y cuerpos geométricos semejantes, es la razón de las longitudes de cualquier par de lados o aristas correspondientes.

scatterplot (p. 164)   A graphic display of bivariate data on a coordinate plane that may be used to show a relationship between two variables.

diagrama de dispersión (pág. 164)   Representación gráfica de datos bivariados sobre un plano de coordenadas, que puede usarse para mostrar una relación entre dos variables.

scientific notation (p. 28)   A number is written in scientific notation when it is expressed in the form $a \times 10^n$, where $1 \le a < 10$ and n is an integer.

notación científica (pág. 28)   Un número está escrito en notación científica cuando se expresa en la forma $a \times 10^n$, donde $1 \le a < 10$ y n es un entero.

sector of a circle (p. 224)   The region formed by two radii and an arc of a circle.

sector de un círculo (pág. 224)   Región formada por dos radios y un arco de un círculo.

sequence (p. 59)   An ordered list of numbers. Each number is called a term of the sequence. For example, {0, 1, 2, 3, …} is a sequence in which the 1st term is 0, the 2nd term is 1, the 3rd term is 2, the 4th term is 3, and so on.

sucesión (pág. 59)   Lista ordenada de números. Cada número se llama término de la sucesión. Por ejemplo, {0, 1, 2, 3, …} es una sucesión en que el 1er término es 0, el 2° término es 1, el 3er término es 2, el 4° término es 3, y así sucesivamente.

similar figures (p. 230)   Figures in which the lengths of the corresponding sides are in proportion and the corresponding angles are congruent.

figuras semejantes (pág. 230)   Figuras en que las longitudes de los lados correspondientes están en proporción y los ángulos correspondientes son congruentes.

similar solids (p. 334)   Solids with the same shape but not necessarily the same size.

cuerpos geométricos semejantes (pág. 334) Cuerpos geométricos que tienen la misma forma, pero no necesariamente el mismo tamaño.

simple random sample (SRS) (p. 281)   In a simple random sample, subjects are chosen according to a fair method that involves chance, like flipping a coin, pulling names from a hat, or using a random number table.

muestra aleatoria simple (MAS) (pág. 281) En una muestra aleatoria simple, los objetos se escogen de acuerdo con un método justo regido por la suerte, como por ejemplo lanzar una moneda, sacar nombres de un sombrero, o usar una tabla de números aleatorios.

slant height of a pyramid (p. 325)   The height of a triangular lateral face.

altura inclinada de una pirámide regular (pág. 325) Altura de alguna de las caras laterales triangulares.

slope (p. 140)   The slope of a line is the ratio $\frac{\text{change in } y}{\text{change in } x}$ between any two points that lie on the line.

pendiente (pág. 140)   La pendiente de una recta es la razón $\frac{\text{cambio en } y}{\text{cambio en } x}$ entre cualquier par de puntos que yacen sobre una recta.

slope-intercept form (p. 150)   The slope-intercept form of a linear equation is $y = mx + b$, where m is the slope and b is the y-intercept.

forma pendiente-intercepto (pág. 150) La forma pendiente-intercepto de una ecuación lineal es $y = mx + b$, donde m es la pendiente y b es el intercepto en el eje de las y.

solid (p. 317)   A three-dimensional figure having length, width, and height.

cuerpo geométrico (pág. 317)   Figura tridimensional que tiene longitud, ancho y altura.

solution (pp. 68, 101)   Any value that makes an equation or inequality true when substituted for the variable.

solución (págs. 68, 101)   Cualquier valor que hace verdadera una ecuación o desigualdad al reemplazar la variable.

solution of a system of equations (p. 171)   The point or set of points that makes all equations in the system true.

solución de un sistema de ecuaciones (pág. 171) Punto o conjunto de puntos que hace verdaderas todas las ecuaciones del sistema.

stratified sample (p. 281)   A stratified sample divides a population into groups of individuals who share a particular characteristic so that each group can be sampled separately.

muestra estratificada (pág, 281)   Una muestra estratificada divide una población en grupos de individuos que comparten una característica especial de modo que cada grupo puede muestrearse por separado.

supplementary angles (p. 188)   Two angles whose measures have a sum of 180°.

ángulos suplementarios (pág. 188)   Dos ángulos cuyas medidas suman 180°.

system of linear equations (p. 171)   Two or more linear equations using the same variables.

sistema de ecuaciones lineales (pág. 171)   Dos o más ecuaciones lineales que usan las mismas variables.

T

theoretical probability (p. 255)   The ratio of the number of outcomes in which the event can occur to the total number of outcomes in the probability experiment.

probabilidad teórica (pág. 255)   Razón del número de maneras en que puede ocurrir un suceso al número de resultados posibles de un experimento de probabilidad.

transformation (p. 196)   A change in the position or size of a figure on a plane.

transformación (pág. 196)   Cambio en la posición o el tamaño de una figura sobre un plano.

translation (p. 196)   A transformation that moves each point of a figure the same distance and in the same direction.

traslación (pág. 196)   Transformación que mueve cada punto de una figura la misma distancia y en la misma dirección.

transversal (p. 190)   A line that intersects two or more lines at different points.

transversal (pág. 190)   Recta que interseca dos o más rectas en diferentes puntos.

tree diagram (p. 256)   A graphic organizer for listing the possible outcomes of an experiment.

diagrama de árbol (pág. 256)   Organizador gráfico para registrar los resultados posibles de un experimento.

trend line (p. 165)   A line that helps explain the relationship between two quantities on a graph. A trend line indicates the general course or tendency of a set of data.

línea de tendencia (pág. 165)   Línea que ayuda a explicar la relación entre dos cantidades en una gráfica. Una línea de tendencia indica el curso general o tendencia de un conjunto de datos.

U

univariate data (p. 276)   A set of data with only one category of measurement.

datos univariados (pág. 276)   Conjunto de datos con sólo una categoría de medición.

upper quartile (p. 267)   The median of the upper half of an ordered set of data.

cuartil superior (pág. 267)   Mediana de la mitad superior de un conjunto de datos ordenados.

V

vertex (p. 193)   The common endpoint of two rays that form an angle.

vértice (pág. 193)   Extremo común de dos rayos que forman un ángulo.

vertical angles (p. 193)   A pair of angles formed by two intersecting lines. Vertical angles share a common vertex but no common sides.

ángulos opuestos por el vértice (pág. 193)   Pares de ángulos que se forman cuando dos rectas se intersecan. Los ángulos opuestos por el vértice comparten un vértice en común, pero no rayos comunes.

vertical reflection (p. 197)   If a pre-image is reflected over a horizontal line, the transformation is a vertical reflection.

reflexión vertical (pág. 197)   Si una preimagen se refleja sobre una recta horizontal, la transformación es una reflexión vertical.

X

x-intercept (p. 153)   The point where a line crosses the x-axis. Its coordinates will be of the form $(a, 0)$, where a is a real number.

intercepto en x (pág. 153)   Punto donde una recta cruza el eje de las x. Sus coordenadas serán de la forma (a, 0), donde a es un número real.

Y

y-intercept (p. 140)   The point where a line crosses the y-axis. Its coordinates will be of the form $(0, a)$, where a is a real number.

intercepto en y (pág. 115)   Punto donde una línea cruza el eje de las y. Sus coordenadas serán de la forma (0, a), donde a es un número real.

Verbal & Visual Word Association

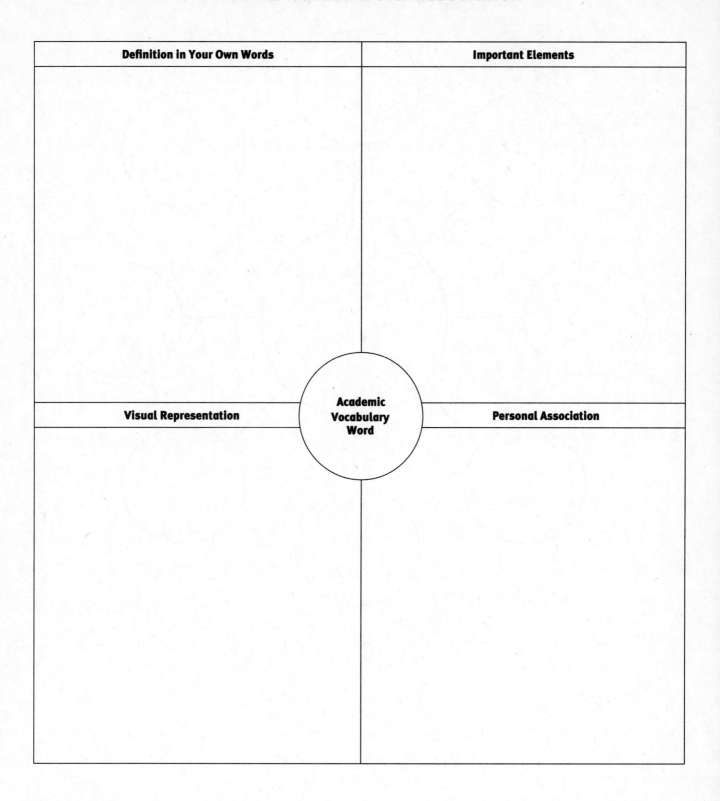

Definition in Your Own Words	Important Elements
Visual Representation	**Personal Association**

Academic Vocabulary Word

Eight Circle Spider

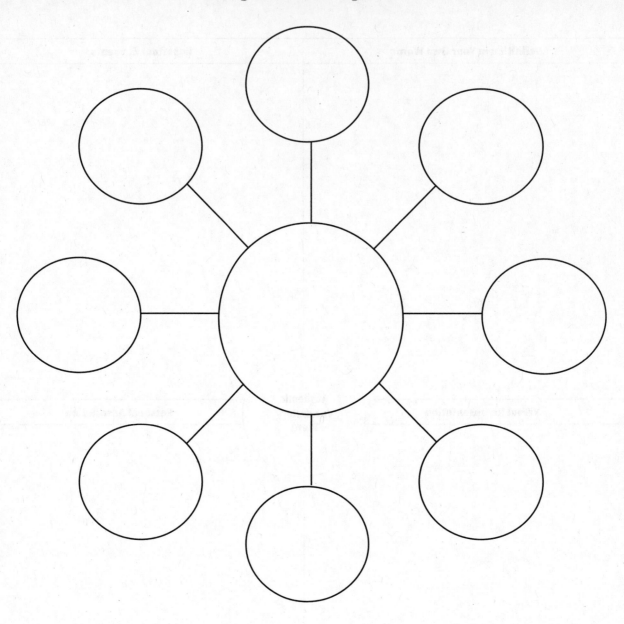

Venn Diagram

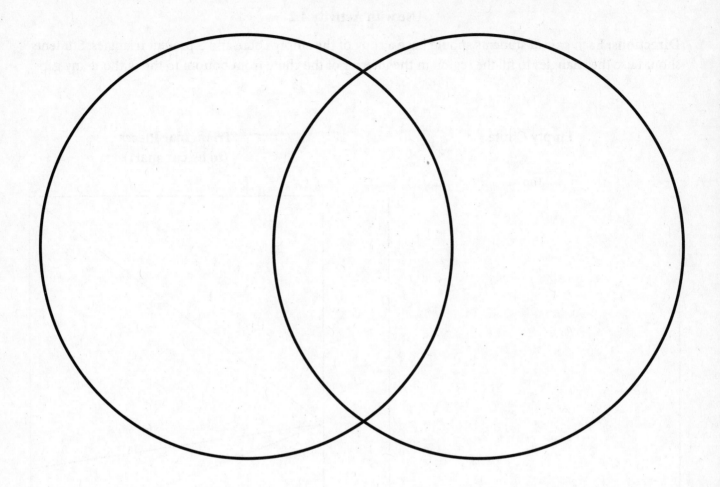

Use with Activity 4.2

Directions: Each pair of students should have a copy of the empty chute and 5 pre-cut triangles. Students should use the triangles to fill the region in the interior of the chute from bottom to top without any gaps.

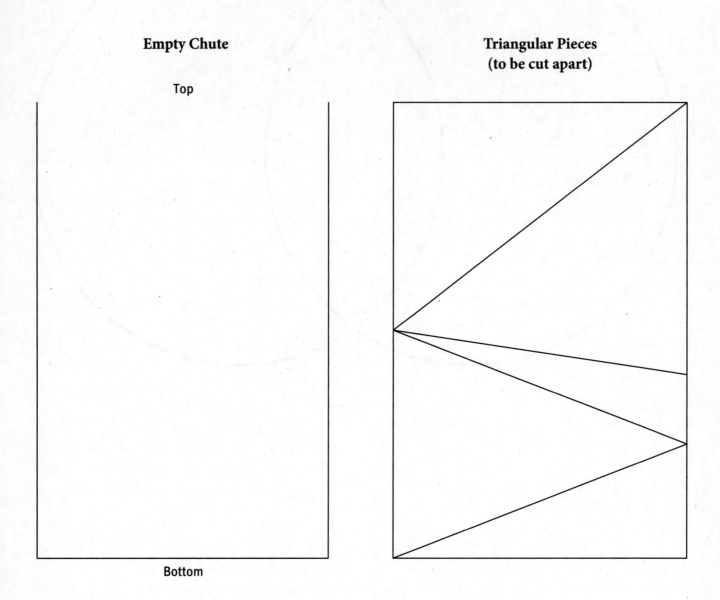

Empty Chute

Top

Bottom

Triangular Pieces
(to be cut apart)

Blackline Master 2

Graphic Organizer for Vocabulary

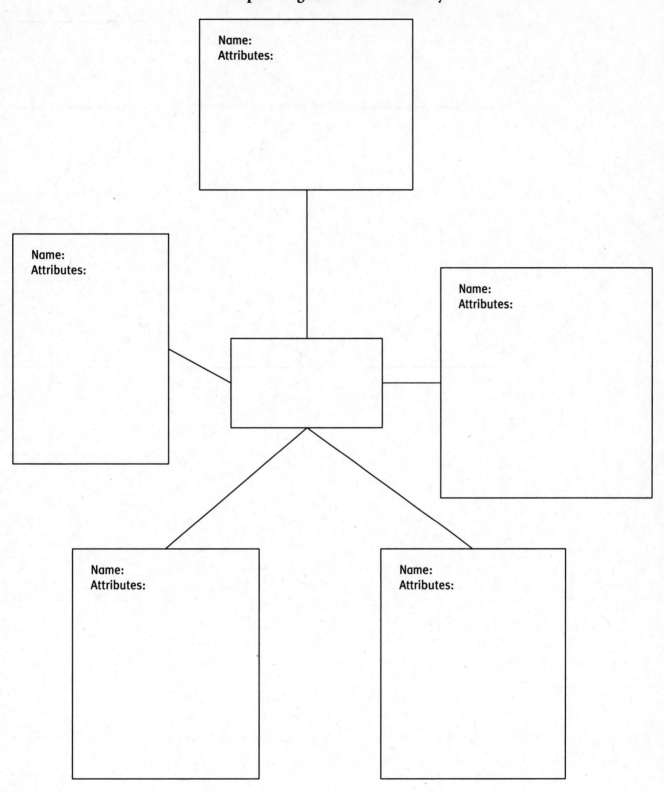

Tree Diagram

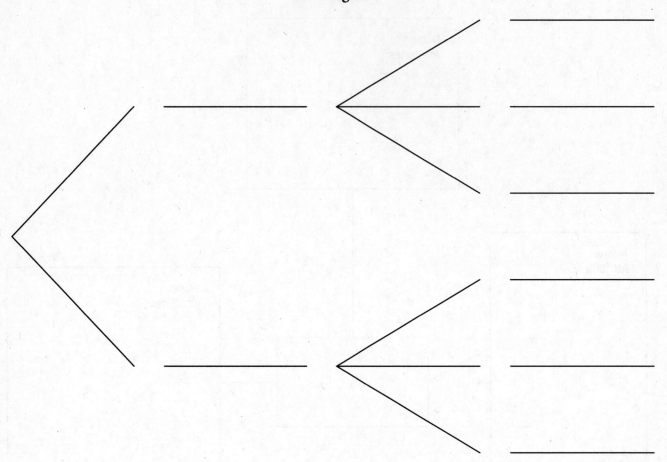

Tree Diagram

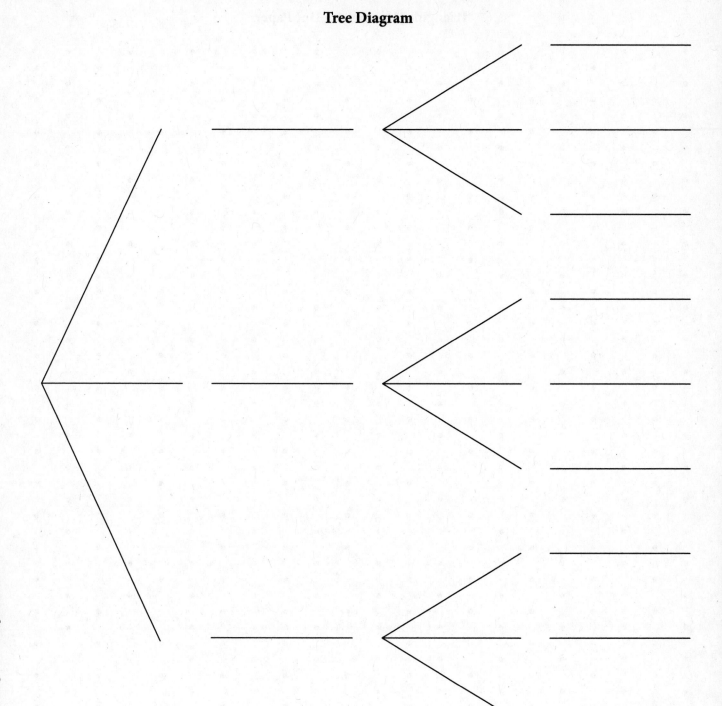

Blackline Master 5: Isometric Dot Paper

Triangular (Isometric) Dot Paper

Blackline Master 6: Square Dot Paper

Square Dot Paper

Blackline Master 7: Hundred Grid

Hundred Grid

Blackline Master 8: 5-by-5 Coordinate Grids

−5 to 5 Coordinate Grids

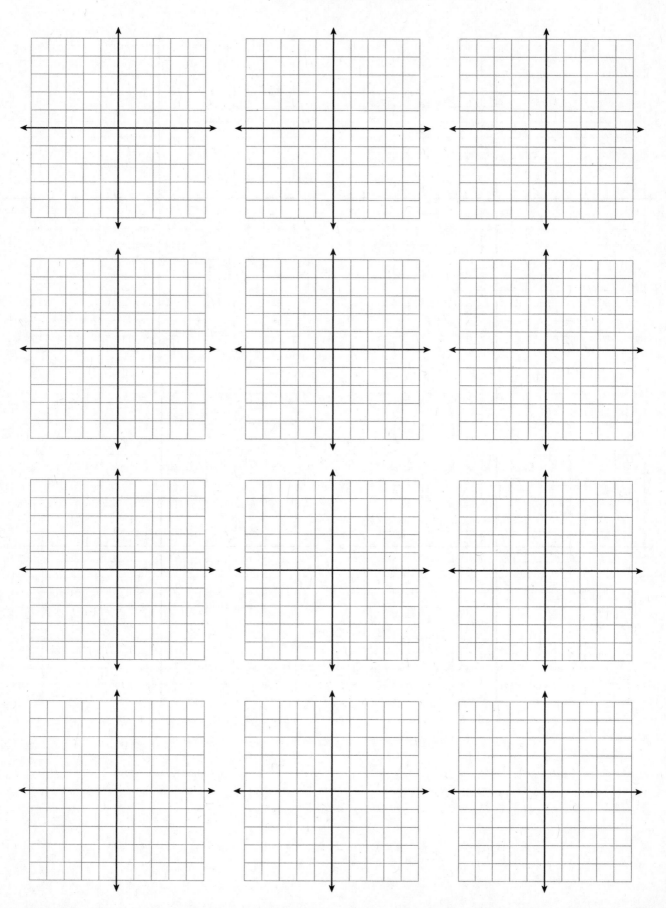

Blackline Master 9: 20 × 20 Coordinate Grids

20 × 20 Grids

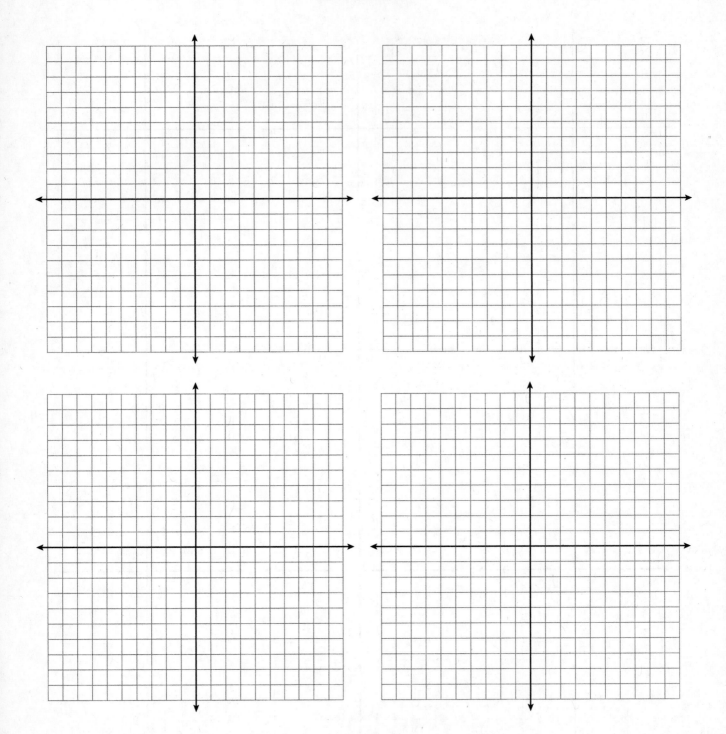

1st Quadrant Grids

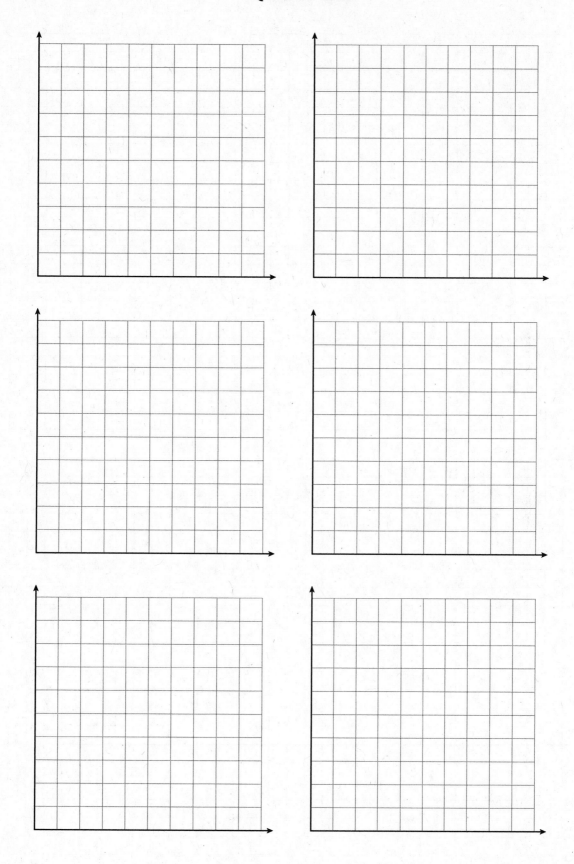

Blackline Master 11: Percent Grids

Percent Grids

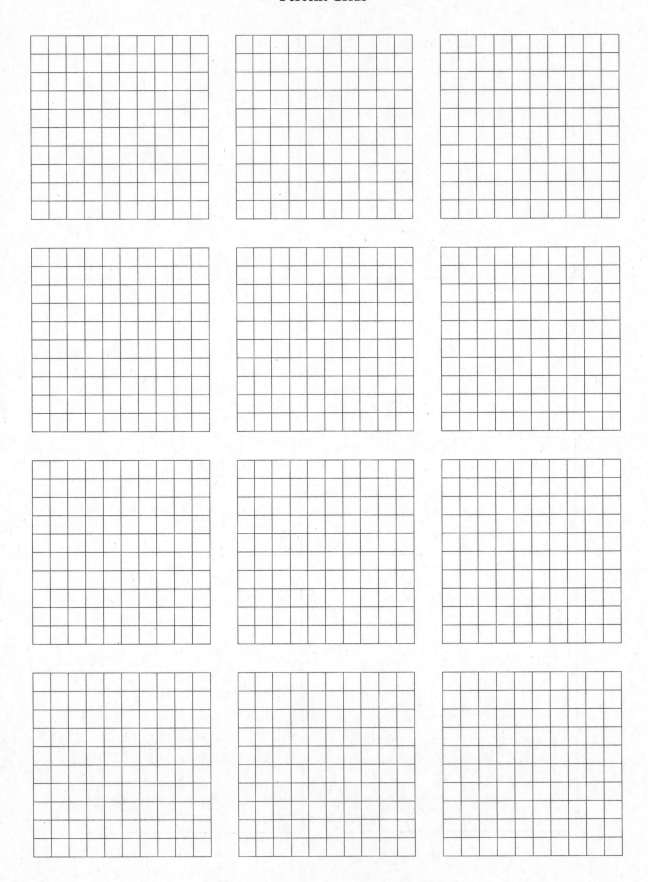

Blackline Master 12: Number Lines

Number Lines

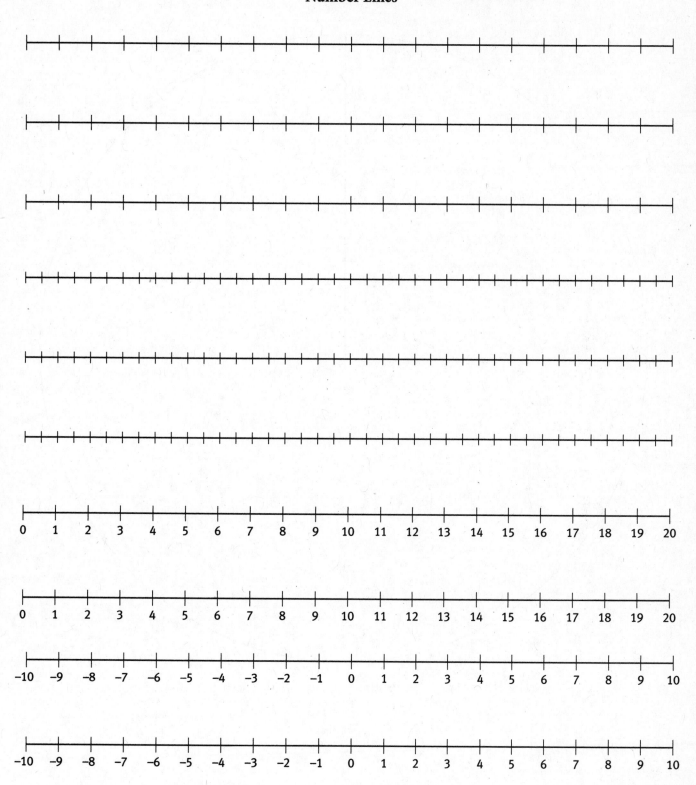

Circle Graph

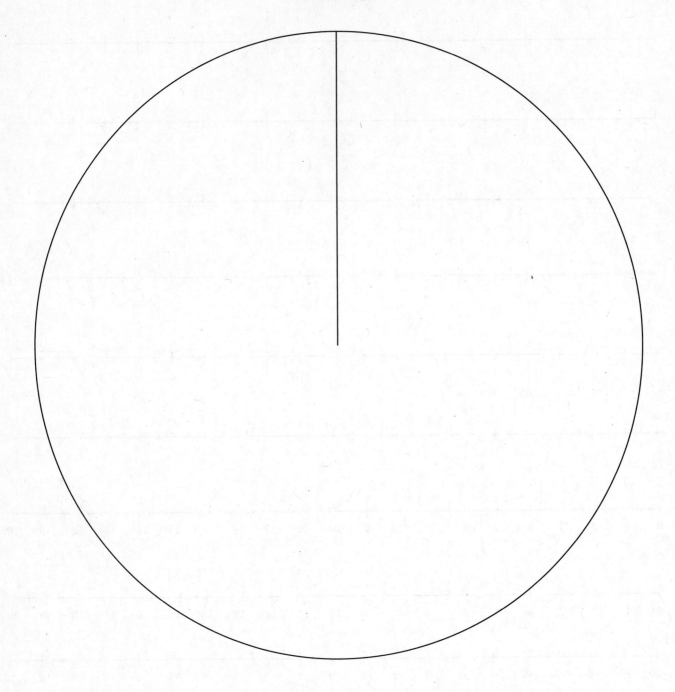

Circle Graphs

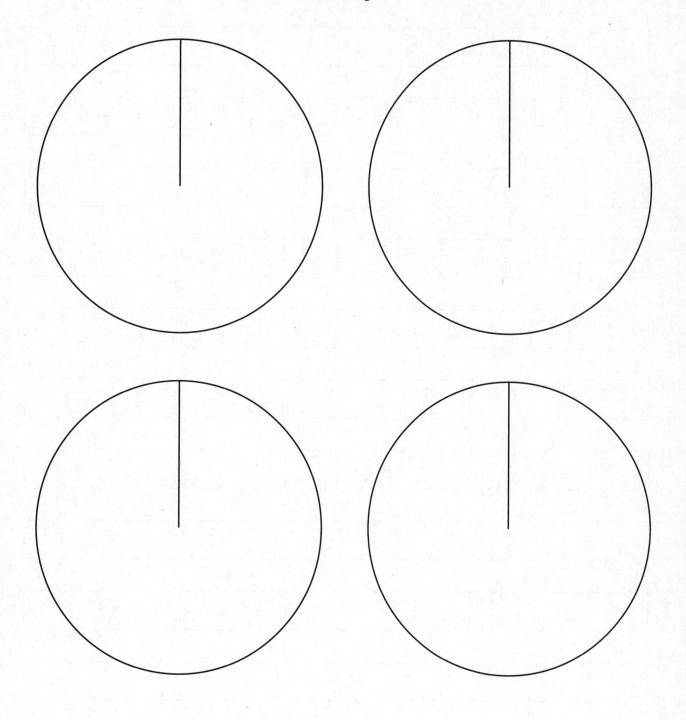

Blackline Master 15: Fraction Bars

Fraction Bars

| $\frac{1}{12}$ | $\frac{1}{12}$ | $\frac{1}{12}$ | $\frac{1}{12}$ | $\frac{1}{12}$ | $\frac{1}{12}$ | $\frac{1}{12}$ | $\frac{1}{12}$ | $\frac{1}{12}$ | $\frac{1}{12}$ | $\frac{1}{12}$ | $\frac{1}{12}$ |

| $\frac{1}{11}$ | $\frac{1}{11}$ | $\frac{1}{11}$ | $\frac{1}{11}$ | $\frac{1}{11}$ | $\frac{1}{11}$ | $\frac{1}{11}$ | $\frac{1}{11}$ | $\frac{1}{11}$ | $\frac{1}{11}$ | $\frac{1}{11}$ |

| $\frac{1}{10}$ | $\frac{1}{10}$ | $\frac{1}{10}$ | $\frac{1}{10}$ | $\frac{1}{10}$ | $\frac{1}{10}$ | $\frac{1}{10}$ | $\frac{1}{10}$ | $\frac{1}{10}$ | $\frac{1}{10}$ |

| $\frac{1}{9}$ | $\frac{1}{9}$ | $\frac{1}{9}$ | $\frac{1}{9}$ | $\frac{1}{9}$ | $\frac{1}{9}$ | $\frac{1}{9}$ | $\frac{1}{9}$ | $\frac{1}{9}$ |

| $\frac{1}{8}$ | $\frac{1}{8}$ | $\frac{1}{8}$ | $\frac{1}{8}$ | $\frac{1}{8}$ | $\frac{1}{8}$ | $\frac{1}{8}$ | $\frac{1}{8}$ |

| $\frac{1}{7}$ | $\frac{1}{7}$ | $\frac{1}{7}$ | $\frac{1}{7}$ | $\frac{1}{7}$ | $\frac{1}{7}$ | $\frac{1}{7}$ |

| $\frac{1}{6}$ | $\frac{1}{6}$ | $\frac{1}{6}$ | $\frac{1}{6}$ | $\frac{1}{6}$ | $\frac{1}{6}$ |

| $\frac{1}{5}$ | $\frac{1}{5}$ | $\frac{1}{5}$ | $\frac{1}{5}$ | $\frac{1}{5}$ |

| $\frac{1}{4}$ | $\frac{1}{4}$ | $\frac{1}{4}$ | $\frac{1}{4}$ |

| $\frac{1}{3}$ | $\frac{1}{3}$ | $\frac{1}{3}$ |

| $\frac{1}{2}$ | $\frac{1}{2}$ |

| 1 |

Blackline Master 16: Rectangular Prism Net

Rectangular Prism Net

Blackline Master 17: Triangular Prism Net

Triangular Prism Net

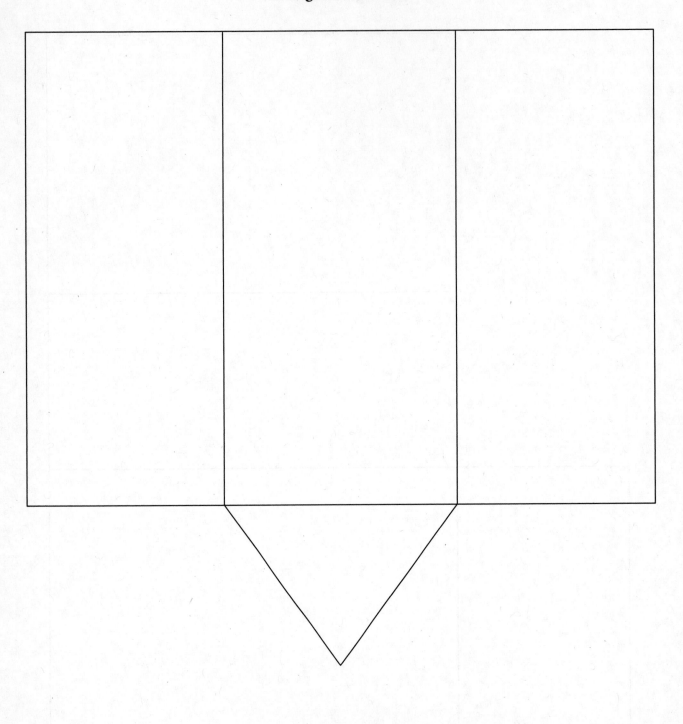

Venn Diagram

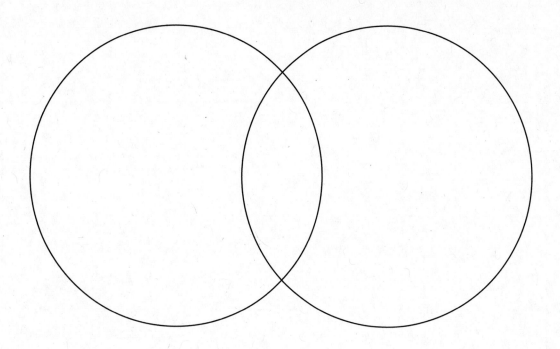

Blackline Master 19: 1 Inch Grid

1 Inch Grid

Blackline Master 20: Tables and Coordinate Grids

Tables and Coordinate Grids

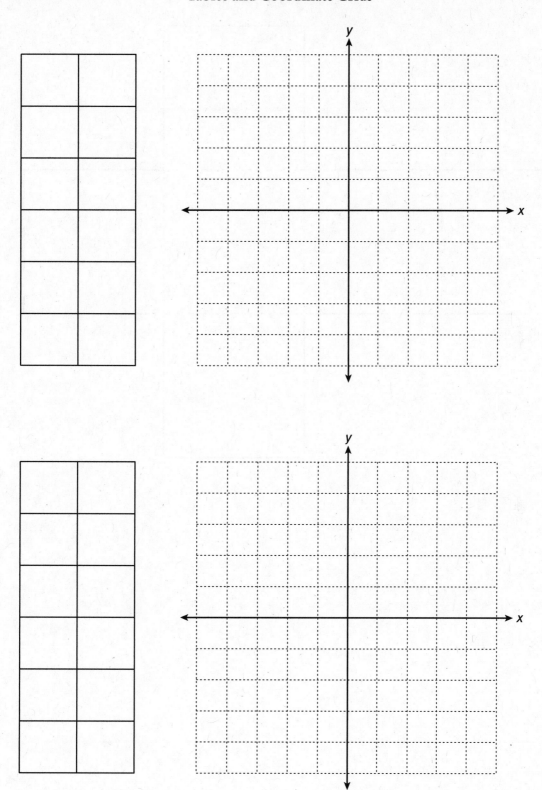

Blackline Master 21: Cube Template

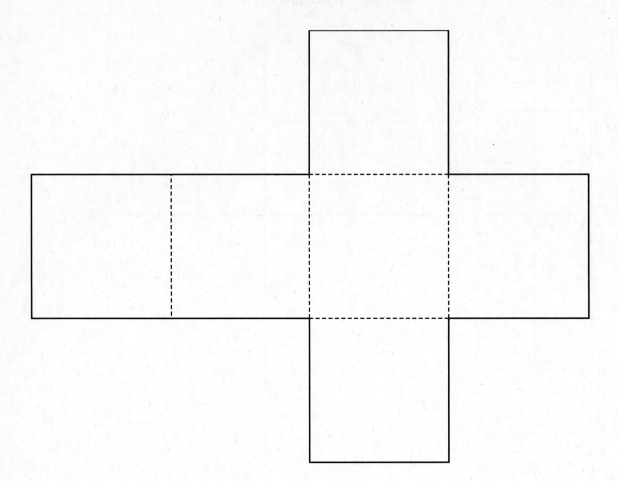

Blackline Master 22: Cone Template

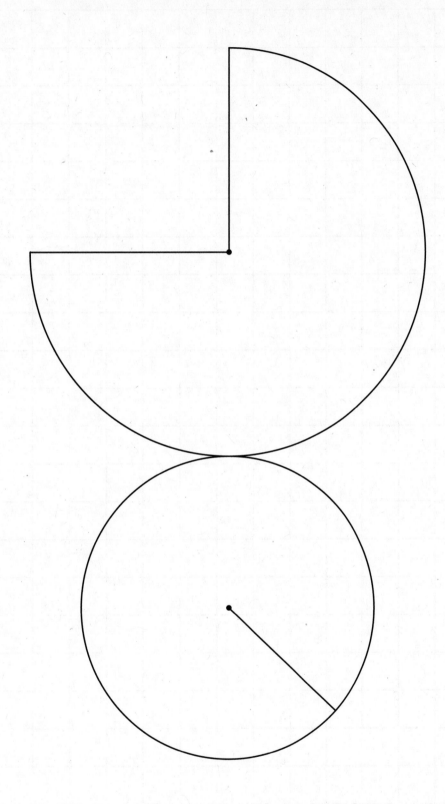

Blackline Master 23: Centimeter Grid Paper

Index

Evaluate
  algebraic expression, 81–82
  defined, 58
Event
  complementary, 258–259
  defined, 254
  dependent, 261
  independent, 255
  mutually exclusive, 261
Experimental probability, 254–255
Exponents
  base, 14
  defined, 14
  division, 18
  multiplication, 18
  powers, 16–17
  of zero, 16–17, 18
Expression
  defined, 58
  evaluate, 81–82
  simplify, 81–82
  writing patterns for, 57–66
Exterior angles, 191–192

F

Fahrenheit degrees, 84
Figure
  n^{th} figure, 64
Formulas
  area
    of trapezoid, 84
    of triangle, 84
  circumference of circle, 84
  defined, 84
  Euler's, 84
  simple interest, 84
  temperature
    in Celsius, 84
    in Fahrenheit, 84
Fractions
  addition, 35
  division, 38–40
  multiplication, 36–37
  musical notes as, 31–35
  subtraction, 35
Functions, 125–133
  continuous, 131–133
  defined, 128
  discrete, 131–133
  identifying
    graphing, 129–131
    mapping, 128
    table, 129
  input and output, 126
  ordered pairs, 126

G

Geometry
  angles
    complementary, 188–189
    congruent, 190–191
    corresponding, 193
    defined, 188
    equilateral triangle, 208
    exterior, 191–192
    heptagon, 209
    hexagon, 206–208
    interior, 192
    isosceles triangle, 204, 206–207
    octagon, 209

pentagon, 205, 208
square, 208
sum of triangle, 200–202
supplementary, 188–189
of transversal, 190–193
vertical, 193
Pythagorean theorem
  to find measurements, 304–309
  to verify right triangles, 311–314
solids
  changing dimensions, 333–336
  defined, 317
  surface area of, 317–327
  volume of, 329–332
surface area
  cylinder, 323–324
  hexagonal prism, 318
  prisms, 320–321
  rectangular prism, 320, 322
  square pyramid, 324–326
  triangular prism, 319, 327
volume
  cone, 331
  cylinder, 330–331
  prism, 330
  pyramid, 330
  sphere, 331

H

Heptagon
  angles of, 209
  as regular polygon, 209
Hexagon
  angles of, 206–208
  as regular polygon, 206–209
Hexagonal prism
  surface area, 318
Histogram
  class interval, 284
Horizontal line
  slope of, 156, 158
Horizontal reflection, 197
Hypotenuse
  defined, 303
  Pythagorean Theorem and,
    304–309

I

Independent events, 255
Inequalities
  compound, 105
  defined, 99
  division
    negative numbers, 103–106
  multiplication
    negative numbers, 103–106
  number line and, 101–104, 106
  solving and graphing, 99–106
  strict inequality, 101
Input, 126
Interior angles, 192
Interquartile range, 268
Inverse operations
  concept of, 38–39
  defined, 71
  to solve equations, 71
Irrational number
  defined, 44
  estimating, 44–45

Isosceles triangle
  angles of, 204, 206–207
  defined, 204

L

Lateral area, 318
Lateral face, 318, 325
Leg, of isosceles triangle, 204
Legs, of triangle, 303
Linear data, 122
Linear equation
  slope-intercept form, 150–151
  system of, 171–174
Linear patterns, 117–122
  rate of change, 119
Linear relationships
  horizontal line, 156, 158
  introduction to, 117–122
  slope, 137–143
  slope-intercept form, 150–151
  vertical line, 157–158
  x-intercept, 153–159
  y-intercept, 140–143, 159
Line graph, 278
Line of good fit, 276–277
Line plot, 284–285
Literal equation
  defined, 83
  formulas, 84
  solving, 83
Lower quartile, 267

M

Mapping
  to identify function, 128
Mean, 265
Measures of central tendency
  box-and-whisker plot, 267–269
  defined, 265
  mean, 265
  median, 265
  mode, 265
Median, 265
Mental math
  to solve simple equations, 69, 75
Mode, 265
Multiplication
  Associative Property of, 14, 80
  Commutative Property of, 29–30, 80
  converting units, 235–240
  decimals, 25–27
  Distributive Property of Multiplication
    Over Addition, 80
  division as inverse operation of, 39
  Equality Property of, 85–87
  exponents, 18
  fractions, 36–37
  inequalities
    negative numbers, 103–106
  Multiplicative Identity Property, 80
  Multiplicative Inverse Property, 80
  scientific notation, 29–30
  words/phrases for, 70
Multiplicative Identity Property, 80
Multiplicative Inverse Property, 80
Multi-step equations
  combining like terms, 91–97
  modeling, 91–95

solving, 96–98
subtracting equal amounts, 91–97
Mutually exclusive, 261

N

Negative association, 165
Negative numbers
  inequalities
    division, 103–106
    multiplication, 103–106
Nets, 317–328
Non-linear patterns, 120–121
n^{th} figure, 64
Number line
  compound inequalities, 105
  graphing inequalities, 101–104, 106
  to solve equations, 72
  strict inequality, 101
Numbers
  irrational, 44–45
  rational, 44
  rectangular, 65
  triangular, 65
Numerical data, 266

O

Octagon
  angles of, 209
  as regular polygon, 209
Ordered pair, 126
Outcome, 254
Outliers, 266
  scatter plot and, 277
Output, 126

P

Patterns
  consecutive terms, 60
  constant difference, 60–61, 63–64
  investigating, 3–12
  linear, 117–123
  non-linear, 120–121
  rate of change, 119
  rectangular numbers, 65
  as sequences, 59–60
  triangular numbers, 65
  writing expressions for, 57–66
Pentagon
  angles, 205
  as regular polygon, 205
Percent
  calculating, 221–223
  circle graph and, 227
  as decimal, 224
  decrease, 216–217
  increase, 216–217
  proportions and, 216–217
Polygon
  regular, 203–209
    equilateral triangle, 203, 208
    heptagon, 209
    hexagon, 206–208
    octagon, 209
    pentagon, 205, 208
    square, 203, 208
Positive association, 165
Power
  of 0, 16–17, 18

defined, 16
Prism
  volume, 330
Probability
  complementary events, 258–259
  dependent events, 261
  event, 254
  experimental, 254–255
  independent events, 255
  mutually exclusive, 261
  outcome, 254
  simple random sample, 281
  simulation, 282–283
  stratified sample, 281–282
  theoretical, 255
  tree diagram, 256–257
Properties
  Additive Identity, 80
  Additive Inverse, 80
  Associative Property of Addition, 80
  Associative Property of Multiplication, 14, 80
  Commutative Property of Addition, 80
  Commutative Property of Multiplication, 29–30, 80
  defined, 79
  Distributive Property of Multiplication Over Addition, 80
  Equality, 85–87
  Multiplicative Identity, 80
  Multiplicative Inverse, 80
  to solve equations, 85–87
  Transitive Property of Equality, 173
Proportions
  percent increase/decrease, 216–217
  scale drawings, 218–219
  scale factor, 231–232
  writing, 214–215
Pyramid
  slant height, 325
  square, 324–326
  triangular, 327
  volume, 330
Pythagoreans, 57
Pythagorean Theorem
  defined, 304
  to find hypotenuse/leg length, 304–309
  verifying right triangles, 311–314
Pythagorean Triple, 313–314

R

Range, 269
  continuous data, 131
  defined, 127
  discrete data, 131
Rate of change
  defined, 119
  linear relationship, 122–123
  as ratio, 139
  slope as constant, 140
Rational number
  defined, 44
  estimating irrational numbers with, 44–45
Ratios
  defined, 139
  proportions, 214–217

rate of change as, 139
  scale drawings, 218–219
  scale factor, 231–232
  similar figures, 229–233
  unit conversions, 235–240
Reading Math, 44, 69, 85, 140
Reciprocal
  defined, 38
  dividing fractions, 38–40
Rectangular numbers, 65
Rectangular prism
  scale factor of similar, 334
  surface area, 320, 322
Reflection, 196–199
  defined, 196
  horizontal, 197
  vertical, 197
Regular polygon, 203–209
  defined, 203
  equilateral triangle, 203, 208
  heptagon, 209
  hexagon, 206–208
  octagon, 209
  pentagon, 205, 208
  square, 203, 208
Relation
  defined, 127
  domain, 127
  range, 127
Right triangle
  Pythagorean theorem, 304–309, 311–314
Rotations, 196–199

S

Samples
  simple random, 281
  stratified, 281–282
Scale drawings
  defined, 218
  proportions, 218
Scale factor, 231–232
  similar solids, 334
Scatter plot
  bivariate data, 164–168
  line of good fit, 276–277
  negative association, 164–167
  outlier, 277
  positive association, 164–167
  trend line, 164
Scientific notation
  Commutative Property of Multiplication, 29
  defined, 28
  multiplication, 29–30
  writing number in, 28–29
Sector, 224
Sequence
  defined, 59
  patterns written as, 59–60
Set
  defined, 127
  domain, 127
  range, 127
Similar figures, 229–233
Similar solids, 334
Simple interest
  formula for, 84
Simple random sample, 281

Photo Credits

Unit 6: St. Peter's Basilica, Rome (p. 333), iStockphoto